# Troubleshooting and Repairing
# AUDIO EQUIPMENT

I dedicate this book to Leah Horrigan who has deciphered and unscrambled many words while typing these pages.

# Troubleshooting and Repairing
# AUDIO EQUIPMENT

### Homer L. Davidson

TAB BOOKS

Blue Ridge Summit, PA

FIRST EDITION
SIXTH PRINTING

**Library of Congress Cataloging-in-Publication Data**

Davidson, Homer L.
　　Troubleshooting and repairing audio equipment.

　　Includes index.
　　1. High-fidelity sound systems—Repairing.　I. Title.
TK7881.7.D43　1987　　621.38′0282′0288　　87-7102
ISBN 0-8306-7167-6
ISBN 0-8306-2867-3 (pbk.)

TAB BOOKS offers software for sale. For information and a catalog, please contact TAB Software Department, Blue Ridge Summit, PA 17294-0850.

Questions regarding the content of this book should be addressed to:

Reader Inquiry Branch
TAB BOOKS
Blue Ridge Summit, PA 17294-0850

# Contents

# Introduction

This book covers practically all of the electronic players within the consumer electronics entertainment field. The purpose of the book is to acquaint the experimenter, tinkerer, home owner, or hobbyist, whether beginner or intermediate, with how each unit works and how to make simple repairs. Even the TV technician who was only taught how to service the TV chassis may learn how to repair other electronic products.

The book has 12 chapters dealing with repairs on the cassette pocket stereo player, the compact stereo tape deck, boom-box player, deluxe AM-FM-MPX tuner, the deluxe amp, auto stereo cassette player, the turntable, the compact disc player (CD), the auto cassette disc player (CD), telephone answering machines, and stereo speakers.

The first chapter of the book tells you how, when, and where to make various tests of transistors and IC components. The basic test equipment and how to use them are discussed here. Knowing how to locate the defective component with critical voltage, resistance, and DMM tests often solves most solid-state breakdowns.

A few hints and tips on servicing the compact cassette portable player are given in Chapter 2. In addition to speed problems, simple sound and earphone problems are also thoroughly explained. A complete discussion of the compact cassette player and the various recording problems are found in Chapter 3. AM-FM-MPX and high-powered amplifier problems and servicing are found in Chapter 4 on troubleshooting the boom-box cassette player. A number of actual case histories are found at the end of most chapters.

Chapters 9 and 10 describe how noiseless high-fidelity compact disc players work at home and in the auto. Troubleshooting the various sections with the scope and critical adjustments often solves difficult repair problems in compact disc players.

Telephone answering machines are now found in the home, office, and businesses. How they work, their problems, and how to solve them are discussed in Chapter 11. Stereo speaker repairs are dealt with in Chapter 12. The names and addresses of all manufacturers in the electronic entertainment field covered in this book are found in the Appendix.

Many manufacturers have contributed electronic data and circuits for use in this book and to them I offer many thanks. A special thanks is due Panasonic Consumer Electronics, RCA Corporation, and Radio Shack for the service literature and schematics used throughout the book. Their assistance helped make this book possible.

# Chapter 1

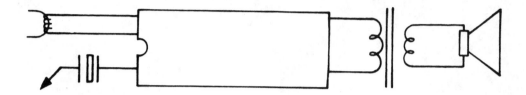

# How, When, and
# Where to Make Tests

IN ADDITION TO THE COLOR TV RECEIVER, MOST other consumer electronics and entertainment electronics items are a combination of both electronic and mechanical components. Both radio and audio circuits are combined in the compact stereo tape decks, boom-box players, portable players, and the telephone-answering machines. Electronic audio circuits are found in turntables and high-powered amplifiers (Fig. 1-1). Special video circuits are used in VCRs. The home auto CD player, using electronic laser sensing, produces almost noiseless music with a dynamic range and accuracy never seen before.

Although electronic and mechanical movements have been used in consumer electronics products for many years, we have not even seen the beginning of the many new products yet to come in the years ahead. Electronics and mechanics are a powerful combination for making life easier and more comfortable in this busy world (Fig. 1-2). Especially today, the electronic entertainment product is better constructed and stands up a lot longer. However, when the two are combined together, sooner or later breakdown occurs.

## REQUIRED TEST EQUIPMENT

To keep the electronic units in tip-top shape, a few basic test instruments are required. The beginning hobbyist often has a VOM, DMM, and noise generator handy for continuity, voltage and resistance measurements. The intermediate hobbyist or electronic student may know how to operate the oscilloscope, audio signal generator, and external audio amplifier. The electronic technician should have a frequency counter, advanced digital-multimeter, transistor testers, distortion analyzer, dual-trace scope, digital capacitor meter, test gauges and disc upon the service bench to provide accurate and precise adjustments upon audio and video products. A remote-control transmitter tester is a handy gadget to test those infrared-and ultrasonic-type remotes.

## VOM and DMM

From the beginning, the volt-ohm-current me-

Fig. 1-1. Here the record turntable is getting a good cleanup after installing a new cartridge and stylus.

ter (VOM) has been the old standby tester of the electronic industry. Everyone must have a portable VOM meter. Fairly accurate voltage, ohm, and current measurements can be made with the VOM pocket meter. Today the digital multimeter (DMM) has practically replaced the VOM (Fig. 1-3). In addition to normal voltage and resistance measurements, the DMM can make accurate low-voltage and resistance measurements required with transistors and integrated circuits (IC). Open or shorted tape head and motor windings are easily located within the tape, disc, and VCR player/recorder. With the additional diode test, you may check for an open or leaky junction of the suspected transistor on the DMM. The low-priced pocket-type DMM is a handy-dandy tester that can solve most service problems related to electronic and mechanical operations.

## Noise Signal Injector

You may quickly locate the defective stage with the hand-held noise signal generator at both audio and rf circuits of the AM-FM table and car radio. The signal may be injected at the oscillator and i-f stages clear through to the speaker since the generated harmonics may appear in the MHz range. Simply inject the noise signal at the base and collector of each transistor until the noise is heard in the speaker. Then take voltage and resistance measurements. You may assume the IC component is defective when a signal is heard at the input and no signal at the output terminal.

Fig. 1-2. The small personal cassette player is only one of the many electronic products that provides easy listening and entertainment.

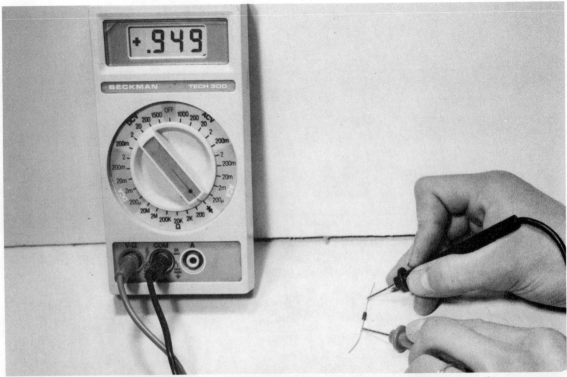

Fig. 1-3. The digital multimeter has practically replaced the VOM meter. Besides accurate voltage and resistance measurements on transistors and IC components, the DMM can also test diodes and transistors in the circuit.

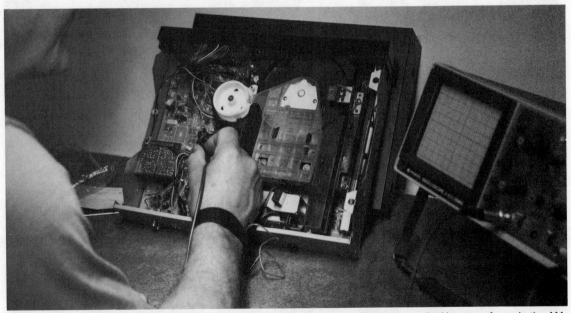

Fig. 1-4. The dual-trace oscilloscope is the ideal test instrument for making alignments and taking waveforms in the AM-FM-MPX, VCR, and compact-disc circuits.

## The Dual-Trace Oscilloscope

Although the scope has appeared on the service bench for many years in TV servicing, the new dual-trace 45-100 MHz test instrument is ideal for video and audio tests (Fig. 1-4). Both audio stereo channels may be checked at the same time, indicating weak, distorted, and intermittent components. The dual-trace scope may be used in AM-FM-MPX alignment procedures. Compact-disc signal tracing, alignment and offset adjustments are critical tests made with the oscilloscope (Fig. 1-5). Locating correct waveforms and adjustments in the VCR circuits requires a high frequency scope.

## Miscellaneous Test Equipment

The digital multimeter is the ideal instrument in taking critical voltage measurements, while the VTVM is required in compact disc and receiver alignment procedures. The audio-frequency-oscillator generator is used in signal tracing and distortion tests with the critical audio circuits. A digital capacitor meter can locate the intermittent or open capacitor in audio or video circuits (Fig. 1-6), while the frequency counter, distortion analyzer, and laser power meters can perform critical adjustments in the audio and compact disc players. Although many of the miscellaneous test instruments

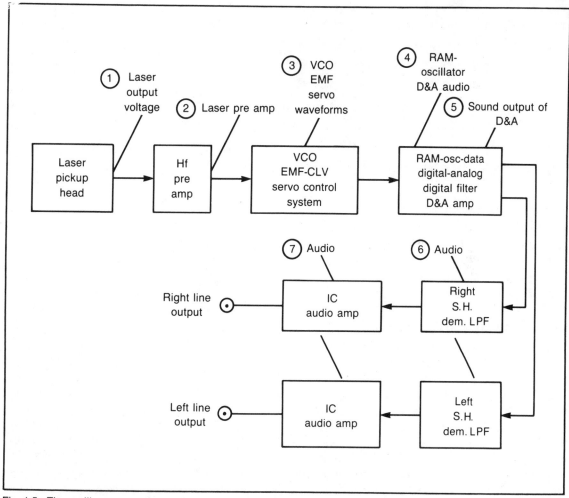

Fig. 1-5. The oscilloscope can be used to signal-trace the various waveforms of the different circuits in the compact disc player.

Fig. 1-6. The digital-capacitor meter can quickly locate open or dried-up coupling and filter capacitors in the audio circuits of electronic entertainment products.

are not required by the beginner or intermediate student, the electronics technician must be able to operate most test equipment in order to service today's diverse assortment of electronic devices.

## SIMPLE TROUBLESHOOTING PROCEDURES

Before attempting to replace the defective component, a few concise troubleshooting procedures should be followed. The defective component may be located with a block or schematic diagram, voltage and resistance measurements, and accurate transistor or IC component tests. Try to isolate the defective stage with symptoms and the block diagram (Fig. 1-7). After locating the defective stage on the schematic, take critical voltage and resistance measurements, and then accurate transistor and IC tests.

## HOW TO LOCATE THE DEFECTIVE COMPONENT

The open or leaky transistor and IC components are easily located with transistor and critical voltage measurements (Fig. 1-8). Usually the open transistor indicates a higher than normal voltage at the collector terminal. Remember, the open transistor under test may be shocked into operation when the test probes are applied to the transistor leads. Usually the leaky transistor shows a low-ohm measurement between at least two elements of the transistor. The diode and transistor tests of the DMM will quickly indicate a leaky or open transistor.

The defective IC component may be located with critical voltage measurements, signal in, and signal out test procedures. Usually, if the IC com-

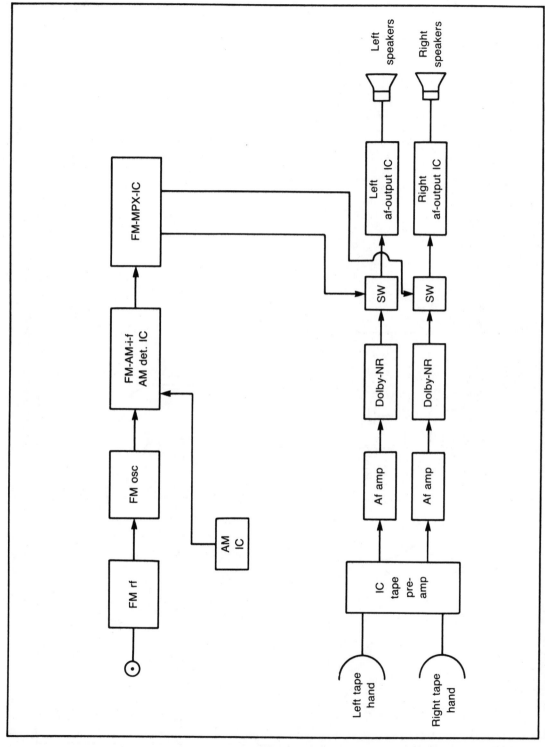

Fig. 1-7. Isolate the defective stage on the block diagram and apply it to the schematic to locate the defective component using signal-tracing methods.

7

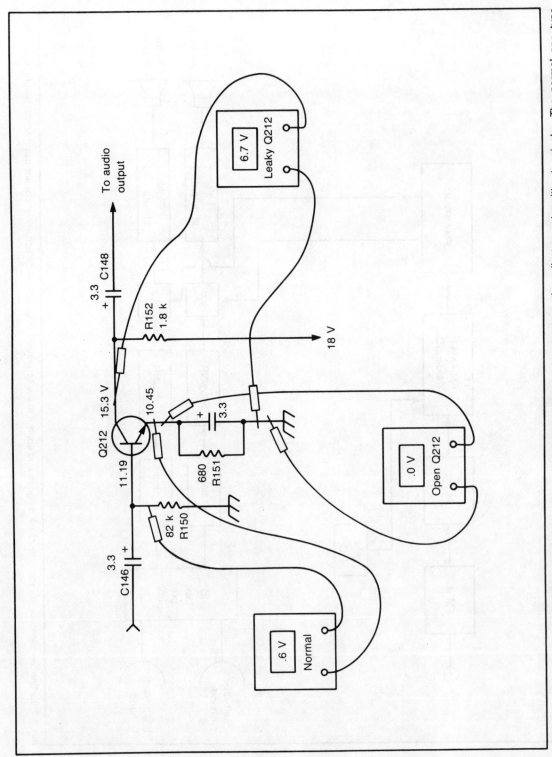

Fig. 1-8. An open or leaky transistor can be located using critical voltage measurements on the collector and emitter terminals. The normal npn type transistor should have a .6-volt forward bias voltage.

ponent has very low voltage upon the supply terminal when an rf or af signal is injected at the input terminal, and no signal at the output, you may assume the IC or components surrounding the IC are defective. The same test applies when the signal is found at the input but none is found at the output terminal of the IC component. Critical voltage, resistance, and capacitor checks of components tied to the IC will locate the defective part.

The intermittent transistor or IC component may be located with critical, monitored-voltage tests, signal in and out, and audio signal-tracing methods. Often, the intermittent transistor or IC component may be shocked into normal operation, when test leads are applied to the component or nearby. Several coats of cold spray or heat from a hair dryer may cause the intermittent component to act up. Rf and audio signal-tracing procedures may locate the defective component.

### The Digital Multimeter (DMM)

The digital multimeter is one of the most versatile test instruments devised in the past few years. Very low and critical voltage measurements made

with the DMM can locate a defective transistor, IC, or leaky component. Usually, a quick low-voltage measurement between emitter and base terminal indicates if the transistor is defective (Fig. 1-9). Npn transistor bias voltage is .6 volts with a .3-volt bias for geranium transistors. The junction of the transistor may be further tested with the diode-transistor test.

Improper or real low voltages upon the IC component may indicate a leaky integrated circuit. Very low voltages upon certain IC terminals may indicate a defective IC. If the supply voltage is very low upon the supply voltage terminal, you may assume the IC is leaky. To perform the low-voltage measurement, remove one lead of the suspected bypass capacitor tied to the IC terminal. Now take another capacitor test. The signal in and out test of the IC while running red hot will quickly locate the leaky or shorted IC component (Fig. 1-10).

### VOLTAGE AND RESISTANCE MEASUREMENTS WITH THE DIGITAL MULTIMETER

The digital multimeter is the ideal instrument to take critical voltage and resistance measure-

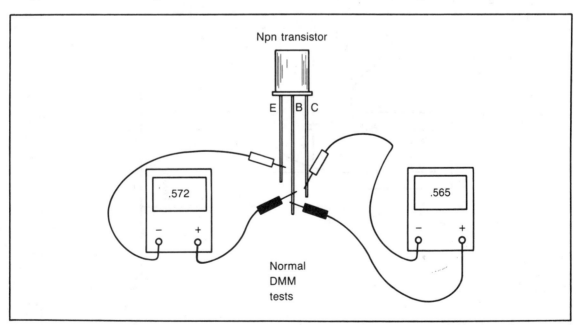

Fig. 1-9. The junction of a transistor may be tested in or out of the circuit with the DMM. The base terminal of the transistor is always common to the other collector and emitter terminals.

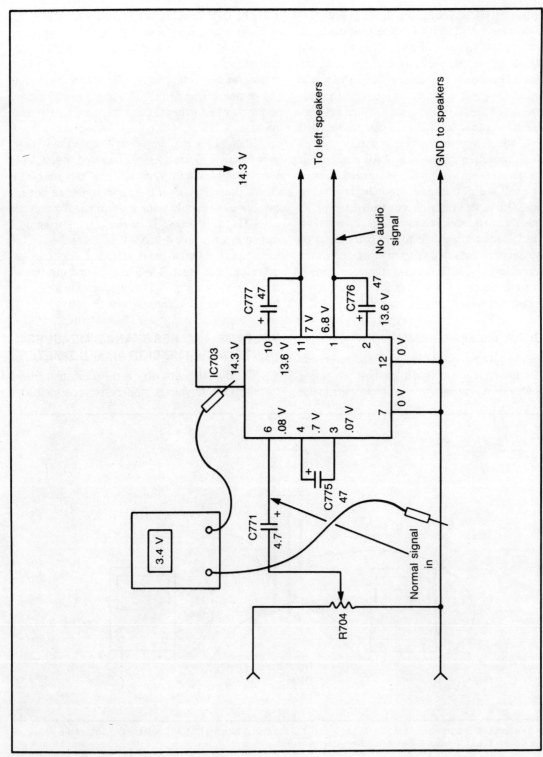

Fig. 1-10. Critical voltages on the IC terminals may indicate a leaky or open component. Low voltage at the voltage supply terminal often indicates a leaky IC.

ments for in-circuit tests. Besides taking very low voltages upon the transistor, the bias voltage test will indicate if the transistor is defective. When no bias voltage (.6V) measurement is found between base and collector terminal of an npn transistor, you may assume the transistor is defective. If the collector voltage is higher than normal, with no emitter voltage, the transistor is open. Very low collector with higher than normal base and emitter voltage may indicate a leaky transistor. The emitter voltage may be quite high if the emitter resistor is open.

Critical voltage measurements on the IC component may indicate a leaky or open IC (Fig. 1-11). First, measure the supply voltage terminal of the IC component. Very low terminal voltage may indicate a leaky IC. Higher voltages upon other ele-

ments of the suspected IC may indicate open internal components. If the supply voltage terminal is very low, remove the IC terminal with solder wick and take another voltage measurement at the pin. The IC component may be leaky if the supply voltage rises above normal. Now, take a resistance measurement of the supply IC pin to ground. A measurement under 1 k ohms indicates a leaky IC component (Fig. 1-12).

Accurate resistance measurements of transistor and IC bias resistors may turn up an open or an increase of resistance. Take accurate resistance measurements between each IC pin and common ground and compare with the schematic. If the resistance is fairly low, remove the suspected pin from the circuit and take another measurement. If the resistance measurement is now increased, sus-

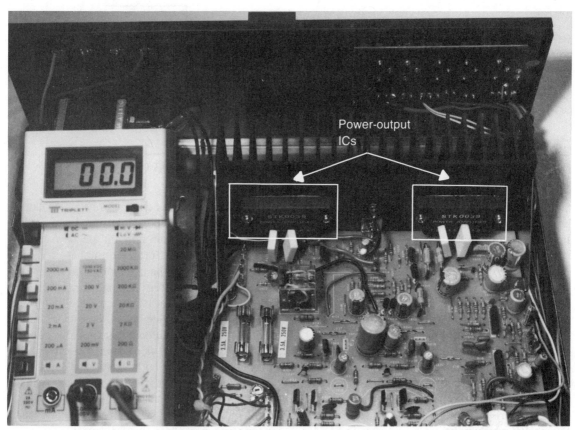

Fig. 1-11. When lower than normal voltages are found on the IC, suspect a defective power supply or leaky IC. Remove the voltage supply pin from the circuit and see if the voltage increases, indicating a leaky IC component.

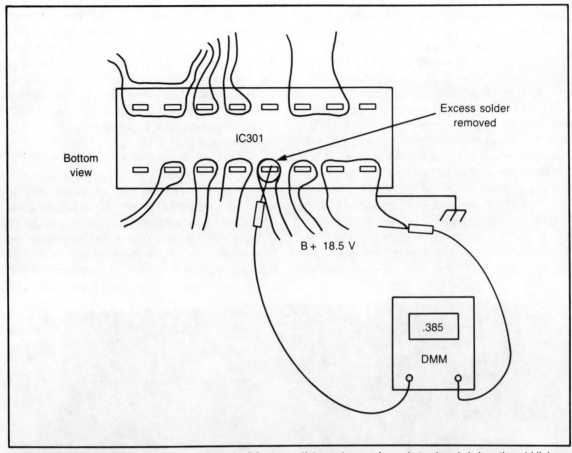

Fig. 1-12. Remove the suspected leaky pin from the PC wiring. If the resistance from pin to chassis is less than 1 kilohms, suspect a leaky IC.

pect a leaky IC. Sometimes a leaky capacitor may be located with accurate resistance tests between IC pins and ground.

## HOW TO TEST TRANSISTORS IN-CIRCUIT

Transistors may be checked in the circuit with accurate voltage measurements, transistor tester, and the diode-transistor test of the DMM. Accurate forward bias-voltage measurement between emitter and base terminals may indicate if the transistor is normal. The normal silicon npn type will have a .6 volt and the pnp germanium transistors a 0.3-volt bias measurement (Fig. 1-13).

There are many good transistor testers upon the market which make in-circuit tests. The DMM diode-transistor test is accurate and within minutes

all of the transistors of the audio channels can be tested. Remember, the base terminal is the common test point between npn and pnp transistors. Place the positive test probe to the base terminal of the transistor and the black probe to the collector and then the emitter terminal. A normal comparable resistance measurement will be found between base and collector and base and emitter terminals. If the measurement is very low, suspect a leaky transistor, and also a leaky transistor with a low measurement in both directions. You should have only one reading in the forward direction with a normal transistor. A measurement in both directions indicates a leaky one. Reverse the test leads for the pnp types. Place the negative (black) probe at the base terminal and take the same tests. Of course, the open transistor will have no measurement in any direction.

## Too Hot to Touch

Suspect a leaky transistor or IC component when it runs very hot (Fig. 1-14). Some power output ICs and transistors operate at a normally warm temperature. You may find a warm regulator transistor within the low-voltage power supply. All other transistors should not be too warm to touch. Sometimes with a change in the bias resistors or with an increase in the supply voltage, the IC or transistor will run warm. Often, a hot power-output IC or transistor is leaky or has a leaky driver or bias diode in the directly coupled input circuits. Most high-powered audio amplifiers output ICs or transistors may operate warm with higher supply voltages. High distortion and weak sound may result from leaky power output transistors or IC components.

## HOW TO SIGNAL TRACE THE VARIOUS STAGES

Signal tracing is another quick method for locating the defective stage and component. The noise generator, scope, and external audio amp may be used for signal tracing in the rf and audio circuit of any consumer electronics product. A pencil-type signal injector may quickly signal-trace the radio circuits from antenna through to the speaker. The scope can check those missing waveforms of the VCR and compact disc player, while the external audio amp may be used to check the audio signal in radios, amplifiers, cassette tape, and the compact disc players. Also, signal-tracing methods may locate distorted and intermittent circuits.

Base

Emitter

Pnp germanium transistors

Fig. 1-13. The normal npn-type transistor has a .6-volt forward bias voltage between emitter and base, while the pnp geranium transistor has a .3-volt bias.

Power ICs

Large bias resistors

Fig. 1-14. The too hot to touch transistor or IC component often indicates a leaky or shorted condition. Sometimes the IC body may turn grey when overheated. Usually burned terminal pin connections are found on the PC board.

## IDENTIFYING CORRECT COMPONENTS

Sometimes transistors, ICs, capacitors, and various resistors are difficult to identify in some electronic chassis. The transistor may be marked with code numbers or with the actual type of transistor. If the numbers are smeared or cannot be seen clearly with a magnifying glass, replacement may be very difficult. You may find some IC components which have run quite warm and the markings on the components are blurred or difficult to make out. Small resistors may be burned into or the color code may not be clear enough for correct replacement. Within the new compact-disc players, many of the chip type components are ICs, capacitors, and resistors which may all look alike but have different code numbers (Fig. 1-15).

The defective part can be identified from the manufacturer's schematic and layout charts in the service manual. In some cases, you may be able to service some units without the schematic, but with most repairs, the service manual is a must item and may save a lot of service time. You may find that tests are being made in the wrong section of the chassis without a schematic diagram. A good service manual will save you a lot of time and money in the long run. Service manuals may be ordered from the dealer, service depot, and manufacturer. Be sure to include the exact make and model number.

## PARTS SUBSTITUTION

No part operates or replaces better than the original one. The wrong size and shape can make the mounting procedure difficult in the case of

Fig. 1-15. In VCRs and compact disc player ICs, resistors and capacitor chips may look alike, with only a code numbering system to tell them apart. Check the manufacturer's service literature.

universal replacements (Fig. 1-16). Always replace with the original part number whenever possible. Of course, the original part number may not be available for several months or not at all if the manufacturer is no longer in the business. Then you must substitute another component for the defective one.

Most universal transistors and IC components can be replaced in the commercial entertainment units without any problems. Simply identify the part number and look up the universal replacement in a solid-state replacement manual. There are many solid-state replacement guides on the market, such as RCA, GE, Sylvania, Zenith, Motorola, Workman, and TAB Books. The universal replacement parts data may be included in *Howard Sams Photofacts*.

Capacitors and resistors may be replaced with other replacements except in special compact-disc chip components. Make sure the capacity and operating voltage of the capacitors are the same or

higher. Of course, your ear cannot hear the difference when replacing a bypass or coupling capacitor or .01 $\mu$F with a .015 $\mu$F capacitor. Likewise, a defective filter capacitor of 1000 $\mu$F at 25 volts may be replaced with a 2000 $\mu$F of 35 volts with better filtering action (Fig. 1-17). Critical bias resistors should have the same resistance and wattage or a larger wattage replacement.

If possible, replace the volume or tone controls with the same part number. You may find the universal replacement is too large and will not fit. When the original is not available, you may have to replace it with a universal control. Make sure the control has a flat or knurled shaft. The resistance of the control should be quite close. For instance, a 10k volume control may be replaced with a 15k control without any problems. Of course, you may have to drill out for a larger mounting hole.

Transformer replacement should be made with the original component. This is not to say there are universal transformers that may replace the defec-

Fig. 1-16. Function and sliding switches found in the cassette player must be replaced with the original part when found defective. They should be ordered through the manufacturer's dealer, distributor, service depot, or direct from the manufacturer.

tive one. Replacing with the original transformer is quick, mounts correctly, and the color-coded wires are the same. Sometimes, with universal replacements, new holes must be drilled in the chassis. The biggest problem is to make it fit in the area where the old transformer was removed.

## BEFORE REPLACEMENT

After locating the defective component, mark down where each terminal goes to the transistors. Make sure pin 1 is located on the board before removing the defective IC component which is mounted flat upon the chassis (Fig. 1-18). Of course, power ICs with leads or terminals out of one side cannot be mounted in backwards. However, the IC that mounts directly into the PC wiring can be

mounted in backwards, producing a damaged new replacement and a chassis that does not operate. Sometimes additional parts on the board are damaged by the wrong replacement.

Double-check the mounting position of critical IC processors and CPU units found in VCR and compact disc players. These many-legged components mount and solder directly on the flat side of the PC wiring. You may find chip-type devices within the compact disc player that mount into the wiring surface and are soldered at each end. Check for correct mounting and handling of these delicate chips.

## SAFETY PRECAUTIONS

When working around electronic entertainment

16

Fig. 1-17. Most electrolytic capacitors can be replaced with universal types as long as they will fit upon the board and have the same capacitance and operating voltage.

equipment, always remember that the ac power line and higher voltages are dangerous. Be careful in making voltage tests with the unit operating. Keep the metal chassis away from pipes and grounded metal with the ac-dc chassis. Service the defective device using an isolation transformer. Entertainment products with power transformers may eliminate the grounded chassis and are less hazardous to service. Always respect ac and dc voltage measurements and components when working on a ''hot'' chassis.

When handling or replacing IC processors, keep the body grounded to prevent electrostatic breakdown charges from damaging the new replacement. The wrist-strap device drains away the static electricity build-up on the human body (Fig. 1-19). Extra care must be exercised while servicing the compact disc player since the work table

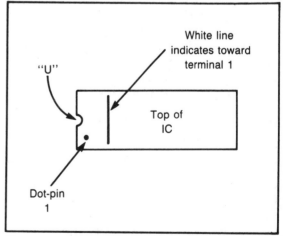

Fig. 1-18. Locate pin 1 or the U identification pin of the IC or processor before removing the defective component from the PC wiring. Installing backwards may damage other components.

Fig. 1-19. Wear a wrist-strap when servicing or replacing critical CPU or IC processors in VCRs and compact disc players.

should be at the same ground potential with player and test equipment. Be very careful not to stare at the laser beam while servicing the compact disc player. The critical CPU processor and laser optical-assemblies replacements come in a conductive bag to prevent electrostatic damage.

Some manufacturers prefer that the tempera-ture from the soldering iron should be under 270° during servicing and replacing of critical components on the PC board. To keep the temperature below this level, a silicon diode is placed in series with the soldering iron (Fig. 1-20). The diode may be inserted in series with one lead of a short ac-extension cable. Do not leave the soldering iron tip more than

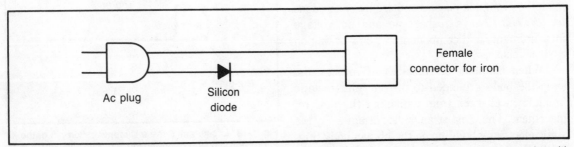

Ac plug

Silicon
diode

Female
connector for iron

Fig. 1-20. The temperature of the soldering iron may be lowered by inserting a heavy-duty silicon diode in series with one leg of the ac cord.

Fig. 1-21. Do not dig into critical circuits of the VCR or compact disc player unless you have the correct test equipment. Leave critical alignment and adjustments up to the electronics technician who specializes in these repairs.

four or five seconds upon the circuit board connection. Do not apply force on the conductor when soldering or unsoldering.

## WHEN NOT TO TOUCH

There are many sections of the complicated TV-chassis, high-powered amplifier, VCR, and compact disc machines that even the electronics technician will not touch. If you do not have the correct equipment for making alignment or waveform adjustments, do not touch those alignments or adjustment screws. Leave these repairs to the electronics technician who is a specialist in servicing these special sections. You may add a few costly items to the repair bill if you make a mistake.

Of course, this does not mean you cannot make several hundred different repairs on these machines. Just stay out of difficult situations unless you have the know-how and correct test equip-

ment. Do not try to peak up the alignment screws within the AM-FM-MPX stereo section unless you have correct FM-MPX stereo alignment test equipment. Do not dig into the VCR color circuits with poor color and try to make color trap and oscillator adjustments without correct alignment equipment (Fig. 1-21). Do not try to improve the compact-disc music by making rf offset, focus offset, and tracking adjustments without a good oscilloscope and test disc.

Simply stay out of those critical and difficult sections you know nothing about or do not have the correct test equipment for. Take the unit to those who are specialists in your own home town. Today, many electronic firms specialize in VCR and compact-disc repairs. Take the unit back to the dealer you purchased it from or to the manufacturer's servicing depot. Many manufacturers have an (800) number to call for factory service located in the operation manual.

# Chapter 2

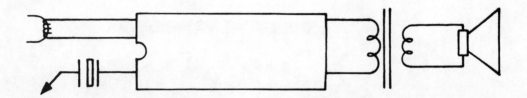

# Servicing the Compact
# Cassette Portable Stereo Player

TODAY, NO MATTER WHERE YOU LOOK, YOU may see the compact stereo cassette player in action. In the early morning hours, the tape player provides music for those running or walking. Car or truck drivers are seen with earphones clasped over their ears listening to miniature tape player music as they whiz by. Children are seen jumping up and down listening to their favorite music (Fig. 2-1). Teenagers skate down the street with music from the cassette player looking like they are in a different world. Finally, after many hours of operation, the compact cassette player stops and needs repairs.

The portable cassette tape player may be the size of a package of cigarettes or a book. Some have only earphones, while others have both earphones and speaker operation. The tape player may also contain an AM-FM-MPX stereo radio. Most produce stereo music while other models have monaural sound. You may find a few with both play and recording features.

The microcassette and mini-cassette recorders

may have one or two speeds. Dolby sound may be found in the take-along stereo portable players. Dual-stereo controls, auto-reverse, and auto stop are added features. You may find LED FM stereo and battery indicators in the latest models. Whatever the features, the small stereo cassette player is here to stay.

## CHECK THOSE BATTERIES

Most portable stereo cassette players operate from 2, 3, or 4 AA batteries. Several C cells may be found in larger models. Some models have a built-in charger feature for nickel-cadmium batteries. You may have a cassette player that operates on both batteries and ac or with a separate ac-dc adapter.

Weak or defective batteries cause the most problems with personal cassette players. If the sound becomes weak or the music slows down, suspect one or two batteries. A weak battery may cause the player to operate one hour and appear

Fig. 2-1. The portable mini-cassette player comes in many sizes and shapes. Most come with a set of earphones.

dead the next. Check those batteries before tearing into the tape player.

The batteries may be checked on a regular low-priced battery tester, VOM, DMM, or a home-made LED tester. Each battery may be tested individually with a commercial battery tester. Turn the player on and take voltage measurements across each battery to locate the weak or dead battery with the VOM or digital multimeter (DMM) while the batteries are under load.

## HOME-BUILT BATTERY TESTER

A mini-battery checker may be constructed around several small LEDs and a Bakelite mini-box (Fig. 2-2). Choose five 1.5-volt light-emitting diodes (LED) for the indicators. Five red and one black banana jacks are used for the various voltage test points. Only a dozen parts are needed with a pair of test leads to complete the project.

All LEDs are wired in series with a tap off lead to each positive voltage test point (Fig. 2-3). The black banana jack is used for the common test probe. A red test probe is applied across the positive terminal of the battery to be tested. Mount all components on the front panel of a small plastic mini-box. Make sure the collector terminal of each LED is soldered to the positive voltage terminal. The good battery will indicate a bright LED light when a single battery is tested across the common and + 1.5-volt jacks. A weak battery will show a dim or no light of the LED.

Parts List for LED Battery Checker:

5 red banana jacks (Radio Shack 274-725 or equivalent).
1 black banana jack (Radio Shack 274-725 or equivalent).

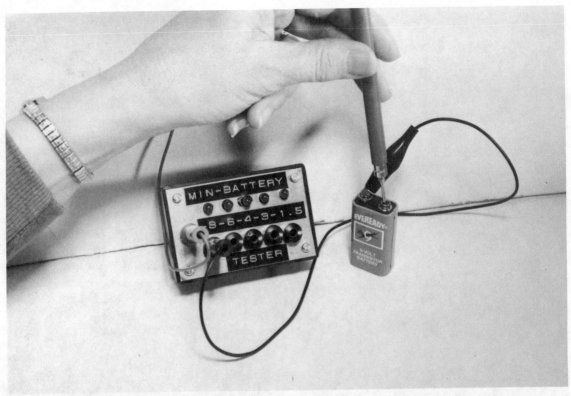

Fig. 2-2. You can build your own battery LED checker with only a few components. Check the batteries when the player slows down or becomes weak.

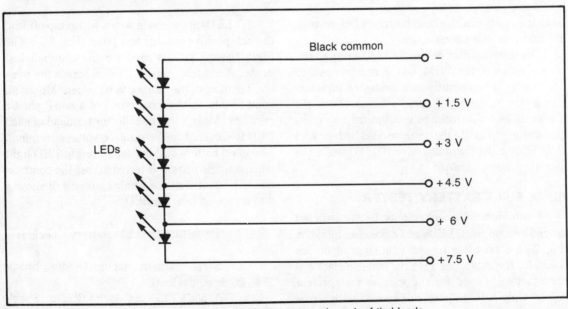

Fig. 2-3. The LED battery checker is made up of a dozen parts and a pair of tied leads.

5 1.5-volt light-emitting diode LEDs (Radio Shack 276-040 or equivalent).

1 Bakelite box 4 × 2¼ × 2¼ inch (Radio Shack 270-231 or equivalent).

1 pair of banana test leads.

## BATTERY REPLACEMENT

Always replace the defective batteries with heavy-duty types. Extra-life cells such as energizers, metal-clad, and alkaline batteries provide longer playing time for the cassette player. Nickel-cadmium batteries can be charged over and over again but cost three times as much as the heavy-duty-type battery. Choose a battery that is enclosed in metal so it will not leak all over the battery terminals. Remove all batteries if the player is not to be used for a great length of time. Suspect a leaky power-output transistor or IC component if the batteries do not last very long.

## CORRODED TERMINALS

Poor terminal contacts may result in a dead or intermittent tape player. If the batteries have been left in too long and have leaked over the battery terminals, they must be cleaned off for normal operation. Use a pocket knife or screwdriver blade to clean up the terminals. Get down inside the battery terminals at the back of the battery compartment. Wipe off the battery contacts with a cloth and cleaning solution, and shine up those battery terminals for good music reception.

## NO AC OPERATION

Some portable tape players have a jack which the outside ac adapter plugs into. Check the female jack and male plug where it plugs into the player body for poor connectors. Inspect the female jack for dirty, shorting contacts or broken terminal wires. Make sure the plug makes good contact.

The ac adapter may be checked with the 20V dc scale of the DMM or VOM. Clip the meter leads to the positive and negative terminal of the male plug (Fig. 2-4). Usually, the center end terminal is positive. Plug the adapter into the power line and measure the dc voltage. Most universal ac adapters provide 4.5, 6, and 9 volts dc. Flex the cable and note if the voltage varies, indicating a broken cable.

Suspect a broken cable with no voltage measurement. Remove the adapter from the power line. Often, the cable breaks where it enters the male plug or at the body of the adapter. Lightly pull on the cord and plug close to the male plug. Check if the rubber cable pulls apart. Likewise, check between cable and adapter. If the rubber cable be-

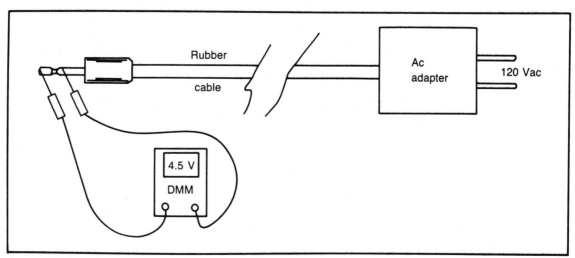

Fig. 2-4. Check for dc voltage at the male plug of the ac adapter. No voltage may indicate a broken lead or a defective power supply.

23

comes thin when pulled, suspect both wires are broken. Another method to check for a broken wire is to run a needle through the cable at the adapter and take a low-ohm resistance measurement at the male plug.

Repair the rubber cable by splicing or resoldering each wire. Remember, the dc voltage at the plug is polarized. Sometimes one wire is silver and the other copper inside the rubber cable. If both wires are copper, check out the wiring with the low-ohm scale of DMM. Determine if the tape player operates with a positive or negatively polarized center-jack terminal, then check the voltage at the broken end with the DMM. Connect the two broken wires and check for correct polarity with dc voltmeter.

## SMALL AC POWER SOURCE

When the ac cord is inserted in some models, the batteries are cut out of the circuit (Fig. 2-5). A simple power supply consists of a power transformer, two rectifiers, switch, and filter capacitor. You may find an external power jack in other models.

Suspect a defective power transformer or power switch when there is no dc voltage at the motor and the output circuit. Check the continuity of the power cord to test the primary winding of the transformer (Fig. 2-6). If no measurement, suspect an open primary winding or a defective ac cord.

Test the diode rectifiers with the diode test of the DMM. Here a duo-diode is contained in one body. The full-wave rectifiers may be replaced with two separate diodes. Remove one end of the diode for an accurate leakage test. Often, the primary winding of the transformer will go open when one diode shorts in the secondary. Do not overlook dirty contacts at the battery and ac shorting switch when the power cord is removed. Spray the switch contacts with cleaning lube and use the blade of a pocket knife to clean them.

## CLEAN UP, CLEAN UP!

A dirty tape lead may cause a dead channel or distorted and weak music. If used extensively, clean up the tape head at the end of the week with alcohol and cloth. Use a cleaning stick if the head is down inside the plastic front piece (Fig. 2-7). Remove all excess oxide from the front of the tape head and tape guides. Do not use a sharp instrument or screwdriver blade to clean off embedded oxide. You may damage or scratch the front of the tape head.

Clean all brown oxide dust from the pressure-pinch roller with alcohol and a cleaning stick. Bear down upon the rubber surface to remove the brown color substance. A good cleanup of the pressure roller will leave a black rubber roller without any signs of brown oxide. Spin the rubber roller to see if it's free. A good cleanup of pulleys and capstan flywheel may cure slow-speed problems.

## SLOW-SPEED PROBLEMS

Slow and erratic speed is the second biggest problem that plagues the mini-cassette player. Excessive drag may be caused by too large a drive belt, oil on the belt, or a cracked belt. A dry capstan flywheel may slow down the tape motion. Dirty or gummed-up idler pulleys may cause slow tape speeds. Weak batteries may produce tape drag.

A defective tape motor may produce slow or no tape motion. Check for a broken belt with no tape motion and you can hear the motor operating. The defective motor may start up if the motor pulley is given a light spin. The erratic or hunting motor may have intermittent tape motion. Fast speed is generally caused by a defective motor. First, determine if the price of the motor is more than the player is worth. Replace the defective motor if there is erratic movement.

Slow speeds may be produced by a dry or binding pressure roller. Suspect excess tape around the roller bearing if the pressure roller does not spin freely (Fig. 2-8). Remove the excess with a pocket knife while rotating the pressure roller in the opposite direction. Clean off the pressure roller after removing excess tape. A drop of light oil on one side of the rubber bearing may help. Wipe off with alcohol and cloth.

If the tape motion is still slow, clean off the belt and motor pulley. Sometimes while waiting for a new belt to arrive, liquid rosin brushed upon the

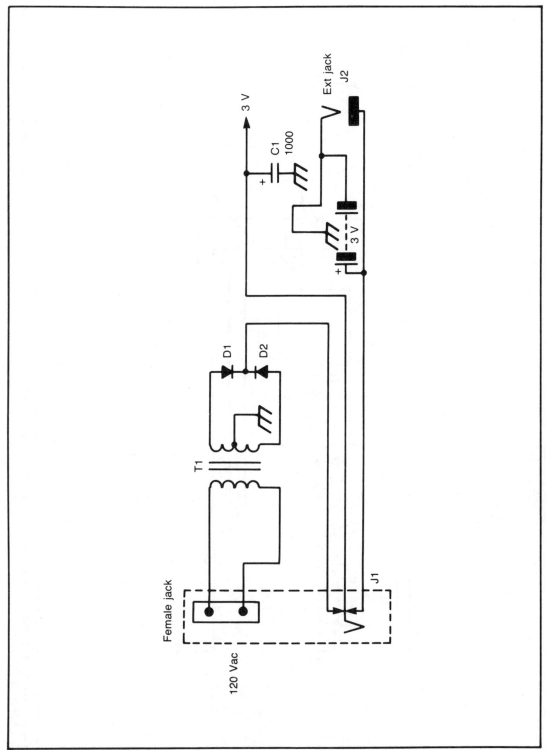

Fig. 2-5. You may find an ac power-supply circuit in some larger models. The batteries are switched out of the circuit with J1 when the ac cord is inserted.

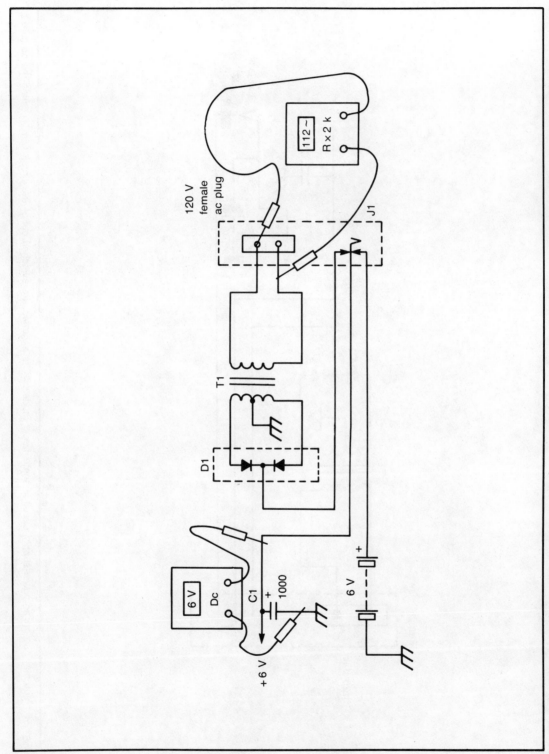

Fig. 2-6. Check for continuity of the primary winding of the power transformer with the low-ohm scale of the DMM. Measure for dc output voltages at the large filter capacitor.

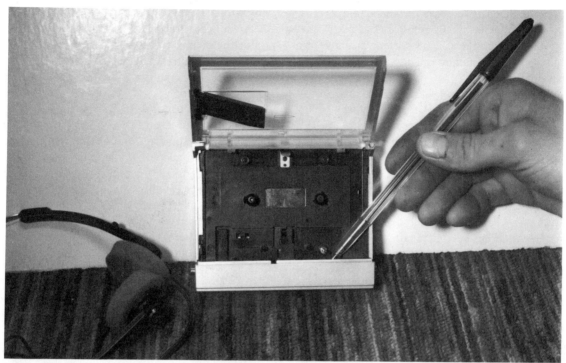

Fig. 2-7. The tape head and pressure-roller assembly are down inside the plastic case. Clean off both with alcohol and cloth.

Fig. 2-8. Excessive tape inside the pressure roller may slow down tape action. Also check the pinch roller for a dry bearing.

motor pulley may improve the speed temporarily. Clean up all idler and drive pulleys. Hold the pulleys away from the contact surface and give it a spin. Suspect a binding bearing if the pulley does not spin freely.

A dry capstan flywheel may cause slow and erratic speeds. Sometimes the speed is normal when first turned on and then slows down. Often the PC board chassis must be removed to get at the flywheel. Leave the flywheel alone if it spins. If not, remove bottom flywheel support and then flywheel. Clean off bearings with alcohol. Apply a drop of light grease on capstan bearing. Clean off capstan and flywheel after it is mounted. A drop of oil upon squeaky bearing may eliminate the noise.

**No Play—No Motion.** A dead tape player may be caused by defective batteries. If the player operates on ac but not batteries, suspect poor battery contacts. Check the ac-dc change-over switch for dirty contacts. Likewise, if the player works on batteries and not ac, check the ac power supply.

Notice if the speaker indicates some sound when the volume control is rotated up or down. Suspect a defective motor if some signs of audio are present but there is no tape rotation. Measure the dc voltage at the tape motor terminals. Replace the tape motor if there is adequate voltage but no rotation.

**Sluggish Play Mode.** Erratic tape motion may result from dry pulley or capstan bearings. A

gummed-up pulley may cause the tape to drag. Check the pinch roller for excessive tape wrapped around the roller bearings. Note if the tape is spilling out or bunching up at the pressure roller. Excessive oxide on the pressure roller may cause sluggish operation.

**Keeps Eating Tape.** Excess tape may be pulled out of the cassette by a sluggish or stopped take-up reel or spindle. The take-up reel may be rotated with a small belt or idler wheel. Check the take-up spindle for dry bearings. A worn, rubber pressure roller may spill out tape from the cassette.

The take-up reel pulley may be slipping due to a slick or worn drive pulley. Clean up all belts and pulleys. Adjust the take-up tension if found. A small spider may be rotated on a higher plane surface for more tension. While in other models, turning a small screw tightens the take-up reel tension.

**Flywheel Thrust Adjustment.** Improper flywheel adjustments may cause the tape to slow down or bind. The flywheel may be frozen if the thrust adjustment is too tight. You may find a small adjustment screw at the rear support plate of the flywheel assembly. Adjust the screw so there will be .05 to .10 millimeter clearance between bearing and flywheel (Fig. 2-9). You may find only a flat plate across the flywheel end bearing without any adjustment. Notice if the metal plate is bent inward. Remove and straighten the flat face-support piece.

**No Fast Forward.** The fast-forward gear en-

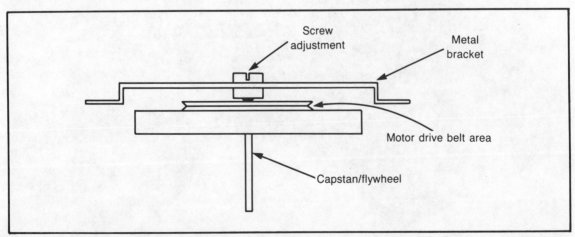

Fig. 2-9. Check the capstan/flywheel for a bent bottom support plate for slow or erratic speeds. Some mini-cassette players have a small adjustment screw for end-play.

Fig. 2-10. Two separate flywheels are found in models with auto reverse. Also, two separate pinch rollers are engaged.

gages the take-up gear or pulley to rapidly pull the tape forward. In most cases the whole play assembly does not come forward in fast-forward mode. Improper seating of the fast-forward gear or slipping of the drive pulley may cause erratic or improper fast-forward action. Check each rubber pulley for wear and cracked areas.

Fast-forward operation may be sluggish or slow because of a defective clutch assembly in older tape players. A good cleanup and resurfacing of the pressure area may help. Clean up the take-up spindle bearings and drive area. Make sure the whole assembly is not loose or out of line. Sometimes, a couple loose screws around the motor mount may produce slow and erratic speeds.

**Improper or No Auto Reverse.** In some mini-cassette players you may find the auto-reverse feature. When the cassette tape is finished or comes to the end of the reel, extra pressure is applied to a ratchet lever, causing the auto-reverse gear to be pulled into action. The tape is reversed and starts to play in the opposite direction. Also, two separate pinch rollers and tape heads are engaged in a mechanical auto-reverse procedure. Two separate capstan/flywheel assemblies are found in these models (Fig. 2-10). Check the auto-reverse gear for gummed bearings. Notice if the ratchet lever is pulling the auto-reverse gear into service. The reverse arm lever may be bent, preventing the reverse gear from sliding into operation.

In some models the tape motion is reversed by two separate reverse switches. The dc motor polarity is reversed in a controlled IC circuit. You may find a separate speed control adjustment with a motor-controlled circuit (Fig. 2-11). Because most motor-controlled and auto-reverse circuits are quite complicated, they should be checked by factory repair depots.

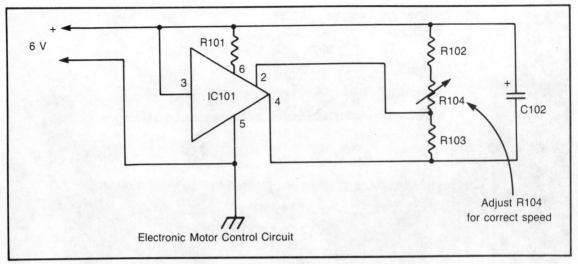

Fig. 2-11. You may find an electronic motor-control circuit in the more expensive models.

**Automatic Stop.** The automatic stop mode may be controlled mechanically or by an electronic auto-stop circuit. A photocoupler may control a transistorized or IC stop circuit. A lot of the mini-cassette and cassette decks have a mechanical stop mode after the cassette is stopped.

The mechanical auto-stop lever is pressed against the tape area (Fig. 2-12). Extra pressure is applied to the stop lever when the tape stops playing. The stop lever may push a long lever against a trip post mounted on the large capstan. Automatically, the stop switch is tripped, shutting down the small dc motor. The auto-stop trip-lever pressure may be checked with a tension gauge when the player is in the play mode.

**Frozen Capstan.** In many of the latest mini-cassette players you may find two capstan flywheel assemblies instead of separate reel assemblies. While other models may have one capstan flywheel assembly with one pressure-roller assembly. Check for a frozen flywheel assembly with no tape action and the motor is rotating. The motor drive belt may be off.

After several years of use, excessive oxide may get down inside the capstan bearing assembly, producing a dry bearing. Gummed up or dry bearings may cause a frozen capstan assembly. Before removing the capstan flywheel, determine if the

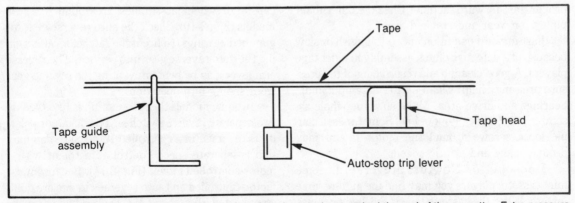

Fig. 2-12. The auto-stop trip lever is put into service when the tape has reached the end of the cassette. Extra pressure applied to the auto trip lever stops the drive motor and tape rotation.

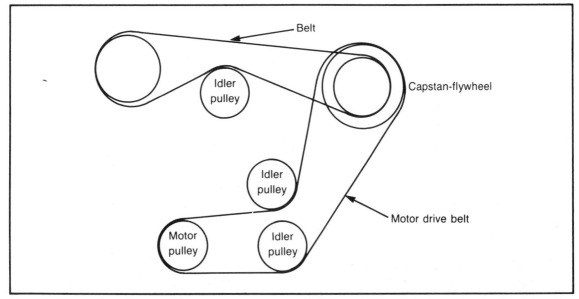

Fig. 2-13. Before removing a worn or loose belt, check the rotation and idler pulley area. Sometimes the motor drive belt drives the capstan/flywheel directly without any idler pulleys in between.

motor belt goes around several pulleys. Often the flywheel drives other tape functions besides tape action (Fig. 2-13).

Remove the bottom support bracket and drive belts. Disengage the flywheel assembly. The flywheel may be rotated to remove it if the bearing is frozen or very dry. Clean out the bearing hole with alcohol and a cleaning stick. Wipe off the drive shaft and flywheel. Get down inside the belt drive grooves. Apply a drop of light grease on the capstan bearing. Replace motor and drive belts, if loose.

## STUCK OR JAMMED BUTTONS

Most all function controls are placed into action by pushing a plastic function button. In turn, each button controls a lever or switch to change each function mode. Sometimes, these plastic buttons will get out of line or bind against the plastic housing. A coat of silicon spray down alongside each button may solve the sticky-button problem.

The plastic lever or button may be repaired if it pops off each time the button is pressed down. Cement the button to the function lever with epoxy cement. Ordinary cement will finally break

loose. Make sure the function lever is straight and not bent out of line. Remember, the recording button will not engage if the indent area is knocked out of the cassette. Locate the protection record trip lever at the back of the cassette area, and pull it down to see if the record button will now engage.

## LOUD RUSHING NOISES

Suspect broken wires at the head terminals if only a loud rush can be heard on both or one stereo channel. Notice if the rush disappears with the volume turned down. Often the top cover must be removed to get at the tape head terminals. These wires break right where they solder to the tape head. Be careful in stripping back the broken wire. Tin the wire and solder to the terminal without any wires connected to it. Use a small low wattage soldering iron.

## NO SOUND OR WEAK SOUND

Clean off the tape head with alcohol and cloth when one stereo channel is dead or weak. The oxide-packed head may produce distortion in addition to weak sound. No sound with a loud rushing noise may be caused by a broken tape-head wire. Check the continuity of the tape-head winding with the low-ohm scale of the DMM or VOM.

Moving a metal screwdriver blade close to the tape head with volume control wide open will indicate whether the tape head and amplifier are alive or not. Place the blade of a screwdriver on the red or white terminal of the tape head. You should hear a loud hum with the volume turned up. If not, check the defective amplifier.

The stereo audio amplifier section may consist of transistors or IC circuits. IC components are found in the latest mini-cassette players. Take critical voltage and resistance measurements on each transistor. Too high collector voltage may indicate an open transistor. Very low voltages on all three terminals of the transistors may indicate a leaky transistor. Check all voltages on the suspected IC terminals. Compare the voltage measurements with the good stereo channel.

You may find only one IC component in one complete stereo channel, while in others one pre-amp IC component may combine both channels with another IC as power output (Fig. 2-14). In the early models transistors were used as pre-amp and af stages with a power IC output. Check Fig. 2-15 for the most dead and weak components in the audio IC output stages.

## DISTORTION

A packed head with oxide may produce weak and distorted music. Check for a weak battery. Sometimes a weak battery will cause motorboating and distortion in the speaker. Inspect the speaker for a dropped or loose cone. Clip another speaker across the speaker terminals or switch speaker leads with the good speaker. Suspect a defective earphone or jack for distortion.

Most distorted music is located in the audio output stages. Isolate the correct earphone with the distorted channel. If both channels are distorted, suspect a weak battery or one audio IC which combines both output channels. Take critical voltage measurements on the output IC with the DMM. Remember, these voltages are very low in mini-cassette players.

The volume was very weak and distorted in the left earphone of a Sharp QT-306D mini-cassette tape player (Fig. 2-16). Voltage measurements were quite normal when taken with a DMM on all IC terminals. Here one IC component combines the entire audio circuit. IC101 was leaky and was replaced with the original part number. Sometimes universal IC replacements are not available for critical IC components, so they must be ordered from the manufacturer or service depot.

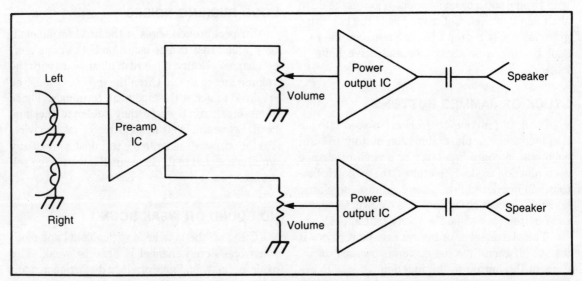

Fig. 2-14. You may find a pre-amp IC in both channels. Separate chips or a complete IC may service both audio output circuits.

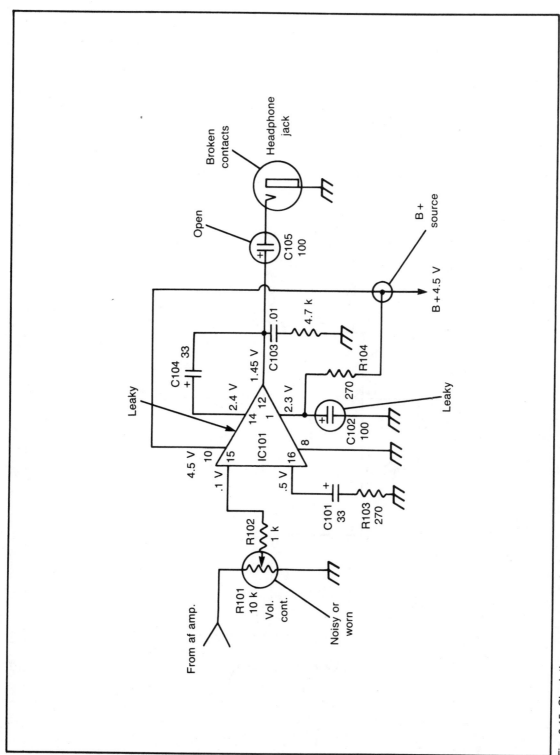

Fig. 2-15. Check these components in the case of dead or weak music.

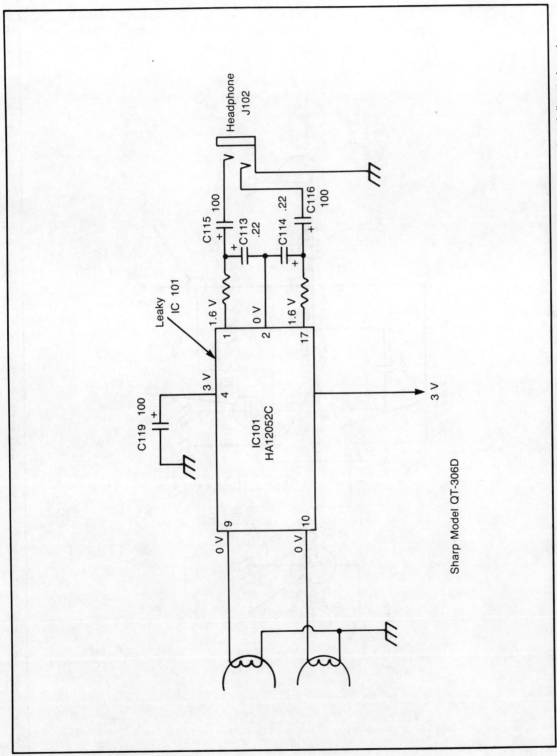

Fig. 2-16. Here one large IC component serves all audio stages in a Sharp Model QT-3060. IC101 was leaky, producing weak and distorted music.

34

## SOLDERING TECHNIQUES

Use a small, pointed soldering iron when working around small components tucked tightly beside each other in the mini-cassette chassis. The low-wattage battery iron is ideal here. You can insert a very small tip and get down to the soldered connection without melting down other components. The heat can easily be controlled with push-button action.

To prevent damage to other components, place masking tape and cardboard around them. Be careful when soldering up or removing solder from the PC chassis not to remove several components at once. Do not place too much heat on the IC or transistor terminals. Tape back all long-wire leads to PC board after soldering and testing out the player.

## EARPHONE REPAIRS

Since the mini-cassette player is handled and used in many different places, the earphone cables may be jerked and torn loose. Check the earphone cables for continuity with the low-ohm range of the DMM. Actually, most stereo earphones are small, 8-ohm speakers enclosed in a plastic and sponge rubber container (Fig. 2-17).

Each earphone may be checked for correct continuity with the low-ohm range of the DMM. Clip one lead to the far end tip and common ground (Fig. 2-18). If this measurement is around 8 ohms, clip the lead to the inside stereo channel of the male plug. Suspect a dead audio channel if both earphones measure up.

Erratic or intermittent music may be caused by a broken earphone cable or plug. Notice if the female jack is broken. Inspect the terminals inside the cassette cabinet. If only the plastic jack assembly is cracked or broken, the jack may be repaired with epoxy cement. These female jack assemblies can be ordered from the manufacturer or service depot.

Check the earphone cable by clipping the me-

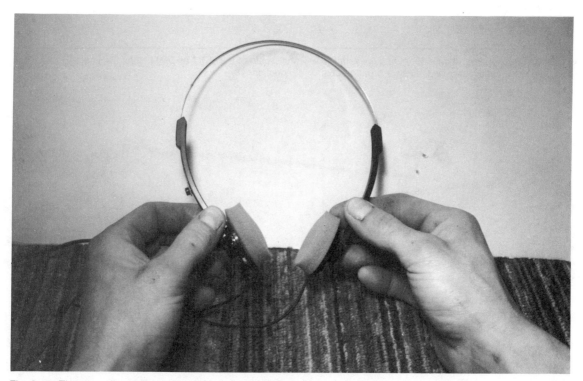

Fig. 2-17. These small earphones have tiny 8-ohm speakers inside the plastic containers. Remove the rubber cushions and pry apart the plastic case to get at the voice-coil terminals.

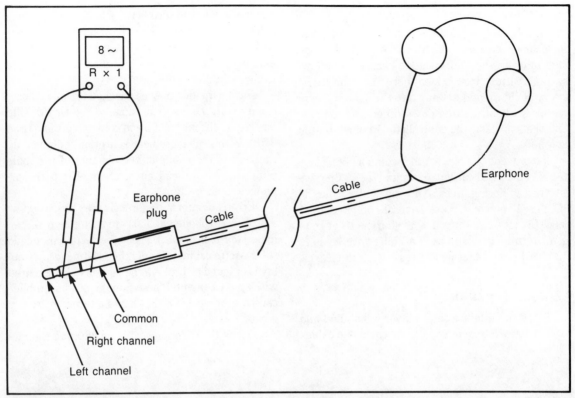

Fig. 2-18. Check the earphones for continuity with the low-ohm scale of the VOM or DMM. Flex the cable to see if the reading goes up and down, indicating a broken cable or connection.

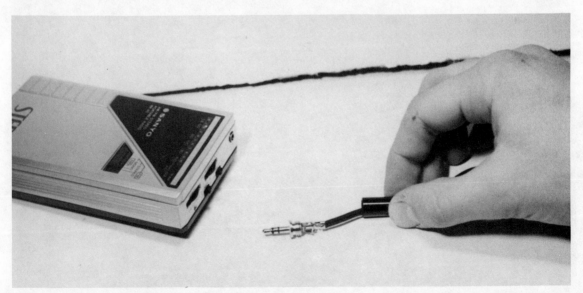

Fig. 2-19. A new male stereo plug should be installed if there is a broken cable or plug. Often the original male plugs are molded right into the rubber cable.

ter to each stereo earphone circuit with the ohm range of the VOM. Flex the earphone cable and notice if the meter hand goes up and down or open. Most cables break right at the male plug or where the cable wires go into each earphone. Cut off the broken cable at the male plug and install a new one found at most electronic mall stores (Fig. 2-19).

## SPEAKER PROBLEMS

A tinny or mushy sound from the speaker may be caused by a dropped or frozen cone (Fig. 2-20). Holes poked into the cone area may also cause noise sounds. The cone may be loose with a noisy vibration sound. No sound from the speaker indicates an open voice coil. Check the low-ohm voice coil with a DMM.

Replace all speakers with the exact impedance and shape. The older speakers may have a resistance of 3.2 ohms. Most speakers used today are the 8-ohm types. These speakers are available at Radio Shack or most wholesale or electronic part stores.

## TEN DO'S AND DON'TS

1. Do use a small, low-wattage soldering iron while working with mini-cassette stereo players.

2. Don't forget to check that the knockout is in place at the back of the cassette when recording. It may be tearing into the record-button assembly when the record button will not press down.

3. Don't purchase cheap or inexpensive cassettes when making a high-quality recording. You get what you pay for.

4. Do clean up the tape heads, reels, spindles, idler, and capstan/flywheel, as this may immediately put that mini-cassette back into operation.

5. Do not over oil or place lubricant on rubber drive pulleys. Wipe off all parts with alcohol and cloth after lubrication.

6. Don't forget to replace all batteries if you find more than one battery weak after they have been in the machine for some length of time.

7. Do remove all batteries from the cassette player if it is going to be stored or will lie around for any length of time to prevent battery leakage

on internal components.

8. Do not force the pushbutton down when they seem to stick or are frozen as you might damage levers or gear assemblies.

9. Don't tear into the chassis with electronic trouble symptoms without a schematic or proper tools.

10. Do use original components for replacement when available. They always fit right and work each time.

## FIVE CASE HISTORIES

Although the following case histories may not concern the exact model you are now working with, they may help to locate the same problem in another mini-cassette player. Here the case histories are listed by make and model numbers.

**Slow Speed—Lloyd's Model V-126.** Here the small cassette player was operating slowly, on both ac and batteries. The dc voltage was checked at the motor assembly and was very low. All batteries were removed and two were badly corroded. Replacing all batteries and cleaning up the battery terminals solved the slow-tape problem. Even the corroded and leaky batteries were pulling down the ac power supply.

**Dead, No Operation—Panasonic Model RQ 3325.** The owner complained of slow operation and now the tape cassette player refused to work. When the nickel-cadmium, rechargeable batteries were removed, the player operated from the ac power line. Here the corroded rechargeable batteries were loading down the B+ source. Replacing the rechargeable batteries solved the dead operation problem.

**Keeps Eating Tapes—GE Model M8455A.** The tape would pull out of the cassette and start to wrap around the pressure roller. All other tape functions were good. Without the cassette in place, the player was switched to play position. At first the take-up reel would rotate, then stop. A worn tire on the drive pulley of the take-up reel would not engage the idler pulley. Replacing the drive pulley solved the tape-eating problem.

Fig. 2-20. Check the speaker voice coil for the correct impedance or an open with the low-ohm range of the DMM. Note if the cone is frozen or has any tears that can cause noise and distortion.

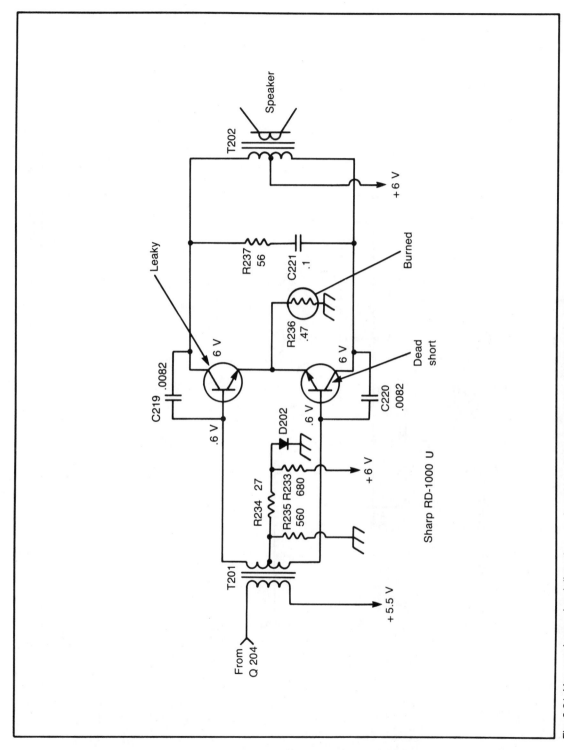

Fig. 2-21. Very weak sound and distortion was found in a Sharp Model RD-1000U. Q205, Q206, and R236 were replaced.

39

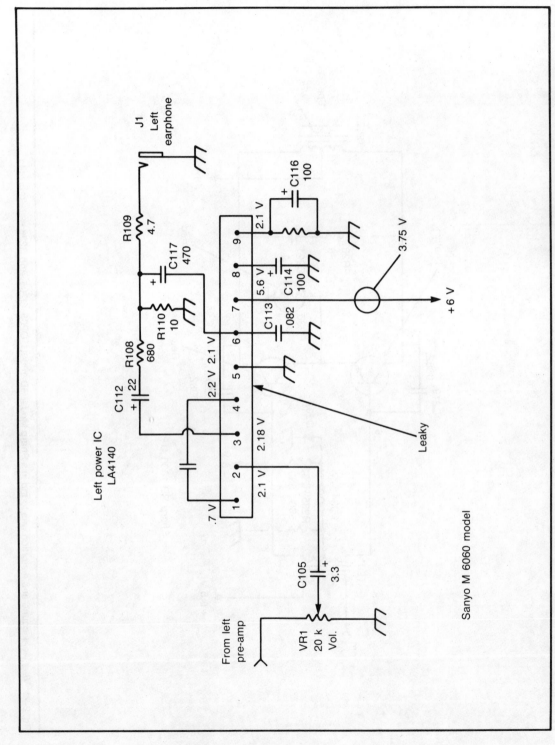

Fig. 2-22. Excessive distortion was noted in the left channel of a Sanyo Model M6060. The power IC, LH-4140, was leaky with only 3.75 volts supply voltage.

**Table 2-1. Mini-Cassette Portable Player Troubleshooting Chart.**

| Symptom | Possible Circuit | Check |
|---|---|---|
| Dead | Batteries | Check batteries; clean battery contacts |
|  | On/off or leaf switch | Clean on/off switch and check connecting wires. |
|  | Ac adapter | Measure dc voltage at male plug of adapter; check for broken cable leads. |
| No rotation | Motor | Measure voltage at motor terminals; replace defective motor. Rotate motor by hand to see if it operates. |
|  | Capstan/flywheel | Frozen capstan bearing. Check for jammed mechanism. |
| Motor rotates; no tape action | Motor belt | Motor belt off; motor belt too loose; motor pulley rotating inside belt area. |
|  | Capstan/flywheel | Frozen bearing; jammed mechanism. |
| Slow tape movement | Good cleanup | Clean all pulleys, reels, spindles, the capstan flywheel bearing, and pressure-roller belts. |
|  | Pinch pressure roller | Check bearing for excess tape or dry bearing; lubricate if necessary. |
|  | Belt | Check all belts—make sure they are tight and clean. Replace cracked or loose belts. Adjust take-up tension. |
| Sluggish fast forward | Take-up reel or spindle | Clean off pulley at rear of take-up reel—remove take-up reel assembly and clean up. Replace worn or cracked rubber pulleys slipping at motor pulley. |
| No auto-reverse | Take-up gear | Notice if take-up gear is meshing; clean up if necessary. Check for worn drive belt. Check binding of ratchet lever. Check switches and electronic motor control circuits in some models. |
| Dead left channel | Audio-output stage | Check output transistors and IC in left channel; measure and compare voltages with normal channel. Shunt speaker coupling capacitor—clip in another speaker. |
| Both channels dead | B+ source and power-output circuits | Measure voltage at the motor and audio-output transistors and ICs. Note if one power output transistor is used for both output circuits; replace defective IC. |
| Distorted right channel | B+ source | Measure voltage at B+ to audio-output transistors or IC. |
|  | Right channel output circuit | Check transistors in circuit. Measure voltages on IC and replace leaky component. Check for mushy speaker. |
| Erratic earphones | Earphone and cable | Check for a break in earphone cables. Check male plug. Measure earphone resistance; if open, then no measurement. |

**No Sound—Sharp Model RD1000U.** Very weak and distorted sound was heard in this AM-FM cassette player. Voltage measurements on both audio-output transistors were way off (Fig. 2-21). Q205 and Q206 were clipped from the chassis, with Q205 leaky and Q206 with a dead short between emitter and collector elements. R236 was found burned. Both transistors were replaced with a SK3124A universal replacement.

**Distortion—Sanyo Model M6060.** Excessive distortion and weak sound were noted in this mini-cassette stereo player with normal sound in the right channel. The supply voltage had dropped to 3.75 volts on both output ICs (Fig. 2-22). All voltage measurements on IC101 were compared with those on IC102. The top wire of the volume control on the left channel was interchanged with the right-channel control ($VR_2$). The music was normal from the pre-amp, IC301. IC101 was replaced with a LH4140 replacement.

# Chapter 3

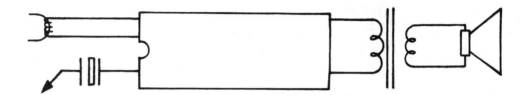

# Servicing the
# Compact Cassette Tape Deck

ALTHOUGH MANY CASSETTE TAPE DECKS may have AM-FM-MPX receiver circuits, only problems with the amplifier, low-voltage power supply, recording circuits, and the cassette player are discussed in this chapter. You may find a separate cassette deck with earphones and line-out operation which is cabled to a separate audio amp (Fig. 3-1). The cassette deck may be included in the compact stereo-component models. Wherever found, cassette deck service problems may include both mechanical and electronic repairs to keep the player operating.

## THE POWER SUPPLY CIRCUITS

A dead cassette player may be caused by a blown fuse or defective ac switch. The on/off switch may be engaged when the play button is pressed or a separate switch on the front panel. Check the play switch for dirty contacts. If the tape motion is erratic when turned on, suspect a dirty switch. Clean up with cleaning spray. Get right down into the switch controls.

With a dead chassis check for an open fuse. Replace with the exact amp rating found on the fuse or marked near the fuse holder. Suspect a defective power transformer, leaky silicon diodes, or output transistors when the fuse blows after replacement. Do not put a larger fuse in the holder. Locate the overloading component.

Quickly test each silicon diode for leakage with the diode scale of the DMM. Remove the end of each diode to perform leakage measurements. Go to the main filter capacitor and take a resistance measurement across the terminals. A low reading (under 50 ohms) may indicate a defective filter capacitor or component in the connecting circuits. Cut loose all wires or leads tied to the filter capacitor and take another measurement. Cut the PC wiring if the capacitor is mounted directly on the PC board.

**Filter Capacitor Failures**. The defective filter capacitor may become leaky, go open, dry up and show signs of white or black substance leaking from the bottom of the capacitor. Often the filter capacitor may contain one large unit (Fig. 3-2). The leaky or shorted electrolytic capacitor will blow

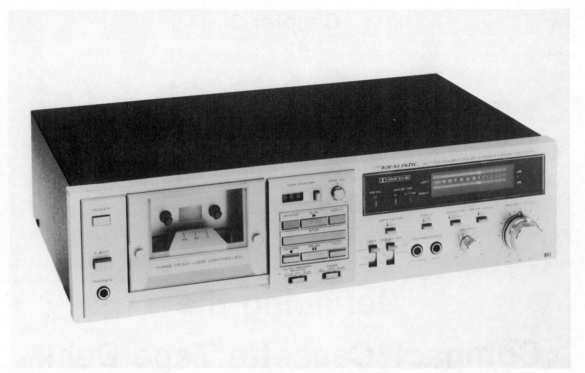

Fig. 3-1. The compact cassette tape deck may be a separate unit or combined with an AM-FM-MPX receiver and a record turntable assembly.

the fuse and load down the power transformer. An open or dried up capacitor may produce hum in the speakers. Sometimes the main positive terminal will break right off inside the capacitor. The filter capacitor may be checked for leakage with the ohm-meter or capacitance tester. Make sure the positive terminal is connected to the positive voltage source or the capacitor may appear warm or blow up with reverse polarity after replacement.

**Installing the Power Transformer**. In

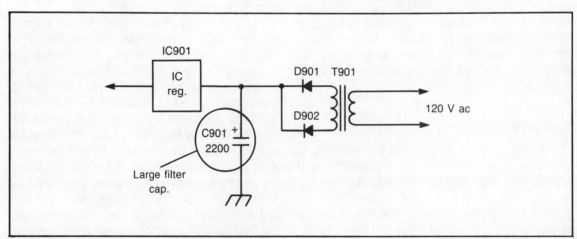

Fig. 3-2. Often only one large electrolytic filter capacitor is found at the positive output terminal of the bridge or full-wave rectifier.

early cassette players, the power transformer might have one or two extra windings for pilot, meter, and dial lights (Fig. 3-3). The B+ voltage source may originate from a fullwave or bridge-type rectifier circuit. A shorted filter capacitor, output transistor, IC, or leaky diode may destroy the power transformer. Sometimes, a shorted pilot-light assembly may open the primary winding of the transformer.

The suspected power transformer may be tested by ac voltage and low ohmmeter tests. Check the primary winding for open test with no motor rotation or sound. Measure the dc output voltage. If the dc voltage is quite low and the transformer hums when plugged into the power line, suspect the overloaded circuit. After checking the silicon diodes, remove the dc load at the main filter capacitor.

Now the dc voltage should increase at the positive terminal of the filter capacitor. Disconnect the transformer secondary leads to the bridge diodes. Plug in the power cord and measure the ac voltage across the two red transformer leads. If the ac voltage is low, and the transformer still hums, suspect a shorted winding in the power transformer. Most shorted transformers will operate very warm. Install a new transformer when it runs red hot without any load on the secondary winding.

Order the exact part number for the power transformer. If the transformer is not available, a universal type may be installed. Make sure the ac secondary voltage and wattage is the same, and the transformer is the same physical size. You may find that the universal transformer is too large to fit in place of the defective one.

Before removing the transformer, mark down where all color coded leads are connected. Cut off the transformer leads one-half inch from the soldered connection. Now the color-coded leads may be replaced with the original replacement. New mounting holes may be needed to mount the universal replacement.

**Voltage Regulated Circuits.** Suspect a defective low-voltage regulator circuit when the audio output circuits and motor are operating but the receiver or pre-amp stages are dead. The voltage-regulated circuits are a simple transistor and zener diode or an IC regulated circuit (Fig. 3-4). The dc voltage from the bridge rectifiers feed directly to the regulating component.

The higher dc voltage provides voltage to the audio-output transistor or IC components, while the regulated 12.2 volts supplies voltage to the motor. Lower, regulated IC voltage is fed to the receiver, pre-amp, and af-amp circuits. Determine what circuits are operating before taking voltage measurements, then measure the voltage source at the defective circuits. Improperly regulated dc voltages are caused by leaky transistors, zener diodes, and IC components.

## THE AMPLIFIER

The audio amplifier may be completely dead,

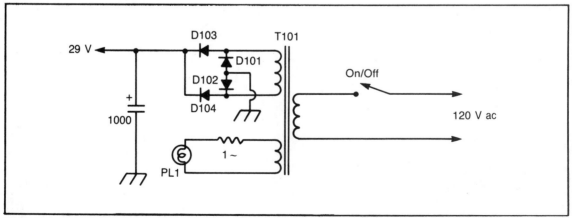

Fig. 3-3. In early models, before LEDs were used as pilot lights, there was an extra winding on the power transformer for different dial light indicators.

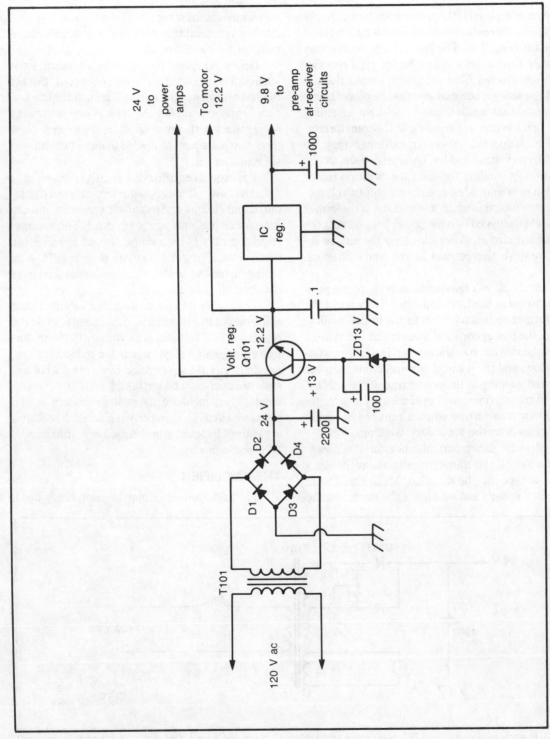

Fig. 3-4. A voltage-regulated circuit usually consists of a regulator transistor, zener diode, and IC regulator. The low IC-regulated voltage is applied to the pre-amp, recording, and front-end receiver circuits.

intermittent, weak in the left channel, noisy in the right channel, or a combination of sound problems. Before starting to work in the amp sections, obtain the correct schematic diagram (Fig. 3-5). It is very difficult to locate the defective component or take accurate voltage without a schematic. Besides critical voltages, transistor or IC parts may be identified from those listed upon the schematic. A block diagram of a dual-cassette player is shown in Fig. 3-6.

**Dead on Both Channels**. Suspect improper voltage source, poor switching, or one dual, IC output when both channels are dead. Do not overlook broken connections at the tape head. Notice if the motor is operating. Clean up the function or play switch with spray cleaning fluid. Work the switch assembly up and down to clean the contacts. Spray

it a couple of times if it still appears erratic.

Determine if the audio-output stages are dead with audio-signal-tracing and voltage tests. Sometimes a dirty or defective headphone jack may prevent music from reaching the speakers. Very low voltage at the power IC may be caused by the power supply or a leaky IC. Remove the B+ pin terminal from the IC and take another measurement. If the voltage returns, the IC is leaky. Suspect a defective power supply component if the voltage remains low.

**No Left Channel.** When either channel is dead and the other normal, you may assume the low-voltage power source is operating. Isolate the signal at the volume control to see if the trouble is in the output or pre-amp stages. Touching the center volume control terminal with a screwdriver

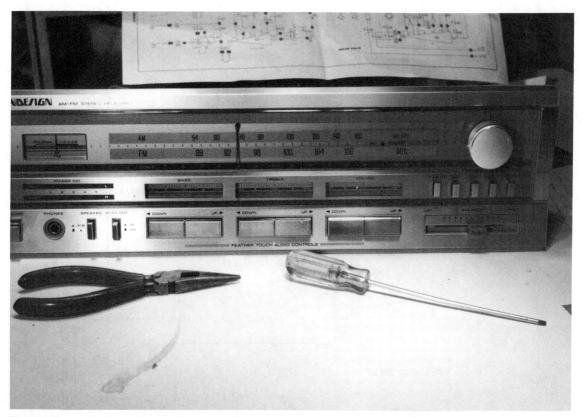

Fig. 3-5. Always obtain the correct schematic before attempting to repair the amplifier or remove circuits in the cassette player/recorder.

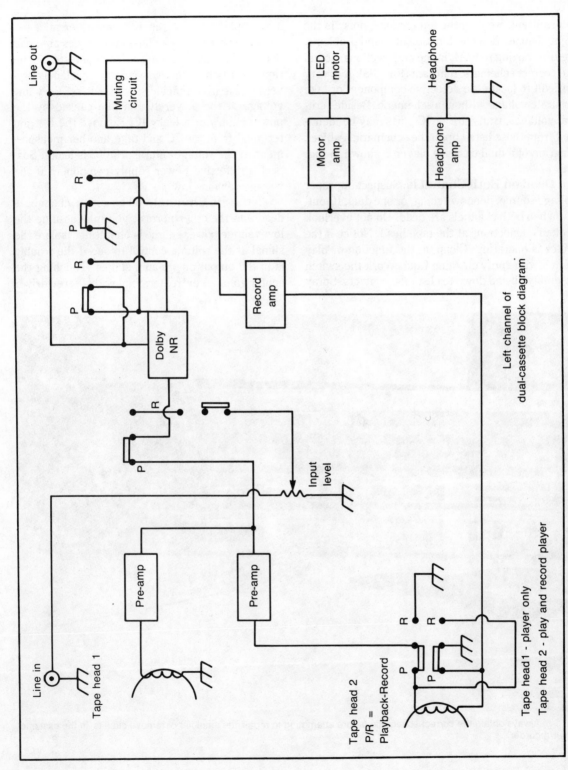

Fig. 3-6. Block diagram of the left channel in a standard stereo cassette deck.

Line out

Muting circuit

LED motor

Motor amp

Headphone

Headphone amp

R
P    P
R
P

Dolby NR

Record amp

Left channel of
dual-cassette block diagram

R

P

Input level

Pre-amp

Pre-amp

Line in

Tape head 1

Tape head 2
P/R =
Playback-Record

R    R

P    P

Tape head1 - player only
Tape head 2 - play and record player

blade or injecting audio signal will cause a hum or audio in the speaker. If not, signal trace the af and audio-output circuits.

Start at the tape head if you have a normal sound-output stage with the volume wide open. Inspect the tape-head terminals for a broken wire. Usually, a loud hissing noise will be heard in the speaker if there is a broken tape-head wire. Inject audio at the tape-head left-channel terminal. Proceed towards the first pre-amp transistor or IC component. Keep going from stage to stage until the audio appears in the speaker.

Suspect an open or shorted tape-head winding if audio is found at the tape-head wire but no music from the cassette. Check for tape-head continuity with the low-ohm scale of the VOM or DMM. The stereo tape-head resistance should be under 1 k ohms. If the resistance is below 100 ohms, suspect an internal short between winding and metal head cover. Remove both leads for this measurement.

**Distorted Right Channel.** Suspect the audio-output circuits when excessive distortion is found in both channels. Make sure the tape head is clean. Distortion may be found in either channel with a dirty tape head. Isolate the distortion with audio signal generator and scope or the external audio amp (Fig. 3-7). Excessive distortion with weak sound may be found when there is a leaky output transistor or IC.

Leaky transistors, ICs and burned bias resistors may produce extreme distortion. Open transistors or electrolytic coupling capacitors may cause some distortion in the sound. In a J. C. Penney 1770 model, the right channel had a slight trace of distortion when the volume was turned up. The right channel was signal-traced when the external audio amp showed distortion at the collector terminal of

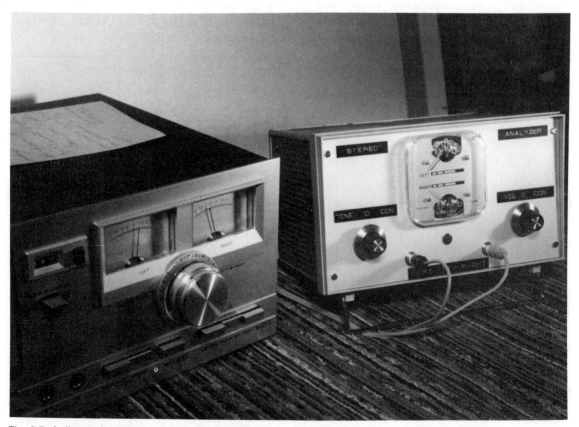

Fig. 3-7. A distorted or weak stereo audio channel may be located with an external audio amplifier.

Q401 (Fig. 3-8). Voltage tests indicated higher collector voltage. After checking the resistance and capacitors in the circuit, Q401 was replaced with an SK3124 universal replacement. When Q401 was under load, the emitter and base terminals became leaky, causing slight distortion with an increase in collector voltage. Q401 was removed from the circuit and tested normal. Sometimes replacing the suspected component is the best method.

**Noisy Right Channel.** Isolate the noisy channel by lowering the volume control. If the noise is still present, suspect a noisy transistor, IC component, or electrolytic coupling capacitor in the audio-output stages. Go directly to the output transistors or IC when a crackling noise with intermittent music is heard in the speaker. Suspect the audio output IC or power supply if the noise is in both channels.

The noisy channel may be located with the scope, external amp, or a shorting capacitor (Fig. 3-9). Scope the various audio stages and notice at which stage the noise is picked up. The shorting capacitor may be used to short out the input and output of each audio stage to ground. Make sure the electrolytic capacitor is discharged each time it is used in the circuit. It's possible to damage a transistor or IC with a charged capacitor. Go to the base and collector circuit of each af or pre-amp transistor until the noise disappears. Now replace the transistor in the noisy circuit. Check the bias resistor and bypass capacitor in the circuit. Do not overlook a small, noisy, electrolytic coupling capacitor between stages.

**Dolby Noise Rejection.** In some models, Dolby noise-reduction circuits are found to reduce the level of background noise normally introduced during tape recordings without changing the frequency response of the audio signal. Dolby B-type noise reduction acts only upon the mid and upper positions of the audio frequency spectrum. At high levels the noise is suppressed, and at low input-signal levels the signal to noise ratio (S/N) decreases and the noise is heard. The Dolby system is designed to solve this problem by boosting the low

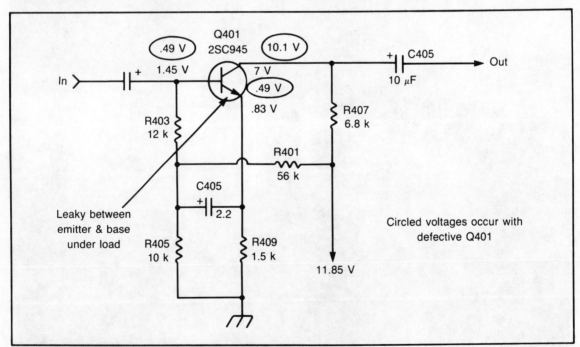

Fig. 3-8. Slight distortion in a J. C. Penney Model 1770 was caused by a leakage between the emitter and base terminals. The transistor tested good, but would break down under load.

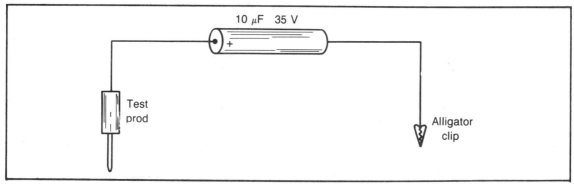

Fig. 3-9. A noisy channel can be located by shorting the audio signal to ground with a small electrolytic capacitor and test probe.

level mid and high frequencies up to a given dB level during recording and alternating the same signals during playback by an equal amount. The amount of boost-alternation depends on the level and frequency of the signal.

**Weak Left Channel.** The weak stage may occur at any point from the tape head to audio-output circuits. Even a dirty tape head may cause a weak channel. The weak signal may be signal traced with the scope or external audio amp with a cassette playing. Use a 1 kHz tone from the audio-signal generator for a slightly unbalanced or weak audio. Go from stage to stage and note where the signal is weak. Compare each stage with the good channel.

Weak audio may be caused by transistors, ICs, bias and emitter resistors, electrolytic coupling, and bypass capacitors. Suspect the 1 $\mu$F or 3.3 $\mu$F coupling capacitor with open conditions. A change in emitter or bias resistors may produce a weak stage. Shunt the electrolytic bypass capacitor across the emitter resistor after locating the weak stage. Check for an open ground or poor wiping contact of the volume control when the volume cannot be turned down in either channel.

**VU Meter Problems.** The VU or level meter may indicate if the sound is normal after the Dolby amp circuits or before the line output terminals in a cassette tape deck. If the meter is moving with the music, you know the channel is good up to this point in the circuit (Fig. 3-10). The audio signal may be signal traced from this point to the audio-output terminals or af stages.

When both speakers are working and either VU meter is dead or stuck in one spot, check the VU meter or connecting circuits. The audio may be signal traced right up to the meter terminals. Suspect an open meter winding or broken terminal wire if voltage is found at the meter but there is no movement. Check the meter movement with the low-ohm range of the DMM. Replace the VU meter, if open. If the meter hand goes up part way and sticks or stops in one place, inspect the meter dial for a warped face plate. The cardboard or meter paper may come loose and curl up, preventing the meter hand from moving. These VU meters may be repaired by removing and cementing the meter scale in place.

## THE CASSETTE PLAYER

The cassette deck may have many features, including a recording system with ac bias and four-track stereo. The erasing system may have ac bias with up to two tracks. Most cassette decks have a frequency response from 30 to 20,000 Hz. Wow and flutter are not over 0.05%-0.06% (WRMS). Some cassette players have Dolby noise-reduction system (Fig. 3-11). Automatic stop and reverse are added features. Light-emitting diodes (LEDs) are used as volume indicators in both stereo channels. With all these added features, many of them break down and must be repaired.

**Cannot Open Cassette Door.** If the door

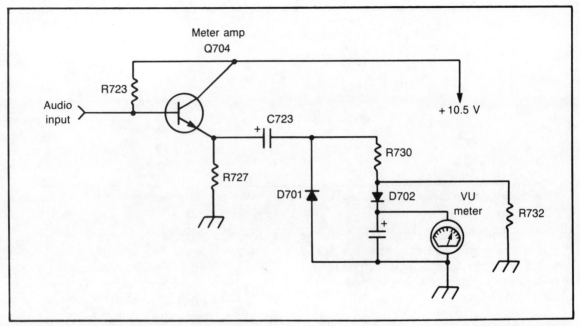

Fig. 3-10. The VU meter may have a meter amp circuit, often located before the line-out jacks in the audio circuits.

Fig. 3-11. You may find special Dolby noise-reduction circuits in some of the expensive cassette decks.

will not release and open with a loaded cassette, suspect the tape is wrapped tightly around the capstan. The excess tape must be cut loose before the door can be opened. Be careful not to damage the door assembly. Remove the front plastic door to get at spilled out tape. Rotate the capstan/flywheel at the back in opposite direction to unwind tape. Suspect a broken or bent release lever when the door will not release at any time. Sometimes the release lever can be seen with the bottom or back cover removed.

**Broken Play Button.** Excessive pressure plied to the play or rewind button may break off the small plastic end piece. The cassette deck must be removed to get at the button assembly. In the J. C. Penney Model 1782, the broken play button is lower than the others (Fig. 3-12). Remove the "C" washers and pull out rod until the broken le-

ver is free. Install a new button assembly and replace rod keeper assembly.

**Broken Pause Release.** Check for a bent pause lock plate or loose rod if the pause control will not shut off the music. The pause button pushes a rod or idler release lever to disengage the pressure roller from the capstan so the tape and music stops. Check for improper adjustment of the cassette. Notice if the release lever is not engaging the small lever on the pressure roller assembly (Fig. 3-13). The lever may be bent, letting the idler release lever slip by without taking the pressure roller off of the capstan drive assembly. A defective pause-lever assembly may result in a no-play mode. The pause control may switch the motor off pause mode.

**Broken Earphone Jack.** No sound at one or both speakers may be caused by dirty contacts

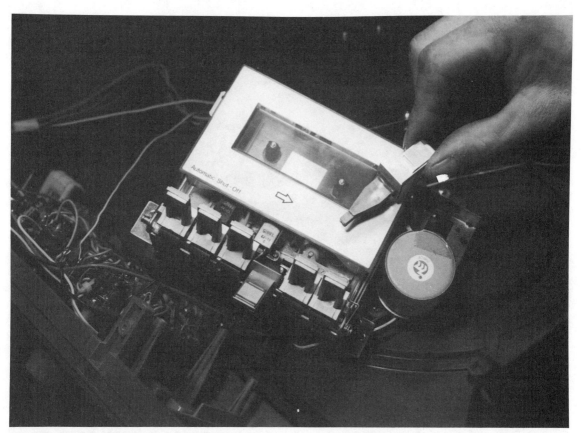

Fig. 3-12. The end of a plastic play or fast-forward button lever may sometimes break off. Replace with the original part number.

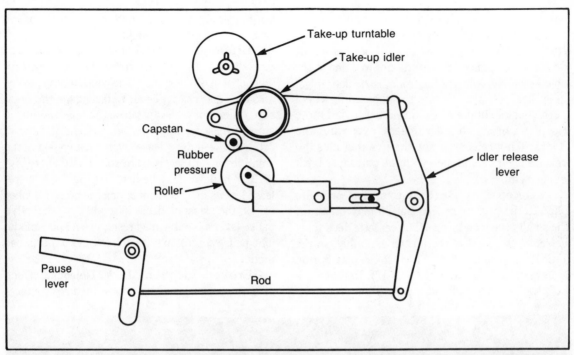

Fig. 3-13. Note if the release lever lifts the pressure-roller assembly away from the capstan in the pause mode.

Fig. 3-14. Replace the headphone jack with the same part number when a cleanup of the shorting contacts does not solve the no sound problem in the speaker or headphone.

or a broken earphone jack (Fig. 3-14). First try to clean up the shorting, internal contacts with tuner lube or spray. Work the male plug back and forth to clean contacts. Replace with the original part number if possible. Mark down all lead connections and small signal-dropping resistors before removing wires. Then remove and replace one wire at a time.

**Intermittent Function Switches.** Dirty or worn function or leaf-type switch contacts may cause intermittent or dead operation in the play mode. Suspect dirty switch contacts when the play button will not hold down in some models. A broken function rotary switch assembly must be replaced with the original part number (Fig. 3-15). Clean up all switch contacts with tuner lube or cleaning spray.

**Eats Tapes.** Excess tape may be pulled out of the cassette because of a worn or bent pressure-roller assembly (Fig. 3-16). Something sticky on the capstan drive assembly may also pull tape. Often, when the tape is not taken up by the take-up reel, the excess tape will wrap around the capstan and

pressure roller. Notice if the take-up reel has stopped or has intermittent operation. Once the tape starts to spill out, it will continue until the player stops.

**Tension Take-Up Wheel Adjustment.** Improper take-up adjustment may cause the tape to spill out of the cassette. In some models a spider spring adjustment is moved to a higher surface on the plastic take-up reel assembly (Fig. 3-17). Rotate the spider ring clockwise for more take-up tension. Some of these adjustments may be made by removing the cassette door and front metal plate covering the cassette spindle or reel assemblies, while in others, the cassette player must be removed to get at these adjustments. Improper take-up tension adjustment may produce erratic fast-forward mode operation. Improper or worn idler wheels may cause erratic take-up reel action.

**Will Not Eject Cassette.** In some models, the cassette will eject and shut off the player when the cassette finishes playing. In the low-priced models, the cassette is ejected by pushing down the eject button. Check for a dry or jammed loading

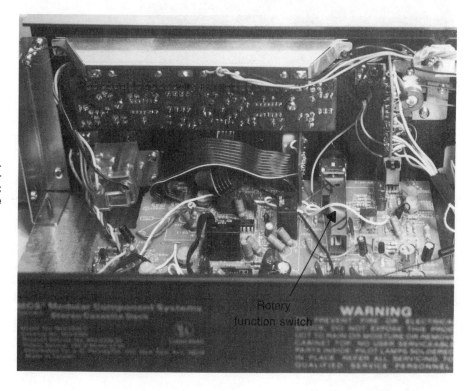

Fig. 3-15. Inspect the rotary function switch for broken contacts or PC wiring areas around the switch.

Rotary function switch

WARNING

Fig. 3-16. Tape spill out may be caused by a worn rubber pressure roller or inoperative take-up reel or turntable.

platform in the automatic-eject system. Lubricate sliding areas with a light coat of grease. Look for a bent bar lever with a ketch assembly in some models. You may find the cassette door will open slowly after the eject button is pushed. Check for broken player assembly or missing "C" washer, if the door does not automatically open up.

**Play Button Keeps Kicking Up.** A dirty play switch may not apply voltage to the solenoid, so the cassette player will not operate until the play switch is held down in some models. Note if the solenoid is energized. The automatic stop system may be shutting down the player if the tape starts and then stops. Check the automatic stop circuits when the player shuts down after a few seconds of operation. Clean up the play switch contacts.

**No Automatic Shut Off.** The electronic automatic shut-off circuit may cause the player to shut off as soon as it is turned on, after a few minutes, or not at all. The automatic shut-off circuit may be controlled with a round magnet rotating close to a sealed magnetic switch or IC component. In some models a Hall IC component is mounted close to the rotating magnet (Fig. 3-18).

When the magnet stops rotating, the IC triggers the electronic control circuit which in turn energizes a control relay, shutting off the player. Instead of the IC, a magnetic sealed switch is mounted close to the revolving magnet, closing and opening the switch terminals in some models. The magnetic switch triggers a multivibrator circuit and in turn causes a transistor to draw current, energizing a solenoid and shutting down the player.

Replace the Hall IC component and magnetic switch in models that shut down at once or in a few seconds. If the magnet stops, check if the belt is broken or off the pulley. The rotating magnet is driven with a rubber belt from the take-up reel. First determine if the automatic shut off is electronic or mechanical. Note if the relay energizes or shuts down. Replace the IC or magnetic switch if the magnet is rotating.

**No Automatic Mechanical Shut Off.** When the cassette comes to the end, extra pressure is applied to a shut-off lever. The trip lever pushes or trips a rod lever which in turn releases a flat locking-bar assembly on the flywheel assembly (Fig. 3-19). A small, protruding shaft on the flywheel locks into the lever, shutting down the player. If the flat locking-bar assembly is bent downward and out of line, the unit will not lock or shut off. When the locking bar is too close, you may hear a click-click noise as the flywheel rotates. Check that the locking bar and trip lever are not

out of line. Replace if the assembly cannot be straightened. Slipping of the take-up reel clutch assembly may not let the player shut off in some models.

**Counter Not Working.** The counter assembly located on the front panel determines the start and stop points of the tape. Suspect a broken or loose belt with no rotation. Inspect the counter assembly for dry or frozen bearings. Spray lubricant cleaning fluid down in the gear assembly of the counter if the assembly is sluggish and erratic in rotation. Replace the jammed or broken counter assembly. The counter is belt-driven from a pulley on take-up reel or spindle.

**Installing a New Tape Head.** After determining if the tape head is open, the front piece damaged, or the head has broken from the mounting plate, order the original one. If the original tape

Fig. 3-17. Move the metal spindle to a higher area on the plastic turntable for more take-up tension. Sometimes this adjustment may be made through the plastic stereo-cassette door.

Fig. 3-18. Suspect a defective IC when the magnet is rotating and the player keeps shutting off. Note if the magnet is rotating.

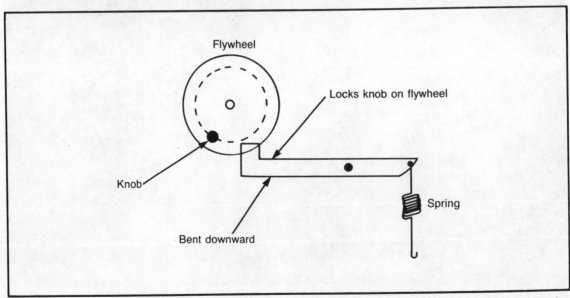

Fig. 3-19. A bent downward flat locking lever may prevent the mechanical automatic shut-off assembly from stopping and shutting off the player.

head cannot be obtained, check the schematic for correct resistance. Universal tape heads may fit with new mounting holes. You may find the same tape head in another manufacturer's model and may be obtained from that source. Often, one side of the cassette tape head is mounted tight to the head bracket, with the adjustable azimuth screw around a tension spring.

Sometimes the tape head has come loose from the mounting, or one mounting screw is missing and is out of line with the moving tape. Replace the tape head if it is broken loose from the mounting plate. Some heads are just spot-welded to the mounting plate.

Mark down all color-coded leads of the tape head. You may find separate connections for the play and record terminals in a stereo tape head (Fig. 3-20), while other tape players use the same head for both play and record. Remove one set of wires and connect to the new head. Try not to remove all the leads at once. Solder each terminal after the tape head is mounted into position. Make sure the head is straight and level with the tape before azimuth adjustment.

**Tape Head Adjustment.** Determine where the azimuth adjustment screw is located. It is usually located alongside the tape head. The azimuth screw along with the spring tension may be adjusted from the front of the cassette area by removing the plastic door. Insert a 6 to 10 kHz test cassette into the player and adjust the azimuth screw for maximum on both right and left channels.

Another method for azimuth adjustment in the line out or speaker outputs is to use two separate VTVMs, one connected to the right and the other to the left channels. Connect a 33- or 47-ohm dummy-load resistor across each speaker terminal (Fig. 3-21). Play a 6 to 10 kHz azimuth test tape.

**Bad Motor.** A defective tape motor may be dead, operate intermittently, or change to different speeds. Monitor the dc voltage across the motor terminals (Fig. 3-22). Check for broken motor wires or defective power circuits if there is no dc voltage. In some models one motor wire may go to the pause control. When the pause control is pushed down, it opens the motor connections. Inspect the

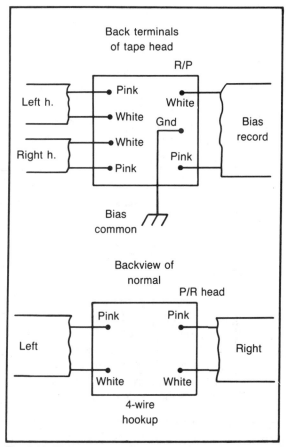

Fig. 3-20. The tape head may consist of a separate record and play tape head in one tape-head assembly. Standard record/play tape-head connections are shown at bottom.

pause-control switch for broken wires. A dirty leaf or play function switch may prevent voltage from reaching the motor terminals.

The motor may start up after the motor pulley is rotated. Sometimes tapping the shell of the motor with the screwdriver handle will make the motor change speeds. Pushing up and down on the motor lead connections may make the motor change speeds (Fig. 3-23). If the cassette is running too fast, inspect the capstan for tape wrapped around it. Check if the motor belt is operating high on the motor pulley to increase the speed. If not, replace the motor with the exact part number.

**Motor Speed Control Circuits.** The motor speed may be adjusted in some players with a

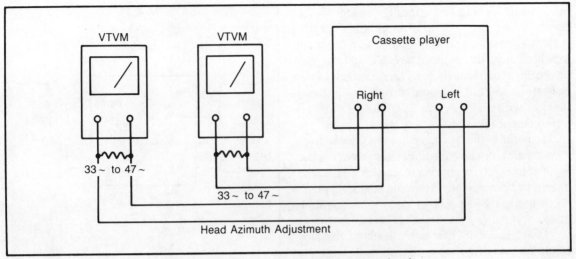

Fig. 3-21. Here two VTVMs are used for azimuth alignment of both stereo tape heads.

screwdriver adjustment at the end of the motor. Many do not have a means of adjusting the motor speed, while others may have a simple motor-control circuit. The motor speed may be adjusted by inserting a 3000-Hz test cassette and adjusting the speed control so the frequency counter at the speaker or line outputs reads the same frequency.

Some motor speed controls are very complicated and should be serviced as given in the exact model service literature. Remove and test each motor regulator transistor out of the circuit for leakage. Replace the suspected transistor even if it checks out as good after all other tests are made. Check all regular and zener diodes with the diode

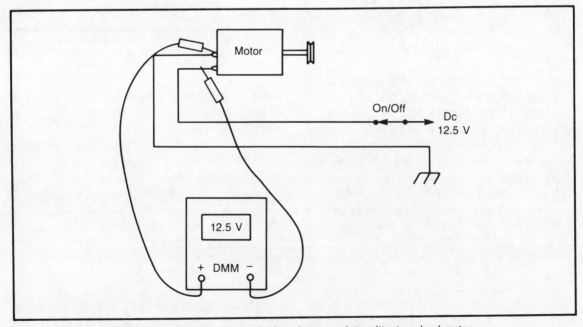

Fig. 3-22. Measure the dc voltage at the motor terminals to locate an intermittent or dead motor.

Fig. 3-23. Replace the tape motor with the original part number when available.

test. Make sure each resistor has the correct resistance. Take voltage measurements and compare with those in the schematic.

**Cassette Torque Meters or Tools.** A tension gauge may be used to check for correct tension of the idler pulley, pressure roller adjustment, and take-up turntable modes. Adjust both pinch rollers with two separate reverse and forward pinch-roller assemblies. Separate torque playback, fast-forward and rewind modes are measured with a torque-meter cassette in some models. For accurate adjustments, follow the manufacturer's various tension or torque procedures. This also applies to level meter, playback sensitivity, overall frequency, and Dolby noise-reduction adjustment tests.

**No Tape Sensor.** With some cassette tape decks a tape-sensor indicator may be a revolving color wheel with a light shining through it to indicate that the tape is moving (Fig. 3-24). Check for a broken belt if the wheel is not rotating. The belt may be lodged between pulley and bearing area. Notice if the light is burned out. Replace with a 12 volt bulb and connecting leads.

**Indicator Lights.** A volume LED VU indicator may consist of several LEDs indicating the volume level that corresponds to the music. Each channel consists of LEDs in a line, which indicates a positive or negative light indication. The LEDs and IC components are mounted upon a separate PC board bolted to the front panel (Fig. 3-25).

Signal trace the audio right up to the IC driver component with a scope or external audio amp when one channel of lights is out. The audio may be taken off after the second or third af transistor or where the line out feeds to the corresponding

Fig. 3-24. A plastic rotating color wheel indicates when the motor is operating. Check for a broken or missing belt when it does not rotate.

jacks (Fig. 3-26). Measure the B+ voltage source terminal. Check each LED diode with one terminal removed with the diode test of the DMM.

## RECORDING PROBLEMS

The same transistors and ICs in the pre-amp, af, and audio-output stages are used in both play and recording modes. In some models with dual-cassette players another pre-amp stage may be used with the recording cassette deck. The same tape heads may be used for both play and recording modes. The tape heads and audio amplifier circuits are switched in play or record procedures.

A separate ac-bias oscillator circuit excites the erase head and recording tape heads (Fig. 3-27). The bias control adjustments determine the amount of bias voltage applied to the recording heads. In more expensive models a dual-transistor bias oscillator may be found with transformer coupling between the bias oscillator and recording heads. A defect in the voltage-regulator bias-control circuit may prevent dc voltage to the oscillator circuits. Check the bias oscillator circuits for poor grounds. Poor recordings may result because of improper bias or no bias voltage.

**No Recording on Both Channels.** Inspect the play/record switch and the bias-oscillator circuits. Check for possible missing ac sine wave at the tape heads if there is no recording in any channel. Spray cleaning fluid down inside the play/record function switch area. Notice if the play/record switch is meshing properly. Sometimes the interconnecting steel wire or lever will not let the switch completely seat in the record mode. Read-

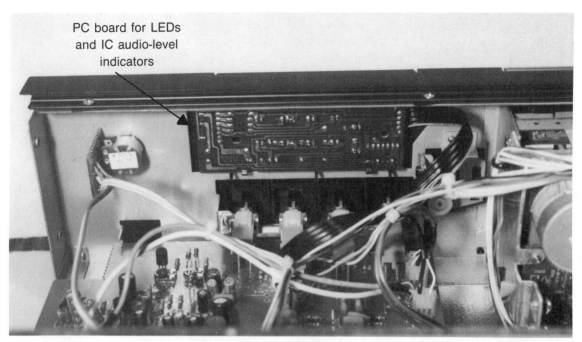

Fig. 3-25. The LED and IC sound-level components are mounted on a separate board located towards the front panel of cassette player.

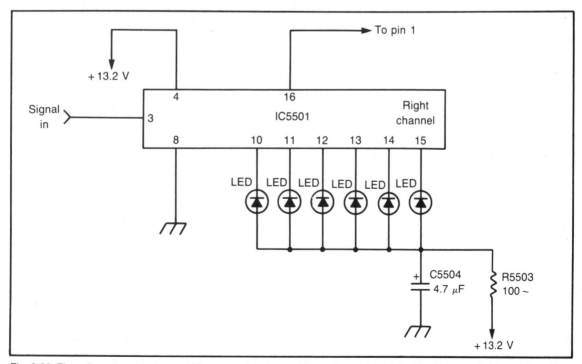

Fig. 3-26. The volume-level diodes and IC may be signal-traced for audio to pin 3 of the IC.   Measure the dc supply voltage at pin 4.

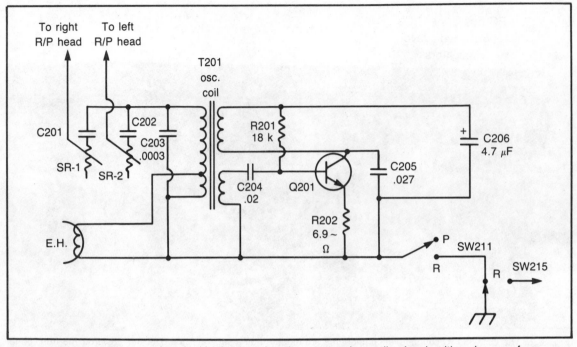

Fig. 3-27. A bias oscillator transistor in this circuit excites the erase and recording heads with a sine waveform.

just the lever and check for a bent lever and for correct seating.

Take a scope waveform to the ungrounded side of the recording heads to see if the ac bias voltage is missing. No sine waveform may indicate the bias oscillator is not working. Measure the dc voltage applied to the collector terminal supplied from the dc voltage source. Some models may have a record-bias-control regulator circuit which supplies voltage to the oscillator circuits (Fig. 3-28). A different voltage is applied with normal (N), CrO$_2$ tape (Cr) and metal tape (M). Check for a leaky transistor or zener diode.

Test the oscillator transistors in the circuit for

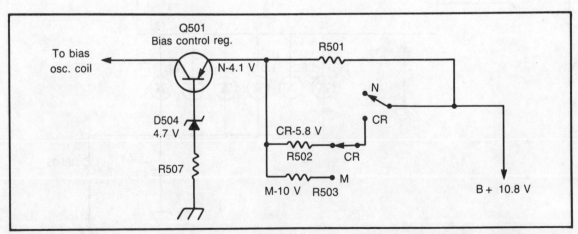

Fig. 3-28. Some models have a bias-control regulator transistor which furnishes regulated dc voltage to the bias oscillator circuits.

open or leakage conditions. Measure the secondary and primary coil windings for good continuity. Remove the erase-head terminals from the oscillator coil and take another resistance measurement. Check each bypass capacitor in the circuit with a capacitor tester. If all other tests fail, install a new oscillator transistor.

**Intermittent Recording.** Intermittent recording problems take a long time to locate. First clean up the recording tape and erase heads. Spray cleaning fluid down inside the record/play function switch. Second, make sure the record switch is seating properly. Third, monitor the ac-bias sine wave at the recording heads with the scope. Suspect the bias-oscillator circuits when the sine wave is missing. Fourth, monitor the dc voltage applied to the bias oscillator stage. Replace the oscillator transistor when correct dc voltage is applied but the sine wave is intermittent. If the intermittent condition continues, spray coolant upon bypass capacitors and oscillator coil until the intermittent component is found.

**Replace Record /Play Function Switch.** When the record/play function switch will not clean up, suspect a broken internal slide bar. Note if the switch assembly seats properly in both play and record modes. Visually inspect the PC wiring around the switch for broken PC-board wiring. A poorly soldered connection on the many switch contacts may prevent normal recordings. A broken plastic shaft or lever may not let the switch change position. Take the low-ohm scale of the VOM or DMM and check the switch contacts on both record and play positions. Several open or bad switching areas may indicate a broken switch assembly. Order a new switch assembly with the original part number.

**No Left Channel Recording.** If the cassette player operates in all channels in play mode and not the left channel, check for a dirty record/play or left tape head. Clean up the recording switch. Make sure the tape head is clean. Suspect a tape head if separate record heads are found in the player.

**Jumbled Recordings.** Improper erasing of the cassette may result in several recordings on one or both channels. Clean up all tape and erase heads. Turn the volume down and start the tape at the be-

ginning. Let the player operate for three minutes in the recording mode. Rewind the cassette. Now replay the cassette from the beginning. If music is still heard, the erase tape head and circuits are not functioning.

Check the erase heads for continuity. Remove one terminal for accurate resistance measurements. The erase-head resistance should be under 1 k ohms. Note if one of the erase head wires is off or there is a poorly soldered connection. Sometimes the ground wire may be broken off. Scope the erase head for a sine waveform. Troubleshoot the bias-oscillator circuits when there is no bias waveform at the erase head or R/P tape heads. It's best to follow the manufacturer's bias-oscillator frequency for correct adjustments since several different methods are used.

**Noisy Recordings.** Determine if the noisy recordings are found in a known cassette in play position. If the noise is only found in record mode, suspect a dirty record/play switch. Clean up the switch with silicon spray. A buzzing noise or a loud hum may be caused by the record/play switch not seating properly. Sometimes, after making a recording and switching to play position, a loud howling noise may develop. Clean up the play/record switch assembly. A loud howling noise on both record and playback with the volume turned up may be caused by an open tape head or connection (Fig. 3-29). Install a 1000 pF capacitor across the erase head if a strong local AM station appears on the recording.

## TEN CASE HISTORIES

Here are ten actual cassette-deck case histories covering most functions and stages in the compact cassette deck. These same problems may occur in any cassette player.

**Slow Fast Forward.** In addition to a sluggish fast-forward mode, the play button would not hold down in a J. C. Penney Model 3551. The drive belt was found off and down around the motor shaft, producing slow play and fast-forward operation. Since the tape pulled slow and hard, the mechanical automatic-stop assembly kicked in, ejecting the play button. A new belt was installed.

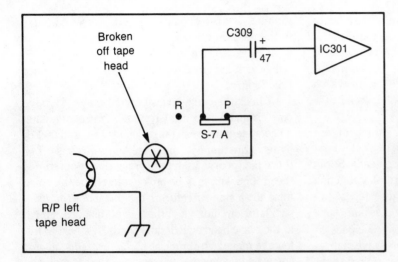

Fig. 3-29. A loud howling noise on a J. C. Penney Model 1770 may be caused by the volume turned up too high and an open tape head or connection.

Both the motor pulley and flywheel were cleaned off with alcohol and cloth.

**Shuts Off After Five or Six Seconds.** Before the tape would start to play, the play button would kick upward in a Sharp RT1155 model. The same thing may occur in this model with a defective part in the auto program search system (APSS). To determine if the APSS system is defective, note if the large solenoid (SOL401) is being energized when the button pops up (Fig. 3-30). If not, the problem may be a mechanical one. Here the flat locking bar was bent out of line, letting the play button "pop" up. Removing and straightening the locking bar solved the intermittent play operation.

In a Sharp RT-3388A computer-controlled stereo-cassette deck, the solenoid would energize and release the lock-plate lever, shutting off the playback mode within seconds. To determine if the solenoid is energized, hold the lock-release lever and feel the pull of the solenoid. In this model the

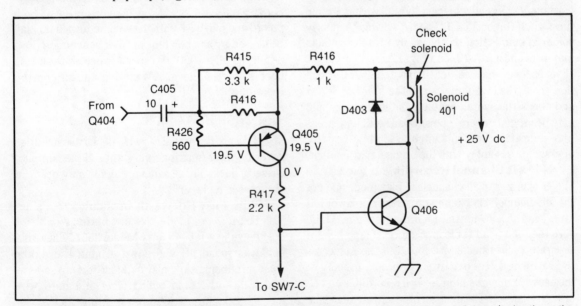

Fig. 3-30. Check for an energized solenoid when the play button shuts off in 5 or 6 seconds and doesn't play the entire cassette.

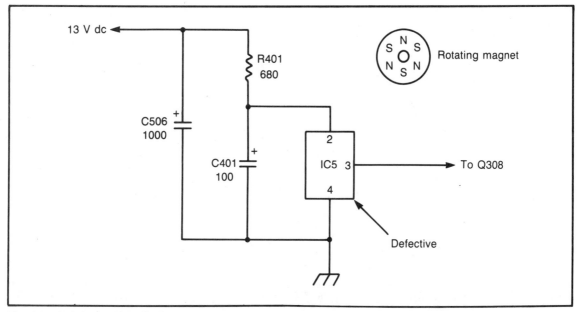

Fig. 3-31. A defective Hall IC (IC5) in a Sharp Model RT-3388A stereo tape deck caused the player button to kick off within a few seconds.

rotating magnet rotates close to a Hall IC (IC5) which feeds to a counting circuit and then the control unit (Fig. 3-31). Premature ejection of the play or record button is caused by a defective IC5. Replace with original part number RH-1X1075AF22.

**No Volume—Tape Motor Runs.** The tape was moving but there was no volume on either channel in a Craig Model 3304 stereo tape deck. No movement of the VU meter indicated af or pre-

amp problems. Although dc voltage was found at the tape motor, no voltage was getting to the stereo amplifier (Fig. 3-32). Regulator transistor TR302 was found open and replaced with a 25C1383 replacement.

**Noisy Left Channel.** Sometimes the noise was very low in the left channel of a J. C. Penney Model 1770, and at other times only a low hiss was heard. The noise was the same when the volume

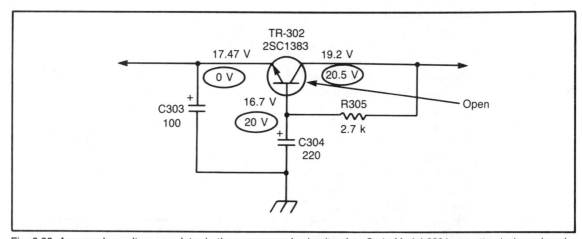

Fig. 3-32. An open low-voltage regulator in the power-supply circuits of a Craig Model 3304 cassette deck produced a no-volume symptom.

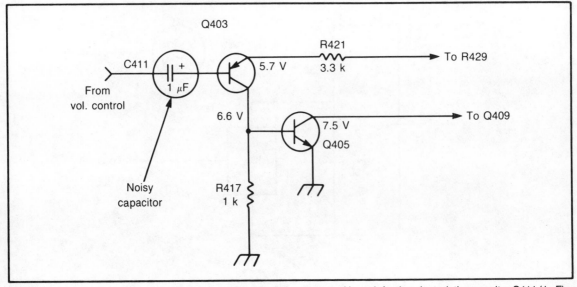

Fig. 3-33. The noisy left channel of a J. C. Penney Model 1770 was caused by a defective electrolytic capacitor C411 (1 μF).

was turned down, indicating the defective component was between the volume control and the speaker. When the base and emitter of Q403 were shorted, the noise disappeared (Fig. 3-33). Shorting the volume-control center terminal to ground did not eliminate the noisy condition. Replacing C411 (1 μF) electrolytic coupling capacitor solved the noisy left channel. Do not overlook noisy ICs or transistors. The noisy stage was located by shorting the emitter to base terminals of each af and pre-amp transistor.

**Intermittent Right Channel.** The intermittent sound symptom was traced to the IC output stage in a Lloyds DD-9720 model. The output IC was replaced with a ECG812 universal replacement, but the right channel was still intermittent. While operating, components were moved with a plastic rod, and when a 47 μF capacitor was touched, the sound cut down. Replacing the 47 μF electrolytic capacitor from pin 8 to ground solved the intermittent right channel.

**Weak Left Channel.** In addition to a weak left channel, the base frequency seemed a little distorted in a J. C. Penney Model 1728. The tone control had little effect in the left channel when rotated. The low-ohm scale of the DMM found the center terminal grounded inside the tone control. Replac-

ing the tone control solved the weak left channel and lower frequency action.

**Whistling Noise.** A loud, shrill noise was heard in a Panasonic SE-1160 cassette player in play mode in the right channel. The feedback noise was signal traced to TR404. A 4.7 μF emitter-bypass capacitor was dried up in the leg of TR404. Replacing the bypass electrolytic capacitor cured the whistling right channel.

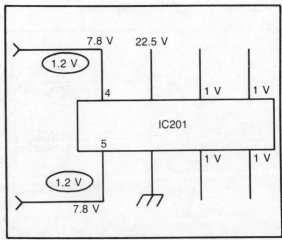

Fig. 3-34. Both channels were dead in a J. C. Penney Model 3207 tape player because of a leaky pre-amp, IC201. IC201 was replaced with a universal ECG824 replacement.

**Table 3-1. Compact Stereo Cassette Deck Troubleshooting Chart.**

| Symptom | Possible Circuit | Check |
|---------|------------------|-------|
| Does not play | Power supply | Check line cord—on/off switch—play/record switch—fuse—measure B + voltage—leaky diodes—burned resistors. |
| No sound—motor rotates | Low-voltage power supply or sound output stages | Measure voltage at large filter capacitor. Measure voltage at output transistor or ICs. Check if both channels are dead. Look for defective earphone jack. |
| Sound indication—no tape movement | Mechanical problems | See if cassette is seating properly. Does the pressure roller engage capstan? |
|  | Tape motor | Check voltage at motor terminals with no tape movement. Belt off or broken. |
| Tape moves—No sound | Low-voltage power supply | Check voltage at IC or voltage-regulator circuit. Check voltage to pre-amp and af circuits. |
|  | Sound output circuits | Signal-trace sound circuits with external amp or scope. Measure voltages on output transistor and ICs. Check output transistors for leakage or open conditions. Replace power IC if both channels are dead. |
| VU meter operates—no sound | Audio output circuits | VU meter movement indicates audio signal up to audio output circuits. Signal-trace audio output circuits to locate defective stage. Measure voltage to output transistors or ICs. Test transistors in circuit. |
| Dead left channel in tape player | From tape head to speaker of audio circuits in left channel. | Isolate sound at volume control. Signal-trace audio with external amp. Test transistors in circuit. Measure voltages in IC to locate defective IC. Compare signals at the same point in the circuit with normal right channel. Possible open tape head. |
| Weak left channel | Left channel audio circuits | Transistors and IC components. Electrolytic coupling capacitors. Electrolytic bypass capacitors. Improper voltage source. |
| Distorted right channel | Transistors and IC audio circuits | Locate distorted stage with scope or external audio amp. Test transistors. Accurate voltage measurement on IC parts. Sub new speaker. Compare with normal left channel. |
| No headphone reception. | Headphone jack | Inspect for broken terminal connections. Replace stereo headphone jack. |
| Motor rotates—no tape action | Motor belt | Motor belt off—loose belt. |

| Symptom | Possible Circuit | Check |
|---|---|---|
| | Capstan/flywheel | Frozen bearings—remove, clean up, and lubricate. |
| Door eject does not open | Door mechanism | Notice if latch releases. Excessive tape around capstan—door will not open. Remove back or bottom cover to get at flywheel assembly. |
| Pulling of tape | Tape-up reel | Stopped or erratic rotation. Check drive idler wheel and pulley. Take-up tension adjustment. |
| | Pressure roller | Worn—needs replacement. |
| Will not eject cassette | Jammed door Mechanical levers | Tape wrapped around capstan and pressure roller, bent reject lever. |
| Play button keeps ejecting | Automatic shut-off circuit | Clean up record/play switch. Notice if solenoid energizes. Is magnet rotating? Check Hall IC. Replace glass enclosed magnetic switch. |
| No recording | Recording circuits | Check erase and tape heads for sine waveform with scope. Check bias oscillator circuit for no waveform. Test bias transistors in the circuit. Measure dc supply voltage to bias oscillator. |
| | Tape head | Open tape head. Check shorted tape head internally to metal cover. |
| Jumbled recordings | Erase head | Open erase head. Broken connection on erase head. |
| | Bias oscillator circuits | Scope erase head for ac sine waveform. Troubleshoot bias oscillator circuit for no waveform. |
| Intermittent recordings | Tape head | Monitor erase and tape head with the scope for waveform. |
| | Bias-oscillator circuits | Monitor dc voltage at bias transistor. |
| | | Check for poor grounds in bias-oscillator circuits. |
| No left channel, normal right-channel recording | Left-channel tape head | Notice if left VU meter is operating. Monitor ac sine waveform at left tape head. |
| | Left pre-amp circuits | Measure voltage at left channel pre-amp stages. Signal-trace recorded music from tape head through pre-amp circuits. Suspect dirty record/play switch assembly. |
| Noisy recordings | Tape head | Clean up tape head. Clean up erase head. |
| | Record/play switch assembly | Clean up play/record switch assembly. Make sure record/play switch is seating properly. |

**Dead on Both Channels.** Voltages in the audio pre-amp IC components were checked in a J. C. Penney Model 3207 since both channels were dead. The voltages on pins 4 and 5 were only 1.2 volts and should have been 7.8 volts (Fig. 3-34). Leaky IC201 was replaced with an ECG824 universal replacement.

**No Recording on Right Channel.** Recording in the left channel was normal with no recording in the right channel of a J. C. Penney 1795 stereo-cassette recorder. The record/play switch was sprayed with cleaning fluid, but there was still no right channel recording. When the player was switched to play mode, both channels were normal. The play/record switch was not seating properly in the record mode. The brace which holds the tension spring of the record/play switch was bent backwards; applying more pressure on the switch assembly corrected the no right record symptom.

Table 3-1 lists some additional problems along with their possible causes and suggested troubleshooting procedures.

# Chapter 4

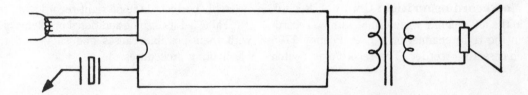

# Servicing the
# Boom-Box Cassette Player

YOU MAY HEAR IT MORE OFTEN THAN YOU SEE it—the boom-box cassette player blasting out on the streets or at the beach. The loud music may be coming from a large cassette player on the shoulder of a teenager at baseball or football games (Fig. 4-1). At other times several young people may be seen break-dancing to music from the boom-box player. One thing for sure, the music is very loud and sometimes not too clear, for it is blasting away at your ears. In addition to the normal repairs, the boom-box player may need additional service because of the rough treatment while being carried around outdoors.

Besides the regular features found in the mini, or small cassette tape player, the boom-box player may have up to six separate speakers. Some have four large 6½ inch PM speakers with two round or horn-type tweeters. Most of the larger players contain an AM-FM-MPX receiver with tape-recording features. You may find two separate cassette players, one for recording and the other for playback modes. The several indicators may include a level meter, battery LED, and Dolby indicator. The large cassette player may be operated from batteries or the ac power line.

## THE POWER SUPPLY

In the early cassette players, the ac power supply consisted of two silicon diodes and the transformers of a fullwave rectifier circuit. Today, the low-voltage power supply contains four diodes in a bridge rectifier circuit (Fig. 4-2). Some portable cassette players may operate from batteries and the external dc adapter source.

The bride-rectifier circuit may be four separate silicon diodes or one large component (Fig. 4-3). Some power supplies contain a 1-amp fuse, while many do not have any type of fuse protection. Either battery or ac power is switched into the circuit when the ac cord is plugged into the player.

Check for a leaky bridge diode or overloading power supply circuit when the fuse is blown. Sometimes a transistor or IC circuit will flash-over, knock out the fuse, and operate without any signs of trouble after the new fuse is installed. Suspect overload-

Fig. 4-1. The large boom-box cassette player may contain 6½-inch heavy-duty speakers.

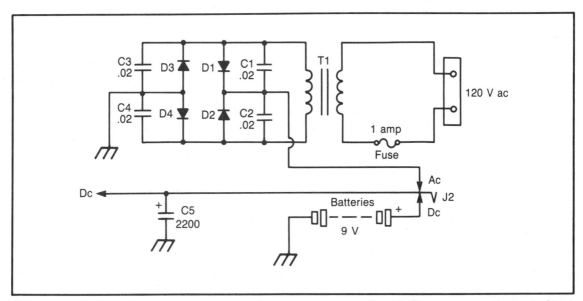

Fig. 4-2. Individual silicon diodes or one large rectifier component may be found in the ac power-supply circuit. Check each diode with the diode test of the DMM.

Fig. 4-3. In the J.C. Penney Model 681-3915, the power supply is mounted on a separate board along with a rectifier component and a transistorized voltage regulator circuit.

ing in the power-supply circuits if the fuse continues to blow.

Inspect the cabinet and components for lightning damage. Check the continuity of the primary and secondary winding of the power transformer. Measure the low ac voltage across the secondary winding of the power transformer. A dead receiver after replacing the fuse may indicate the primary winding is open. Remove one end of each diode and check with the diode test of the DMM.

Although most dc voltage from the ac power supply is not regulated, you may locate a few simple transistor and zener-diode regulator circuits in the higher priced models (Fig. 4-4). The regulated voltage is fed to the radio tuner, pre-amp, and af amplifier circuits. Here low-voltage regulation is provided by Q901 and a zener voltage-reference diode on the base terminal. The regulated 8.5 volts is fed to the AM-FM, pre-amp, and af-amp circuits.

**Critical Voltage Tests.** Measure the dc voltage at the main filter capacitor or at the tape motor terminals. No voltage may indicate a defective or dirty on/off switch. Suspect a defective selector or mechanical switch with voltage at the filter capacitor. Do not overlook the 120- or 220-volt ac switch found in some models. Start at the positive terminal of the bridge rectifier and proceed to the voltage-regulator circuit. Check the voltage at the output IC terminal.

**Broken Ac Plug.** Sometimes when the player is dropped or knocked off the table, the player may land on the ac cord and plug, cracking the plug assembly. Rough treatment of plug insertion may break or crack the plug housing. The switch contacts come apart, resulting in a dead player. Reassemble all components and place a tie-wire around the plug assembly. Use epoxy cement to repair the damaged female plug. Apply epoxy around the plug

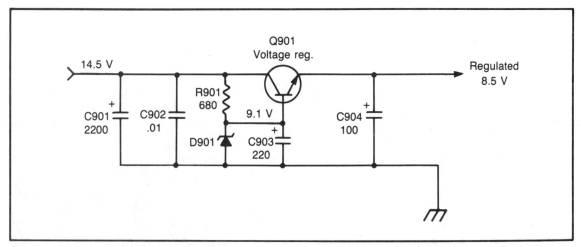

Fig. 4-4. A simple voltage-regulator circuit in the power supply source may consist of a regulator transistor and zener diode. Check both transistor and diode for leaky conditions along with improper voltage source.

and female jack. Let the mixture set overnight before attempting to plug in the ac cord. Order a new female ac-jack assembly if the unit is broken in several pieces.

**Will Not Play on Batteries.** Check the batteries with a battery tester or DMM. Inspect the battery terminals for poor contacts. Clean off the battery contacts with a cleaning fluid and cloth. Make sure the batteries are inserted properly for correct polarity. Measure the voltage across the entire battery assembly if the player does not come on after battery replacement. Check the ac/dc selector switch when the ac cord is inserted. Spray tuner or cleaning fluid down inside the switch terminals. Check the battery terminals for broken wires to chassis ground and the selector switch.

## THE AM-FM-MPX RADIO SECTION

The AM-FM-MPX receiver is very sensitive with good selectivity on distance FM stations. The early manual radio-cassette players contained transistors in every stage (Fig. 4-5). Then IC components were found in the i-f amp set and multiplex circuits (Fig. 4-6). The am converter may be a separate transistor or combined with the IC-i-f amp circuits. Today most boom-box receivers have IC circuits throughout the entire player. The FM front end may contain one IC component with the AM converter, i-f FM and AM and detector in another

IC. IC301 contains the entire multiplex (MPX) system (Fig. 4-7). Usually the left and right channel signals are switched with the selector switch into the audio circuits.

**Dipole Antenna Repair.** The small FM dipole antenna often breaks off at the tip or where it enters the cabinet. The pieces cannot be put back together once they are broken. Many times the rod gets bent in the middle and will not retract (Fig. 4-8). Some dipole antennas push down out of the way into the cabinet, while others fold up against the back side of the receiver. These dipole antennas may be ordered from the manufacturer or repair depot. Replace with a universal replacement if not obtainable.

**Dead Radio.** Note if a switching sound is heard when switched to the AM with the function switch. A loud click or noisy sound may indicate voltage at the selector switch or dirty contacts. Clean up the AM-FM radio and selector switches. Next grab hold of the AM ferrite-rod antenna coil and tune in a strong local station. Check to see if the cassette player is working. If the play is normal, but the radio is dead, take critical voltage measurements on transistor and IC circuits. A schematic diagram is a must to locate the correct components and critical voltage measurements.

**No Radio, No Cassette Player Action.** Go directly to the power supply and battery circuits if

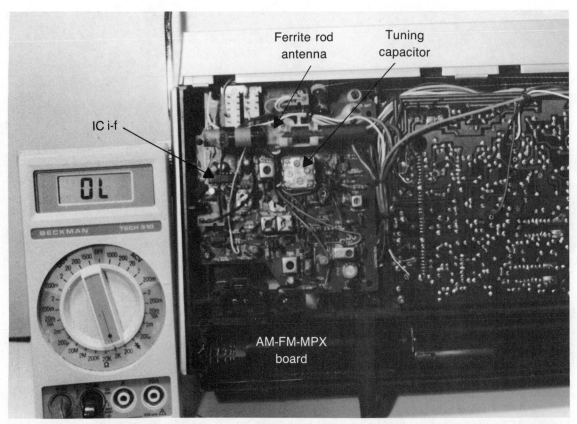

Fig. 4-5. Often the AM-FM-MPX receiver circuits are isolated on a separate chassis in the boom-box player. Transistors and IC components are used in these sections.

the radio and audio sections are both dead. Check the dc voltage at the large filter capacitor. Inspect the on/off and selector switch contacts. Spray tuner or cleaner fluid down inside the contact area. If the voltage is normal, check out the audio-output circuits. Listen for a hum or low music from either speaker. When no sound can be heard from either radio or tape player, suspect the audio-output circuits, poor earphone jack, or a defective power supply.

**No AM or FM.** With music on the cassette player but no radio on either AM or FM, suspect a defective AM-FM i-f-amp IC component. Check the supply voltage at the IC. A burned resistor or leaky zener diode may prevent voltage at the IC component. Check the voltage-regulator transistor for leakage if one is found in the power-supply circuits.

Inject the i-f signal from an rf or noise generator at the input terminal of the i-f-IC. If there is no tone or sound, inject the same signal at the output terminal. A small noise-type generator is ideal for locating a dead stage in the radio circuits.

**No AM—FM Normal.** Suspect a broken AM antenna coil or wire when the FM is normal. Since both the AM and FM signals are amplified by the i-f section, the defective component must be before the i-f stages. Check for a leaky or open AM converter transistor in some models. Replace the i-f-IC if the AM section ties directly into it. Take critical voltage measurements at the IC terminals.

**No FM.** A weak local FM station may indicate a leaky or open FM-rf amp transistor. Suspect a leaky FM oscillator transistor when a loud rushing noise is heard but no tuneable stations. Check the FM mixer stage if no rushing noise but there is a

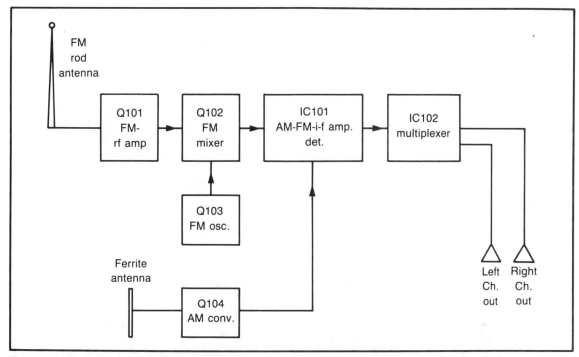

Fig. 4-6. A block diagram of the front-end AM-FM section with transistors and ICs in the i-f and multiplex stages.

normal AM section. Measure the voltage on the FM front-end IC with no FM reception. Replace the FM-IC with normal AM reception.

**Dial-Cord Problems.** Dial-cord replacement may not be as easy as it seems. The dial cord may break at the pointer assembly or at the end of the line of the drum assembly. Excessive wear often occurs at the rotating shaft assembly. Use a dial-

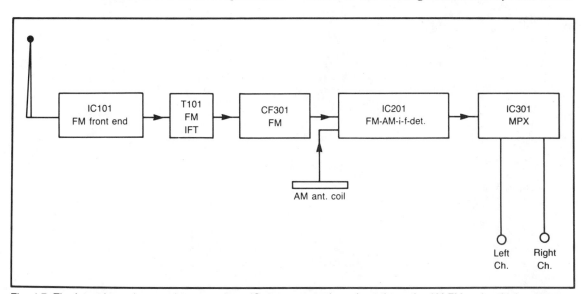

Fig. 4-7. The latest boom-box receivers may have IC components throughout the entire AM-FM and multiplex system.

Fig. 4-8. Weak FM reception may occur because of a broken dipole antenna. Replace with the original, if possible.

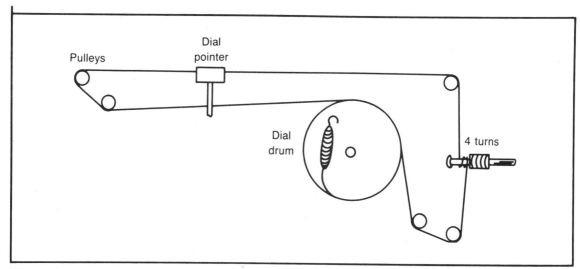

Fig. 4-9. Check for a loose dial cord if there is erratic movement of the dial pointer. Put liquid resin around the dial shaft drive area to prevent slippage.

cord stringing guide, if handy (Fig. 4-9). Most service literature covering a given receiver contains a dial-cord guide.

Dial-cord slippage is found at the tuning-shaft area. Liquid rosin around the shaft area may help. Tighten the loose dial cord at the drum with another dial-cord spring. Drill another small hole in the drum brace if the dial cord has broken out the plastic where the cord is tied. Place a dab of glue or silicon rubber cement over the dial-cord ends to keep them from coming apart.

**Broken Selector Switch.** Sometimes when the player is dropped, the selector knob may take the brunt of the fall and end up with a bent selector shaft or lever. Check around the selector-switch area for broken board connections. If only a few places are cracked, repair with bare hookup wire. Suspect dirty switch contacts or a defective switch when the selector switch operates some functions but not others. Spray cleaning fluid down inside the switching area. Rapidly rotate the switch to help clean up the contacts. The switch contacts may be checked with the low-ohm scale of the DMM. Order a new selector switch from the manufacturer when it cannot be cleaned or repaired.

## THE AMPLIFIER SECTION

Most of the audio stages in the stereo-cassette player have IC components instead of transistors. You may find a pre-amp IC and a single audio-output IC for both channels (Fig. 4-10). The pre-amp IC amplifies the weak signal from the tape heads, while the audio IC contains the complete af and output circuits.

In expensive cassette players with Dolby sound and muting features, the IC takes care of the Dolby sound while two transistors are found in the muting circuits (Fig. 4-11). You may fine line in and out stages with either transistors or IC components. Sound-level indicators may be controlled with one large IC and several LEDs as indicators.

**Pre-amp Circuits.** The pre-amp stages may consist of one or two transistors or one IC for both pre-amp circuits. You may find a pre-amp IC for the tape heads and another pre-amp audio circuit, which feeds into the power-output IC. Most pre-amp stages use a low-voltage and low-noise-level audio circuit (Fig. 4-12).

The IC pre-amp may be switched directly into the Dolby IC or selector-switch assembly. Like the transistor pre-amp stages, the supply voltage is usually under five or seven volts. Likewise, very low voltages are found on the pre-amp IC terminals (Fig. 4-13). One pre-amp IC may serve for both tape-head input amplifiers.

Suspect the audio pre-amp stage if one tape

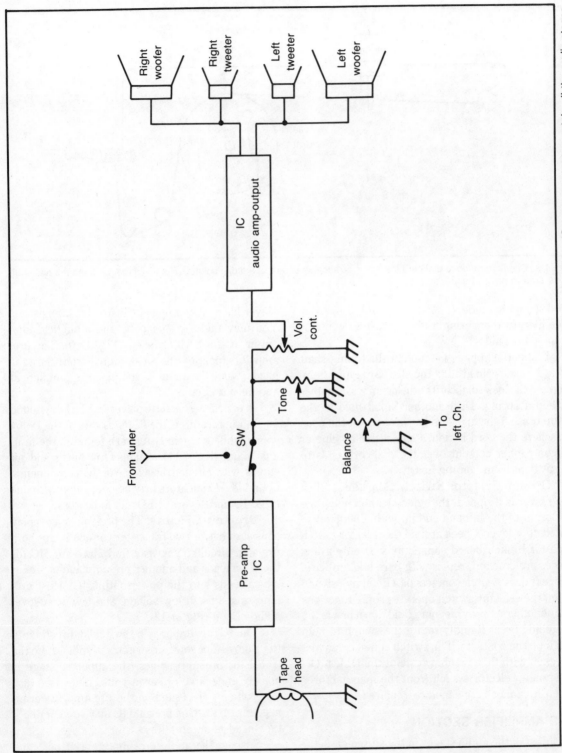

Fig. 4-10. IC circuits may be used throughout the audio section in modern cassette players. One large IC component may contain all the audio stages.

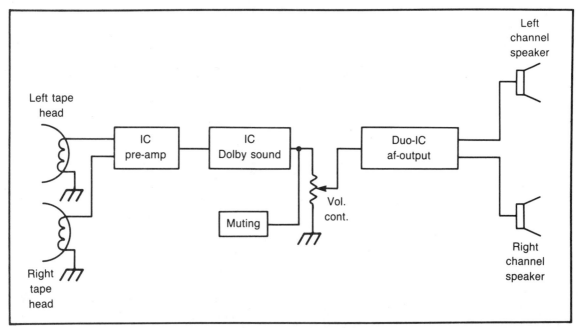

Fig. 4-11. Dolby sound may include one additional IC component between pre-amp and audio stages. Tape muting circuits are directly ahead of the volume control in most models.

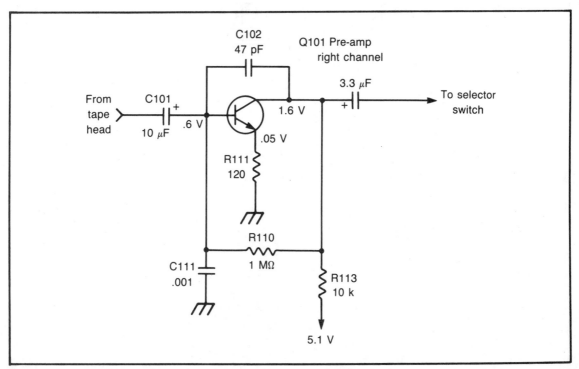

Fig. 4-12. You may find normally very low voltages on the pre-amp transistor circuit, in order to maintain a low noise level. A normal silicon transistor should have a .6-volt bias measurement between emitter and base terminals.

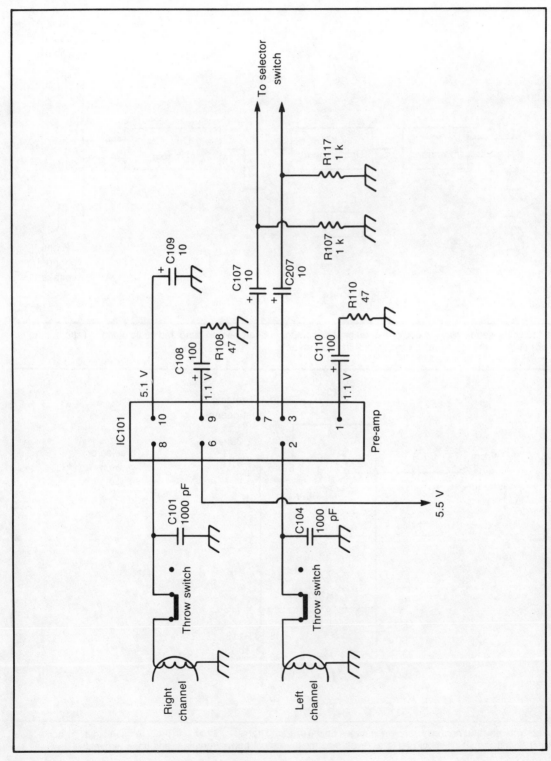

Fig. 4-13. The pre-amp stereo circuits may be contained in one IC component. To prevent hiss and low-level noise, very low voltage is supplied to these circuits.

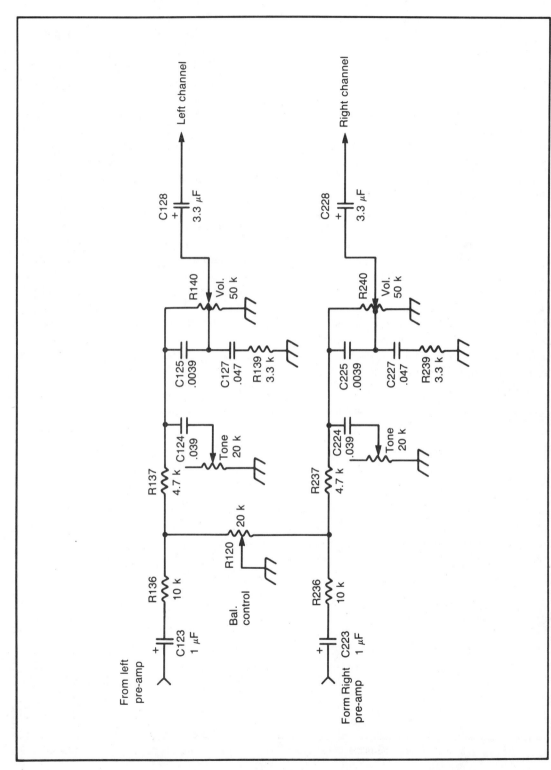

Fig. 4-14. The balance control is found between the left and right stereo channels before the volume control. Erratic or improper audio balance may be caused by a worn or dirty balance control.

channel is weak or dead when one tape channel and both receiver circuits are normal. Check continuity of the tape head with the low-ohm scale of the DMM and compare the measurement with the other good channel. Then measure voltages at the pre-amp transistors or IC components. Do not overlook the supply voltage source at the IC. Very low voltage may indicate a leaky IC or an improper voltage source.

**The Balance Control.** Often the balance control is found between the pre-amp stages and the volume control so both audio channels are equal at the speaker channels (Fig. 4-14). The center tap of the volume control is at ground potential. Suspect a worn or dirty balance control when the sound appears erratic in either channel when the control will not lower any given channel. Try to clean up the control with cleaning spray.

Sometimes the balance control may short internally and lower the audio in one of the stereo channels. Remove the connecting wire from the control with the low audio signal. Note if the sound level returns to normal. Replace the control if it is erratic or worn in spots.

## POWER OUTPUT CIRCUITS

In the low priced cassette players, you may find one large IC component taking care of all the audio circuits. The intermediate player may have one IC for both pre-amp stages with another large IC as both af and power-output ICs. The expensive high-powered units may have transistors in the equalizer sound circuits with a separate af IC component driving a large, dual-stereo IC output (Fig. 4-15). Large six-inch heavy-duty speakers may be found in these models.

The typical stereo-output IC circuit is shown in Fig. 4-16. Here the output from the volume control is fed directly into the input IC terminal. Pin 12 connects to the low-voltage source of 9 volts. The audio output is capacity coupled from pins 11 and 2 through C119 and C120 with the left channel and C220 and C219 of the right channel to the headphone jack. When the headphones are not plugged in, the audio sound is switched to the stereo speakers.

Most power-output ICs are bolted to the chassis or have separate heat sinks to dissipate the heat. After replacing a power IC, place silicon grease on

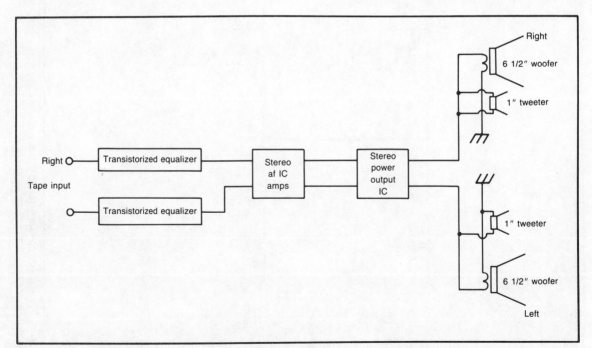

Fig. 4-15. In the large players, transistor equalizer circuits may be found between the tape-head pre-amp and af circuits.

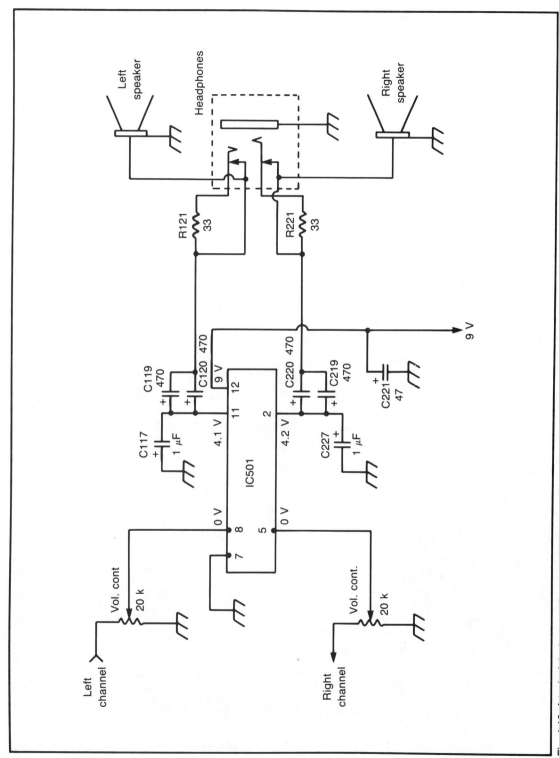

Fig. 4-16. A typical dual-stereo IC output circuit. Only one IC component is used in the less expensive boom-box players.

the metal side of the IC component and metal heat sink. Always replace the metal heat sink before firing up the chassis after replacement. Separate audio IC components may be found mounted on the same heat sink (Fig. 4-17). If not, you may destroy the power-IC replacement within minutes. The power-IC components may be mounted on a separate PC amp board with the pre-amp audio stages close to the tape-head connections (Fig. 4-18).

**No Right Channel.** When either tape channel is dead and the other is normal, the defective component may occur from the tape head through to the speaker. If the receiver plays normally through the right channel, suspect problems in the pre-amp circuits or tape head. Check the audio-output circuits if the right channel is dead on all functions. Start at the volume control and inject the audio signal from a noise or audio signal generator. Proceed from the IC input to the output of a pre-amp and power audio IC circuits to the speaker voice coil until the dead stage is located.

**Dead, No Sound.** Suspect a dual-IC power-output stereo component or improper supply voltage if both channels are dead. Usually one channel will be weak, distorted, or dead, while the other is normal in a combination power-output IC. If the power IC is leaky, you may have weak and distorted sound in both stereo channels.

The defective power IC may be red hot or the heat sink warm with a leaky IC component. Inspect the body of the IC for raised or plastic areas "popped" out of the IC body area (Fig. 4-19). Check for a burned or grey-looking metal IC heat-sink tab, indicating the IC has been operating too warm. Note if any of the long IC terminals have been warm and have poorly soldered connections on PC board.

**Weak Sound.** Locate the weak channel. Determine which IC component is weak in signal. The

Fig. 4-17. Here the separate stereo output ICs are found mounted on the same heat sink in a Sanyo Model M9975L player.

Fig. 4-18. The audio af and power-output IC components are mounted on a separate PC board in a J. C. Penney Model 681-3915 boom-box player. Note each individual metal heat sink.

outside external amp is good for this test. Start at the volume control and check signal in both directions. Besides IC and transistors, do not overlook electrolytic coupling capacitors in the tape-head circuits and between pre-amp and volume control and in the speaker coupling circuits.

After isolating the defective IC component, take accurate voltage and resistance measurements. If the supply source is low at the IC terminal pin, suspect a defective voltage-regulator circuit or leaky sound IC. Remove the IC terminal from the PC wiring with solder wick and soldering gun. Make sure the pin is not connected to the PC wiring. Now fire up the unit and measure the supply voltage source where the pin terminal was mounted. If the voltage returns to normal, replace the leaky power IC.

Pin 12 of a power IC in a Sharp GF-4343 cas-

sette player was low at 2.1 volts. The normal pin voltage should have been around 9 volts (Fig. 4-20). The voltage regulator transistor was running very warm. Pin 12 was removed from the circuit with solder wick. The supply voltage shot up to 11.9 volts in ac operation. Now the tape motor began to turn. After pulling the power plug, a resistance measurement of 5.7 ohms was found from pin 12 to chassis ground. Replacing IC201 restored the dead cassette-tape player.

**Erratic Headphone Jacks.** Intermittent or no sound in one of the speaker channels may be caused by a defective or dirty headphone jack. You may find one large headphone jack or two separate ones for each audio channel (Fig. 4-21). The electrolytic audio-coupling capacitor feeds to the earphone jack before being switched to the speaker. The audio signal may be traced with another PM

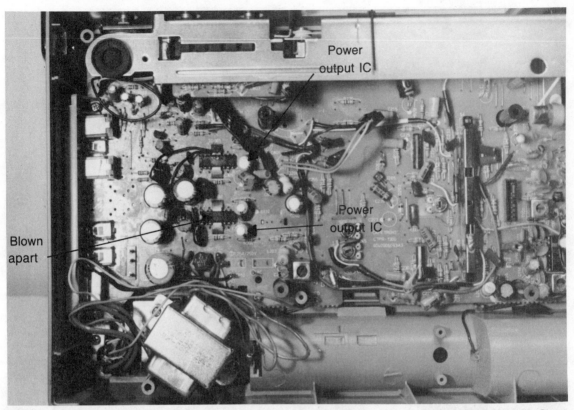

Fig. 4-19. Note how the plastic body has blown off of the lower audio output IC in this MacDonald Model 06-33-63. Check components tied to the IC terminals before replacing a defective IC.

speaker and clip leads from pin 1 and 6 through the headphone jacks to the speaker terminals. Some large stereo players have external speaker jacks for outside speaker hookup. The powerful audio signal is reduced with R101 and R102 (330 Ω) for headphone operation. Spray inside the headphone jack assembly and move the male plug in and out to clean up the shorting speaker terminals. Replace the broken or defective headphone jack when it cannot be cleaned up.

**Tape Head Tests.** Inspect the tape head for broken wire connections. These little wires seem to break off right at the tape-head terminals. Check the resistance of the tape head. Compare this reading with the normal tape head. If there is erratic sound, push down on the tape-head terminals at the back and note if the sound cuts in and out. Sometimes a broken internal-wire connection may cause

intermittent sound.

Although the tape-head azimuth adjustment is not found in small cassette players, check for the adjustment screw alongside the tape head. Azimuth adjustment should be made after tape-head replacement or when the recorded music sounds tinny. Only one adjustment screw is found at the tape head. Actually, azimuth adjustment involves lining up the tape head horizontally with the tape.

Connect a ten-ohm load resistor across the speaker plug terminals. Clip the VTVM leads across the added resistor. Insert a playback cassette test tape at 6 kHz and adjust the azimuth screw for maximum reading on the VTVM. The latest method is to connect a frequency counter across the speaker-jack terminals instead of a VTVM (Fig. 4-22). Adjust the azimuth screw for maximum reading.

## THE SPEAKER SYSTEM

The woofer speakers in the boom-box player may vary from 3½ to 6½ inches diameter. You may find an external speaker jack where larger speakers may be connected. In the deluxe models, a multi-amp three-way six-speaker system is found with two speakers operating in the center from another stereo IC. The speaker impedance may vary from three to ten ohms. Since the power output may vary from two to ten watts of total power, larger speakers are installed with heavy PM magnets (Fig. 4-23). Of course, each stereo output channel is one-half the total output power.

The tweeter speaker may be one-inch in diameter, or a small two-inch horn. The horn tweeter is found in the deluxe models for clear, crisp, high notes. The small tweeter may have a stiff cone or a ceramic-type speaker. These tweeter speakers are connected in parallel with the woofer or have a small wattage resistor in series with the voice coil (Fig. 4-24).

## THE CASSETTE PLAYER

The boom-box cassette player may have two separate cassette decks side-by-side and also recording features. One player is used for playback, while the other operates as playback and recording. In most cassette players the front plastic cover must be removed to get at the cassette deck. Several long screws must be removed to get at the player. Sometimes they feature slide knobs that must be removed before the front cover comes off the main chassis.

**Motor Problems.** The cassette tape speed is 1.781 ps or 4.75 cm/sec. The fast-forward and rewind time may vary from 100 seconds to two minutes with a C60 cassette. Of course, the dual-cassette deck contains two separate motors. The

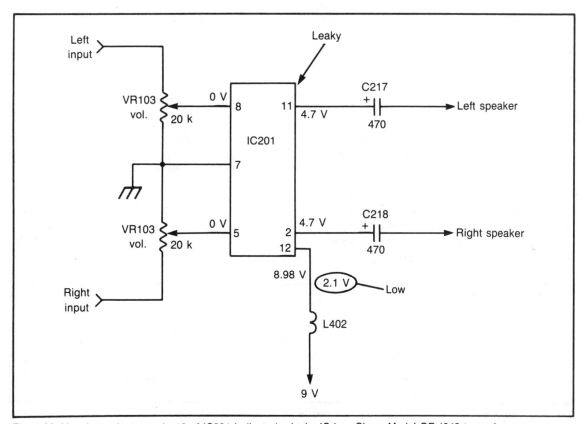

Fig. 4-20. Very low voltage at pin 12 of IC201 indicated a leaky IC in a Sharp Model GF-4343 tape player.

89

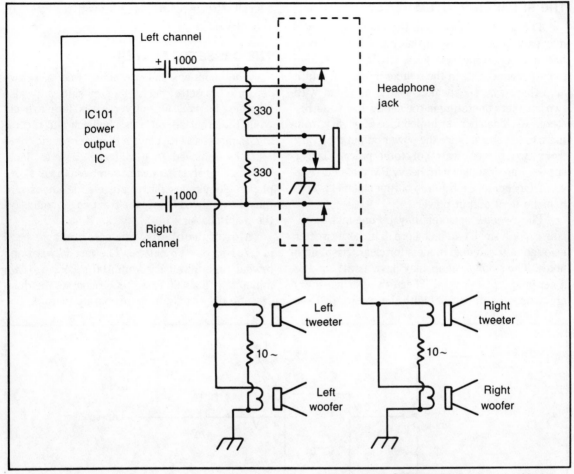

Fig. 4-21. A defective or dirty headphone jack may cause a dead or erratic speaker. Clean up shorting controls with cleaner spray.

small motor drives a capstan flywheel or a separate supply reel with a rubber belt.

A defective motor may stop, have intermittent rotation, slow down, or run fast (Fig. 4-25). The motor may start up if the motor pulley is rotated. Sometimes the motor will start if tapped with the end of a screwdriver. Replace the motor if the above symptoms are present.

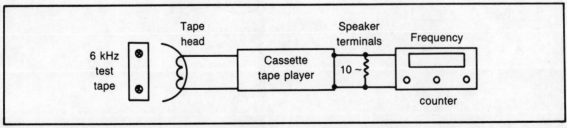

Fig. 4-22. Use a cassette test tape and frequency counter at the speaker terminals for azimuth alignment. Adjust the azimuth screw for maximum on the frequency counter.

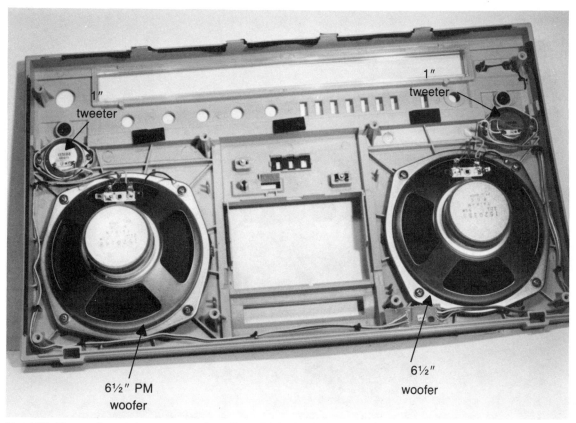

Fig. 4-23. The woofer speakers may vary from 3½ to 6½ inches in the boom-box player. Note the heavy-duty speakers in this Soundesign Model 4689 tape player.

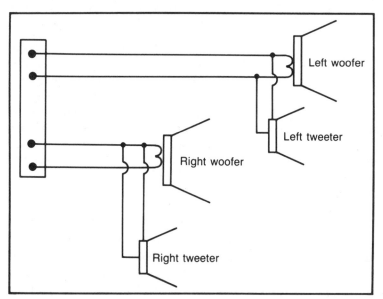

Fig. 4-24. The tweeters are usually 1-inch types and connected in paralleled with the woofers.

Fig. 4-25. Check the dc voltage across the motor terminals. Replace the motor with the exact part number when it is erratic or must be turned to start rotating. Note the direction of tape movement is indicated by the arrow between supply and take-up reel.

Check the suspected motor with a voltage test at the motor terminals. Very low or no voltage may be caused by poor wiring connections or a defective on/off switch. Clean the mechanical on/off switch with cleaning spray. Replace the motor if normal dc voltage is found at the motor terminals but no rotation.

The motor terminals may receive the wrong voltage in an apparently defective motor-control circuit. A transistor or IC circuit may be employed here. Look for a motor-speed control in the circuit (Fig. 4-26). The correct speed should be adjusted with a dummy load connected to one set of speakers and a frequency counter. Insert a 3 kHz test tape and adjust the speed control with a 3 kHz reading on the frequency counter.

**Pinch-Roller Adjustment.** In some models the pressure-roller spring may be set higher in a small hole of the chassis to apply more pressure. In other models you can just bend the spring for more tension. Too much pressure may cause the tape speed to slow down. Improper feeding of tape may be caused by a worn rubber roller or improper tension. Check the pinch roller for tape down between the rubber roller and bearing assembly. The correct method is to use a tension gauge and set the pinch-roller pressure according to the manufacturer's gram settings.

**Auto Shut Off Adjustment.** Mechanical auto shut off occurs when the tape has reached its end of play with the player in playback mode. Improper adjustment of the shut-off lever spring may cause the unit to shut off too soon or not at all. Check for correct clearance and tension at the shut-off lever. Bend the spring by putting more tension on the shut-off lever when it does not trip and less pressure when the lever trips too soon.

**Pause Control.** The pause control may be used when in play or recording modes. A pause lever lifts the pressure-roller assembly away from the capstan to prevent tape movement while the tape motor is still rotating. Make sure the pause control is not on before suspecting improper tape action in the player. A bent pause-control lever may not let the pressure roller engage the capstan assembly.

**Tape Speeds.** Tape speed problems in boom-box players are no different than any other tape deck (Fig. 4-27). Clean up all belts, idler wheels, and pulleys with alcohol and cleaning cloth. You may find flat and square belts in some models. Replace cracked or loose belts. Inspect the pressure roller for tape down inside the bearing area. Replace worn pressure roller, idler wheels, and rub-ber pulleys, if worn.

**Broken Levers or Knobs.** Check for a broken tab end-piece when the button stays down or will not engage the function lever. Sometimes the plastic lever will break right in two. Order a new button assembly. The play and rewind buttons are the first ones to break as they are used the most (Fig. 4-28). A small metal rod must be pulled out of each button assembly until you come to the broken one. Remove a "C" washer at the end of the button assembly. Insert the new lever and replace the small rod assembly.

**Indicator Lights.** LEDs are used extensively as indicator lights in today's boom-box players. Volume-level lights that increase as volume is applied are controlled from an IC component (Fig. 4-29). Each channel has its own set of lights. The LEDs and IC may be mounted on another small PC board mounted towards the front of the dial assembly.

Suspect a leaky IC when no lights will function

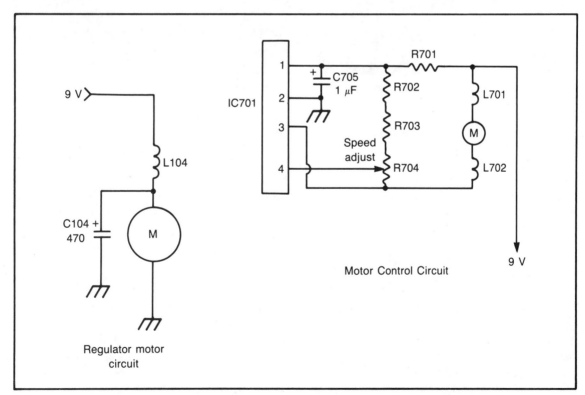

Fig. 4-26. You may find a motor-control circuit in some cassette players. Adjust R703 for the correct speed.

Fig. 4-27. Check motor drive belt, idler wheels, spindles, and reels for improper speeds. Inspect the pressure roller for drag or slow speeds.

or light up. Check the B+ source voltage at the IC. Determine if the correct dc voltage is across the LED. If the correct voltage is measured across each LED but there is no light, suspect a defective LED. Usually only one LED is out in a volume light movement.

## TEN DO'S AND DON'TS

1. Do be careful when installing the IC component. Use a low-wattage or battery-type soldering iron.

2. Do measure all voltages at the IC before replacing it. Make sure a defective resistor or capacitor tied to the IC is not defective instead of the IC.

3. Do not re-install the suspected IC back into the tape sound system when a new one does not

solve the problem. You probably have ruined it in removing it from the PC board.

4. Check for universal IC replacements when the exact part number cannot be located. All universal ICs work nicely in audio and receiver circuits.

5. Do clean up the tape head when weak or distorted music is found in one channel. A dirty tape head while recording may cause the same problems.

6. Do not overlook a blown speaker cone when one channel is dead. Sometimes the cone gets blown out when the player is operated at extremely high volume.

7. Do not be afraid to use a universal speaker for the defective one. Choose one of the same diameter, impedance, and weight of magnet.

8. Do not overlook a defective earphone jack

with one dead channel. Sometimes the internal shorting contacts are bent or broken out of line, preventing good contact.

9. Don't overlook small electrolytic coupling capacitors (1, 3.3 and 4.7 $\mu$F) from causing weak sound. Signal-trace with the external sound amp on each side of the suspected capacitor.

10. Do order the exact part number of critical parts in the tape-player mechanism.

## FIVE CASE HISTORIES

**No Dialing.** Either the dial shaft was loose or there was a broken dial cord in a Panasonic Model RQ-4445. The dial pointer would not move across the dial scale. The chassis was removed from the plastic cabinet to get at the dial assembly. The dial-cord spring had pulled through the piece of plastic dial drum. Another small hole was made to the left of the breakout area with the tip of a battery sol-

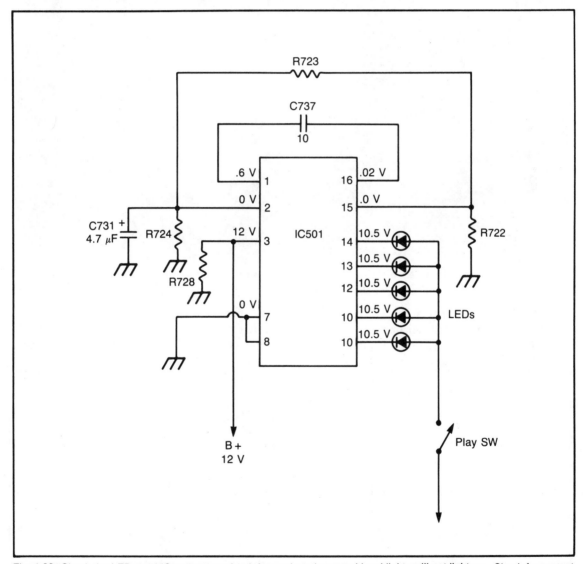

Fig. 4-28. Check the LEDs and IC component for defects when the sound level lights will not light up. Check for correct voltage across the LED terminals.

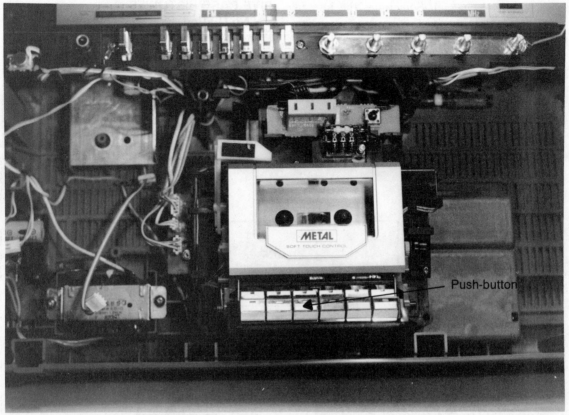

Push-button

Fig. 4-29. Inspect the lever for a piece broken off when it presses down but does not engage the function assembly. Order original buttons or plastic levers from the manufacturer.

dering iron. The spring was slipped through the hole and held in place with silicon rubber cement.

**No Tape Motion.** The tape would not move in a Sanyo Model C3D. After removing the back cover, a voltage test across the motor terminals indicated correct voltage. The motor took off after

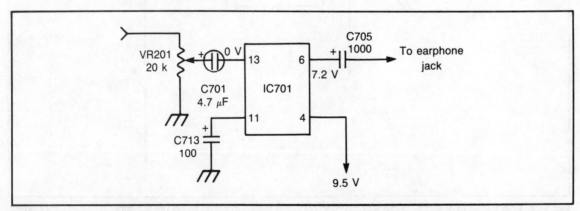

Fig. 4-30. A weak left channel in a Sharp Model 6F-575 was caused by open C701. Very low electrolytic coupling capacitors have a tendency to go open, producing a weak channel.

**Table 4-1. Boom-Box Tape Player Troubleshooting Chart.**

| Symptom | Possible Circuit | Check |
|---|---|---|
| Dead | Dirty tape on/off switch | Clean switch contacts—spray down inside switch area. |
| | Broken battery/ac switch | Inspect switch assembly when ac cord is plugged in. |
| | Low-voltage diodes | Check diodes with diode scale of DMM. |
| No motor rotation | Defective motor | Measure voltage at motor terminals—rotate motor by hand. |
| | Motor switch | Check for bent or defective motor on/off switch assembly. |
| No flywheel rotation | Motor belt | Check for broken or loose motor belt—see if motor belt is off motor pulley. |
| | Capstan/flywheel | Frozen or dry |
| Sluggish pinch-roller movement | Rubber pressure roller | Pinch roller should open freely—inspect pinch-roller bearing for excess tape—check for dry pressure-roller bearing. |
| Erratic auto shut off | Lever spring | Check tension on lever spring of auto shut off. Readjust by bending metal spring. |
| Erratic dialing | Dial assembly | Tighten up dial-cord spring. Install a new stronger spring. Inspect dial cord for frayed or thin cord. Place liquid rosin upon dial-knob shaft assembly. |
| Will not erase | Erase head | Inspect erase head for broken lead connections. Check for missing side-mounting bolt. Check continuity of erase head. |
| Both channels dead | Power output circuits and B+ voltage | Measure B+ voltage at transistor or IC circuits. Check for accurate voltage at IC terminals. |
| Dead right channel | Speaker | Clip another PM speaker to right-channel output. |
| | Earphone jack | Clean up earphone shorting terminals. Replace earphone jack if broken. |
| | Output IC | Locate right-channel IC. Measure IC voltages. Check signal in and out with external audio amp. |
| Weak right channel | Low voltages | Measure all voltage upon IC terminals. Check power supply for low voltages. |
| | IC component | Isolate IC—check signal in and out. |
| | Electrolytic capacitors | Check signal on both sides of speaker, input IC, and volume-control coupling capacitors. Shunt a new one across each suspected bad one. |

giving the motor pulley a spin. Sometimes when the player was shut off, the motor would stop and not start up again. Replacing the motor with the original part number, ATN-171506303, did the trick.

**Will Not Erase.** A J.C. Penney Model 6536 portable cassette player had jumbled recordings. To determine if the erase-head circuits were normal, the played tape was rewound to the beginning of the cassette. The volume control was lowered with the player in record mode. If the erase circuits are operating, the first three minutes of the recording should contain no music. Upon checking the erase head, the white wire was broken from the tape head. After soldering the erase-head wire and cleaning up of heads, the jumbled recordings disappeared.

**Dead Left Channel.** The left channel was dead at the speakers but had normal earphone operation in a MacDonald Model 06-33-63 high-power compact cassette player. Since the earphone operation was normal, the speaker or earphone jack had to be defective. Another PM speaker was clipped across the woofer with no results. Cleaning fluid was sprayed inside the earphone jack and the male plug was worked in and out several times to clean the contacts. This treatment restored the left speaker.

**Weak Left Channel.** The left channel of a Sharp Model GF-375 was fairly weak with loud music from the right speaker. The external amp was used to signal-trace the audio circuits. Weak sound was found at pin 6 of IC701 (Fig. 4-30). Very weak signal was found on input terminal pin 13. The sound was normal for both channel center-terminal connections of the volume control. Upon checking the schematic, C701 was the only component between the volume control and the IC. After several minutes C701 was located. Another 4.7 $\mu$F electrolytic capacitor shunted across it restored the weak left channel. Additional troubleshooting suggestions for sound and mechanical problems may be seen in Table 4-1.

# Chapter 5

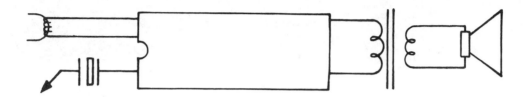

# Deluxe AM-FM-MPX Tuner Tests

HIGH-QUALITY AM-FM CIRCUITS MAY BE found in the compact stereo component system, stereo receiver, AM-FM tuner-amplifier, or in a separate AM-FM-MPX tuner (Fig. 5-1). The latest development is the digitally synthesized tuner with fully automatic tuning circuitry that offers precise reception. The automatic-tuning system automatically searches for receivable stations while a preset tuning system enters station frequencies into memory circuitry to provide one-touch, accurate tuning. In a direct-tuning system, push the number input buttons to register a station frequency and the tuner will move directly to the input station. You may find all of these features in one deluxe AM-FM-MPX tuner chassis.

The digital and synthesizer tuner is controlled like the new TV chassis. The controller selects the station by supplying correct tuning voltage to the AM and FM varactor tuners (Fig. 5-2). The controller has both manual push-button and random-search station-selection capability. Memory, latch, and LED display circuits are tied to the synthesizer controller.

## DIGITAL SYNTHESIZER CONTROL

The phase-locked-loop frequency synthesizer provides electronic control of the AM-FM tuner. Both the AM and FM sections are controlled by signal voltage from the synthesizer control to the varactor tuner.

The FM system is a conventional tuner with varactor diodes in place of the mechanical capacitor with rotator and stator plates. This controlled voltage varies a local oscillator instead of the mechanical tuner. Buffer and prescaler stages are added so that the controller knows to what frequency the local oscillator is tuned. A stop signal is sent to the controller IC to tell the controller when a station is tuned in. When using the stop signal, the controller may stop when searching for a station. The audio is shut off with a muting circuit as it receives a muting signal from the controller when it is in the searching mode.

The AM tuner is a conventional tuner but with varactor diodes replacing the mechanical tuner. A signal voltage from the controller selects the required station. The AM tuner and controller works

Fig. 5-1. The deluxe AM-FM-MPX tuner may be in a separate container by itself or in a radio-receiver like the Radio Shack Model STA-700 pictured here.

in the very same manner as the FM system.

Practically all controller features are performed by IC components. These large synthesizer processors have anywhere from 28 to 42 terminals. The controller also sends signals to the multiplexed drive display, showing the frequency of the tuned station on a multiplexed display. A signal is also sent to control the memory of the LEDs. Besides synthesized control, you may find analog frequency and quartz-locked tuning in the AM-FM tuner.

**The Varactor Tuner.** The FM varactor tuner is tuned with several varactor diodes. A varactor diode will change capacitance when a different voltage is applied to it. By varying the voltage across the diode, a variable capacitor tunes the FM and AM bands like the TV tuner. In many of the early FM chassis, the tuning was controlled by a variable resistance control with a tuning knob. When the variable resistor was rotated, a different voltage was applied to the varactor diode, tuning in the various stations.

Along with the FM varactor tuner, you may find a varactor diode in the rf, mixer, and oscillator stages (Fig. 5-3). The same signal voltage is supplied by the controller. In some chassis there is a test point to measure the controlled voltage. The voltage applied to the varactor diode is a different voltage for each station.

Suspect a defective synthesizer processor when improper or no voltage is found at the varactor di-

ode. The controller or display may be defective with improper lighting of the various LEDs. Check the driver and memory circuits for no memory LED display. Critical voltage measurements at the processor or IC components should locate the problem. Replace all ICs, processors, and varactor diodes with the exact part number.

**FM-FET-Rf-Amp.** Most FM receivers use an FET transistor in the varactor or conventional capacitor rf stage. D3 is the varactor diode in the rf stage of the varactor tuner in Fig. 5-4. Here the tuning voltage applied to D3 is supplied through R4 (33 k). The FM coil (L4) is tuned by varactor diode D4. The same tuning voltage occurs at R7 from the same tuning-voltage source. TP1 is a test point to check the varying voltage supplied by the controller or push-button voltage selection.

**Conventional FET-FM-Rf Amp.** A conventional AM-FM-MPX block diagram is shown in Fig. 5-5. The conventional FM-rf amp is tuned by a mechanical tuner, VC101 (Fig. 5-6). The tuned rf signal selected by VC101 is capacity coupled through C103 to the base terminal of the FET rf transistor. The secondary of L102 is tuned with another section of the mechanical tuner to the base of the mixer transistor, Q2 (Fig. 5-7). Suspect a leaky or open FET rf transistor when only a local FM station can be heard.

**FM Oscillator Buffer Varactor.** The oscillator stages in the varactor tuner may consist of

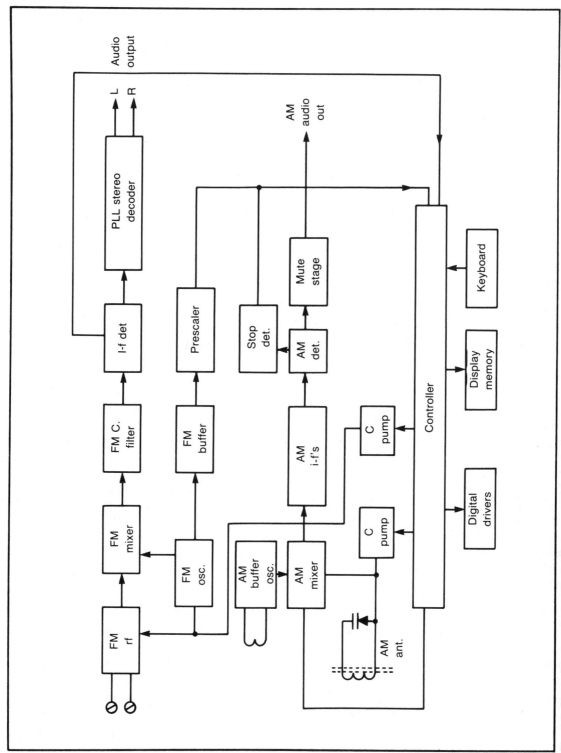

Fig. 5-2. Block diagram of a synthesizer-tuner controller which controls both AM and FM reception.

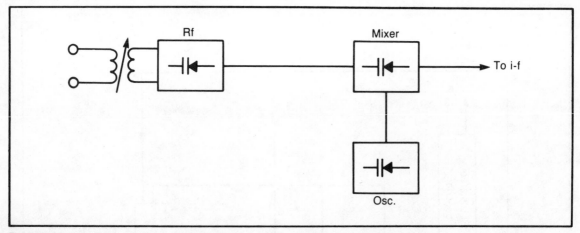

Fig. 5-3. All three FM-rf, oscillator, and mixer stages are tuned with varactor tuners by a control voltage from the controller. In early receivers, the varactor tuners were controlled by a manual variable resistor.

two or more transistors. The varactor diode selects the correct frequency in the oscillator circuit with voltage being controlled by the controller (Fig. 5-8). Suspect a defective oscillator circuit when only a loud hissing noise can be heard but no tunable stations. The same controlled voltage is found at the oscillator, mixer, and rf stages. Check for a variable voltage at point (A) when a different station is tuned in.

**Conventional FM Oscillator Circuit.** The conventional oscillator transistor is coupled to a tuned coil and mechanical capacitor with the oscillator frequency coupled to the mixer stage (Fig. 5-9). The incoming rf tuned station frequency and oscillator frequency results in a mixed signal at the mixer stage. Check the oscillator circuit when no tunable station can be heard. Critical transistor and voltage measurements solve most oscillator-circuit problems. Erratic tuning may be caused by the oscillator plates touching the variable capacitor.

**FM Mixer Circuits.** The only difference between the conventional mixer and varactor circuits is the varactor diode coupled to the mixer transistor. Practically all mixer stages are conventional in operation with the 10.5-MHz i-f frequency coupled to a ceramic i-f network (Fig. 5-10). In the early FM i-f circuits, several transistors are found. A defective mixer stage may create a low hissing noise or a completely dead FM band if there is a leaky or open mixer transistor.

**The AM Varactor Circuits.** You may find that the AM varactor tuner consists of a separate rf FET transistorized stage with a separate IC for the converter and i-f circuits (Fig. 5-11). A varactor tuning diode is found in the rf and converter stage. The same tuning voltage is fed to both tuning circuits. The i-f output is fed to multiplex IC circuits. In large deluxe models you may find entirely separate AM and FM circuits.

**Conventional AM Circuits.** The AM antenna may feed directly into a separate rf transistor or IC component. In some chassis one IC may control all the AM circuits. The AM output is then coupled to the audio switch circuits (Fig. 5-12). Today more and more IC components are found in the AM and FM control and tuning stages.

**FM I-f Circuits.** Even the lower priced receivers have one or two ceramic filter components in the i-f circuits. You may find three in the large FM i-f circuits (Fig. 5-13). In the older circuits you may find three or four separate i-f transistorized stages with large i-f transformers (Fig. 5-14). The ceramic filter stages are quite simple, easier to service, and cause fewer service problems.

You may find all of the AM-FM circuits on one board in compact receiver models (Fig. 5-15). The small tuning capacitor, i-f, and multiplex transformers are shown in the photograph. Here a combination of transistors and IC components forms the AM and FM circuits, while in the larger tuners the

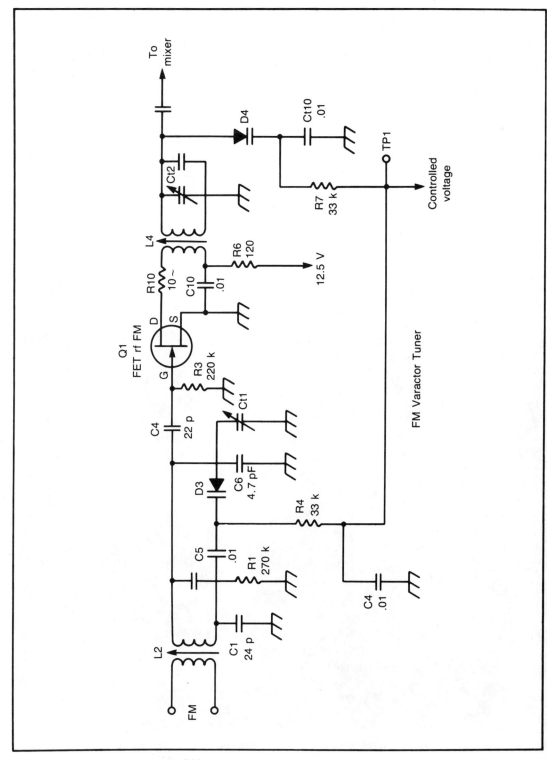

Fig. 5-4. Varactor diode D3 tunes rf coil L2 with a variable voltage through voltage-dropping resistor R4. The rf FET transistor amplifies the tuner signal and is coupled to the mixer stage through L4.

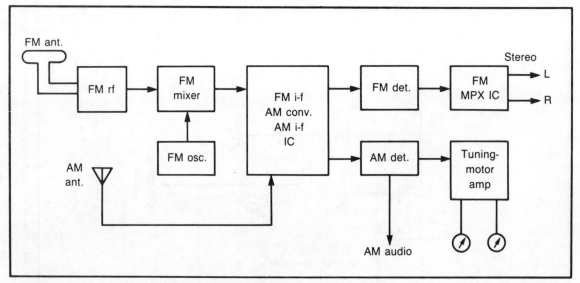

Fig. 5-5. A conventional AM-FM-MPX may have two separate IC components. The FM i-f/AM converter/Am-i-f circuits are contained in the first IC with the second operating the FM MPX circuits.

Fig. 5-6. A mechanical tuner in both AM and FM circuits tunes the different bands in the early conventional tuner circuits.

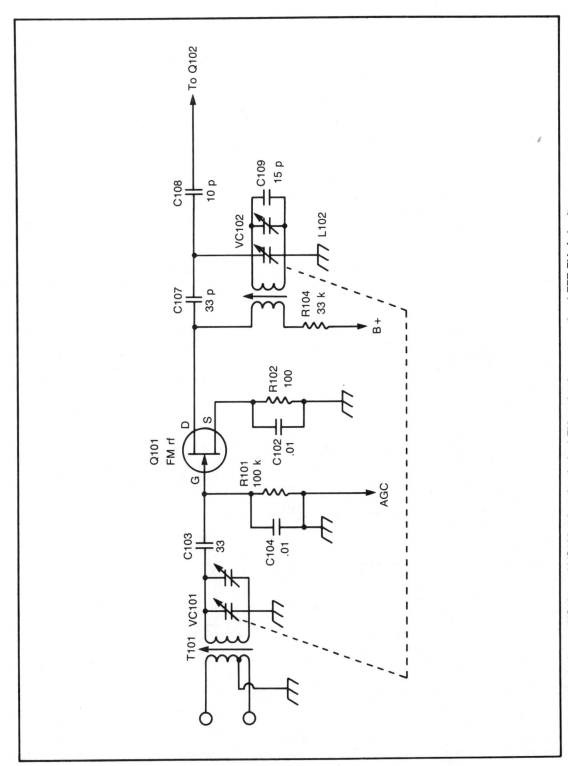

Fig. 5-7. Mechanical tuner VC101 and VC102 select the desired FM station in a conventional FET FM rf circuit.

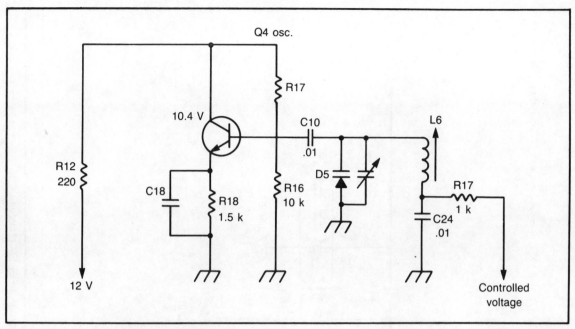

Fig. 5-8. The FM varactor oscillator circuit is tuned by D5 with a variable voltage applied through R17 by a synthesizer controller or manual variable resistor.

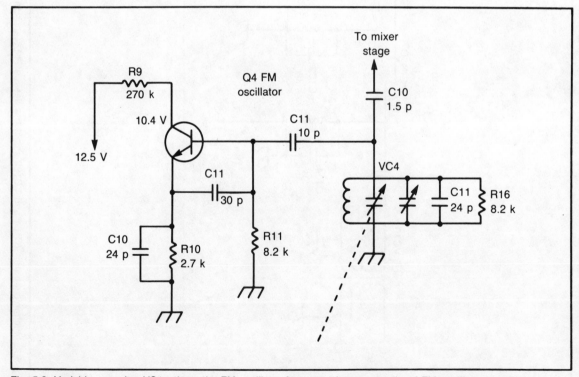

Fig. 5-9. Variable capacitor VC4 selects the FM oscillator frequency in a conventional FM oscillator circuit.

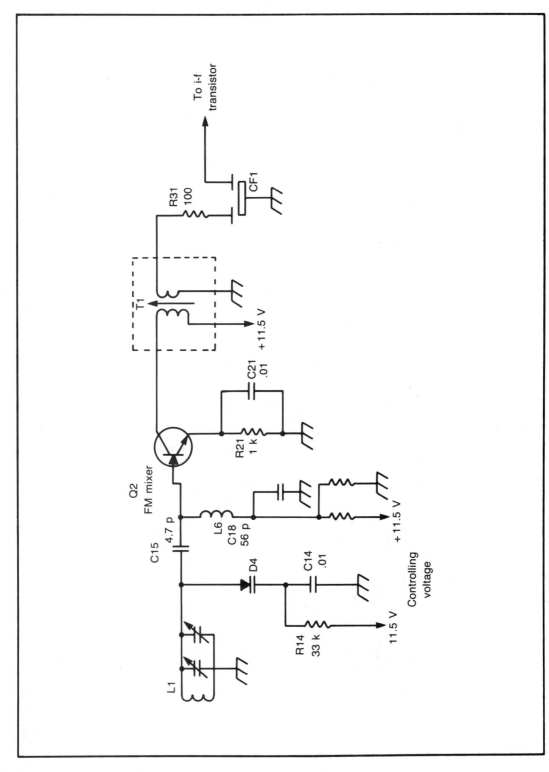

Fig. 5-10. Coil L1 in the base circuit of the FM mixer stage is tuned with varactor tuner D4. The controlled voltage is applied through voltage-dropping resistor R14 (33 k).

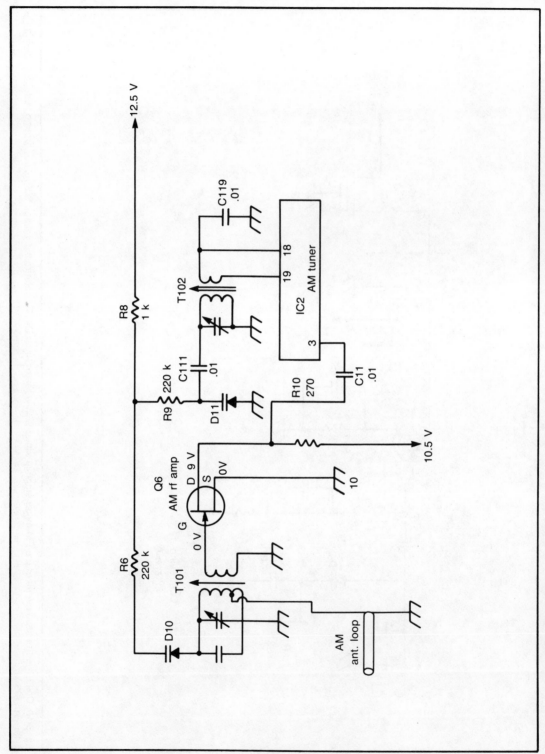

Fig. 5-11. Coils T101 and T102 are tuned by the same controlled voltage fed to varactor diodes D10 and D11. An FET transistor serves as AM rf amp in the AM receiver circuits.

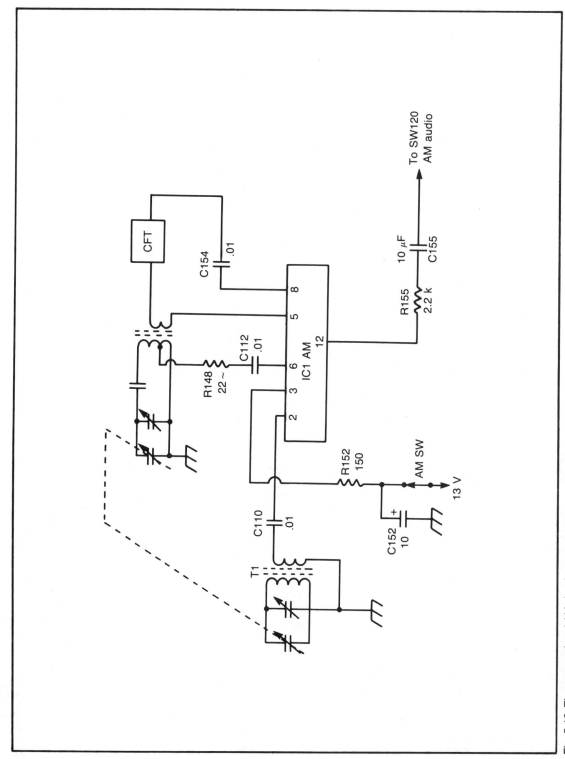

Fig. 5-12. The conventional AM circuits are tuned by a mechanical variable capacitor with one IC serving for all the AM functions in some AM-FM tuners.

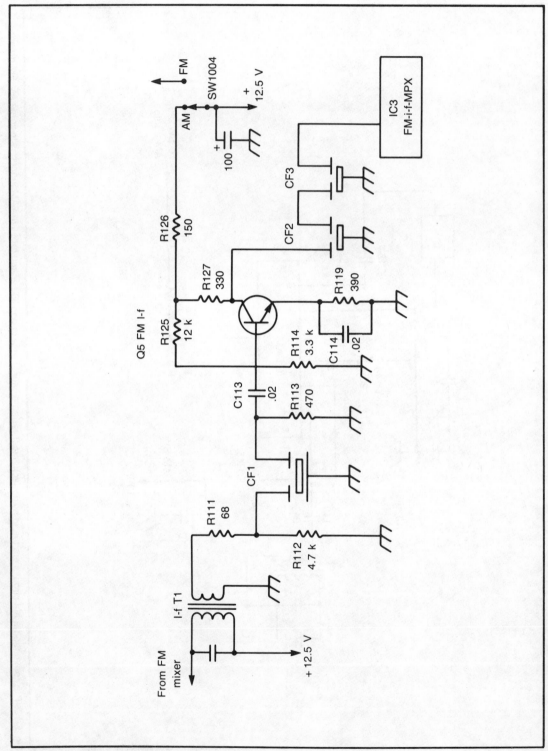

Fig. 5-13. Here three different ceramic filter components are used in the FM i-f circuits of transistor Q5. Many of the new tuners have IC components in i-f and matrix circuits.

Fig. 5-14. Large i-f transformer and matrix coils are found in the early receiver circuits with transistorized stages.

control tuner, AM-FM, and MPX circuits are found on separate boards.

**FM Multiplex Circuits.** The IC component was first introduced in the audio and FM multiplex circuits. The input signal is taken from the last FM i-f stage and fed to IC3 (Fig. 5-16). A 19-kHz adjustment is found at terminal 15. Separation adjustment is found at terminals 4 and 5. The stereo audio is taken from terminals 5 and 7 and fed to the selector-switch assembly. Pin 9 provides signal to the LED driver and tuning LEDs. Excessive whistling and poor sound separation may result from a defective MPX circuit. No stereo or only distorted sound may be caused by a defective multiplexer IC (Fig. 5-17).

## THE POWER SUPPLY

You may find many power-supply voltage sources in the FM-AM-FM stereo synthesizer tuner. Extreme voltage regulation is needed for critical processor and digital circuitry (Fig. 5-18). Simply isolate the defective circuit and check for adequate voltage. If the voltage is low or improper, trace the source back to the low-voltage power circuits.

Although many of the receiver-tuner low-voltage circuits consist of nothing more than full-wave or bridge rectification, you may find several different voltage sources in the deluxe AM-FM-MPX stereo compact system (Fig. 5-19). Here a 14.1-volt source feeds the AM-FM-MPX circuits and equalizer amp with a – 14.1-volt source from the same bridge rectifier. Another bridge rectifier regulator circuit supplies a 17-volt source to all audio circuits. Two separate half-wave diode rectifiers supply voltage to the phono motor and cassette deck motor.

Like most power-supply circuits, large filter

111

Fig. 5-15. In smaller AM-FM-MPX receivers you may find all components mounted on one small PC board. Note how small the FM coils and transformers are compared to the other chassis.

capacitors (2200 μF) are used for critical regulation circuits. Check the regulator transistor for an open or leakage in the case of an improper voltage source. Most zener-diode regulators will increase or short when defective. Scope the 14- and 17-volt sources for excessive hum in the audio circuits. In a dead chassis, look for an open fuse. Suspect a leaky bridge or diode rectifier if the fuse keeps blowing. Check for a shorted power transformer when the lights dim down and the transformer hums without a fuse in the ac line.

**Dead—No AM or FM.** Check the power supply with a dead AM-FM-MPX tuner. Notice if the audio section is normal in the radio receiver. If the phono or cassette player is okay, suspect problems within the front-end circuits of the AM-FM tuner in a compact unit. Check the audio at the line output terminals of the tuner. Inject a 10.5-MHz i-f signal at the mixer input terminal and notice if the

signal can be heard in the speakers. If no audio, troubleshoot the i-f and MPX circuits. Do not forget a dirty AM-FM switch assembly. Check for a broken AM-FM function switch.

The no AM-FM symptom was found in a Soundesign 69D model. No voltage at the AM-FM selector switch indicated trouble in the low-voltage power supply. Zero voltage was measured on the emitter terminal of Q16 with 19.8 volts at the collector terminal (Fig. 5-20). Q16 was found open with the transistor tester. Replacing Q16 with a universal SK3253 transistor replacement solved the no AM-FM symptom.

**No AM—FM Good.** Inspect the AM antenna coil for a broken core or wire connection. Test the AM converter transistor with the diode test of the DMM. Most universal transistor replacements will work nicely in the AM circuits. Measure all voltages at the AM transistor. Suspect a defective IC,

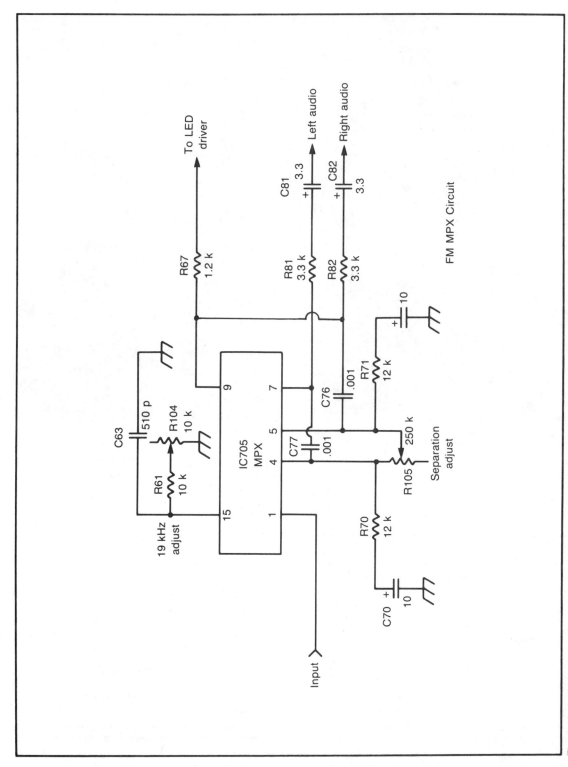

Fig. 5-16. A 19 kHz and separation adjust controls are found in the FM matrix circuits of IC705. The audio output channels are taken from pins 7 and 9.

Fig. 5-17. Here in a more modern receiver the FM i-f and matrix circuits have IC components.

even though the FM i-f stages are supplied by the same IC component when the AM antenna coil feeds directly into the same IC.

**Weak AM.** Go directly to the AM antenna-coil assembly and rf transistor. Note if the antenna coil core is broken in two. Inspect all wiring connections from coil to the PC board circuits. Suspect the rf transistor if only a local station can be heard.

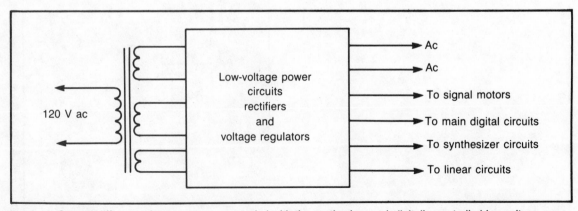

Fig. 5-18. Several different voltage sources are needed with the synthesizer and digitally controlled low-voltage power supplies.

114

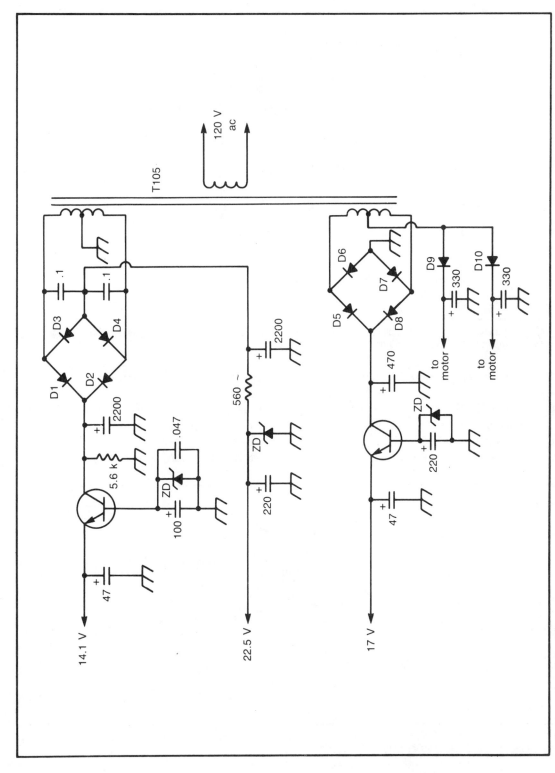

Fig. 5-19. In the large deluxe AM-FM-MPX receivers several different power supplies are used. The 14- and 17-volt sources are regulated with transistors, while the 22-volt supply has a zener diode for voltage regulation.

115

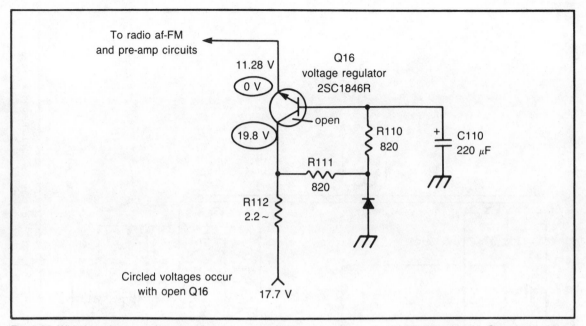

Fig. 5-20. With the voltage regulator transistor open no voltage was applied to the AM-FM circuits of a Soundesign Model 69D. Q16 was replaced with an SK3253 transistor replacement.

The FET rf transistor in a Sanyo GXT300 component system was suspected since the AM section was dead (Fig. 5-21). When voltage measurements were being taken upon Q9, a local station could be heard. The D voltage should be 9.5 but was only 1.2 volts. Replacing the leaky FET, Q9, with a universal 2SK315 transistor solved the weak reception problem.

Weak or no AM may be caused by a poor connection or the AM detector in the AM i-f stage. Sometimes these diodes will become leaky, producing distorted or no AM. A poor anode connection

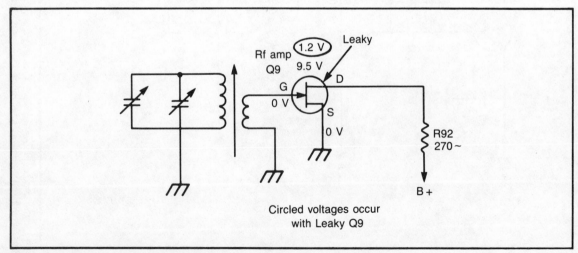

Fig. 5-21. Only a local AM station could be heard in a Sanyo Model 6XT-300 receiver; the rf AM FET was found leaky. Q9 was replaced with a 2SK315 transistor.

116

of D7 in a J.C. Penney 1322 model produced a dead AM symptom (Fig. 5-22). Look for a leaky IC, which may include the AM converter, i-f, and detector circuits. Suspect a defective AM converter if there are no tunable stations on the dial. A leaky capacitor in the AVC or AGC line to the rf or converter transistor may result in only one or two local stations being received.

**Noisy AM.** First, isolate the noisy sound to only the AM circuits. Determine if the noise is in the front end of the tuner or sound circuits by lowering the volume control. Transistors and IC components in the AM and FM circuits may produce a low hissing noise. Short out the base and emitter terminals of each i-f, oscillator, and mixer transistors to pinpoint the noisy stage. Actually, voltage and transistor tests will not uncover a noisy IC or transistor. Replace the suspected IC when the input circuit is grounded out and noise still persists at the output terminal.

**Both AM and FM Quit After Five Minutes.** Suspect something common to both AM and FM circuits when both channels are intermittent. Check the i-f and matrix sections common to both the AM and FM. Measure the voltage at the power supply and voltage-regulator circuits. Monitor the voltage regulator and sound output channels. Inject a 10.5-MHz signal into the i-f stages and note if the sound comes through the speakers, or monitor each stage with the scope.

**No FM—AM Okay.** Determine if a local station may be tuned in for a completely dead FM section. Measure the voltage to the rf, oscillator, and mixer transistors. Suspect a defective voltage-regulator circuit in the case of improper voltage (Fig. 5-23). A leaky rf FET transistor may cause a dead FM stage. Place a test probe to terminal D and see if local stations can be tuned in. Test the rf, oscillator, and mixer transistors in the circuit. Visually inspect the FM circuits for cracked or broken resistors. A poor board connection may cause the dead FM symptom.

Only a loud FM hiss could be heard in an RC-1248A RCA stereo chassis. Voltages were way off in the FM circuits. Accurate voltage measurements were made on the voltage regulator, IC202

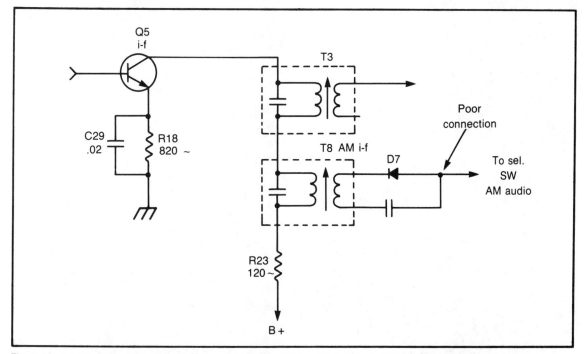

Fig. 5-22. A poor diode connection (D7) caused a dead AM symptom in a J. C. Penney Model 1322 receiver.

Fig. 5-23. The VTVM or DMM are required test instruments for servicing the AM-FM-MPX chassis. Critical voltage and alignment tests are required in tuner repairs.

(Fig. 5-24). All voltages around the IC were higher than normal. Replacing the leaky IC202 fixed the dead FM chassis.

Do not overlook the multiplex stages when there is a dead FM symptom. Note if the stereo light, VU meter, or digital LEDs are working during FM operation. If the lights or LEDs indicate no signal, suspect a leaky MPX IC component. Take accurate voltage measurements on all IC terminals. Sometimes replacing the IC with an indicator light staying on is the only answer.

**Weak FM—Only Local Station.** Go directly to the FM rf stage if there is only one tunable local FM station. Test the FET or transistor for leaky or open conditions. Inspect the chassis for lightning damage, especially if the chassis was connected to the outside FM antenna. Accurate voltage tests may indicate a leaky or shorted LED transistor. Check the first FM-AM i-f transistor or IC component with a weak FM and no AM symptom. Very weak FM with frying noise may be caused by a leaky MPX IC component. Suspect the MPX IC if there is weak and distorted FM reception. A leaky MPX IC may run warm and should operate cool in the FM circuits.

**No FM—Very Weak AM.** In the J.C. Penney Model 2500, both the FM i-f and AM i-f circuitry are in IC201. Since IC201 was common to both bands, accurate voltages were made at each terminal. Voltages on pins 4, 8, 9, and 15 were quite low (Fig. 5-25). Only 1.79 volts was found at pin 4 which was the common voltage source from voltage regulator TR901. At first TR901 was suspected of supplying low voltage to IC201 (4.9V). Actually, IC201 was found to be leaky, causing the no FM and very weak AM symptom.

**Intermittent FM.** Intermittent reception within either the AM or FM band is very difficult to locate. Try to isolate the intermittent to a given stage with accurate transistor and IC voltage measurements. Determine if the FM-AM switch is dirty. Clean all function switches with cleaning fluid. Spray down inside the contact-point area. The intermittent FM problem may be found by applying pressure to components on the chassis with an insulated tool or pencil. Move the i-f transformer to see if the FM music will cut in and out. Poor board connections around transistor and IC terminals may cause intermittent FM reception. Check for an intermittent transistor or IC which combines the first

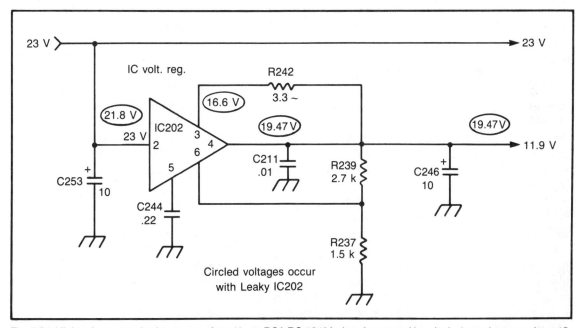

Fig. 5-24. Higher than normal voltages were found in an RCA RC-1248A chassis, caused by a leaky low-voltage regulator IC.

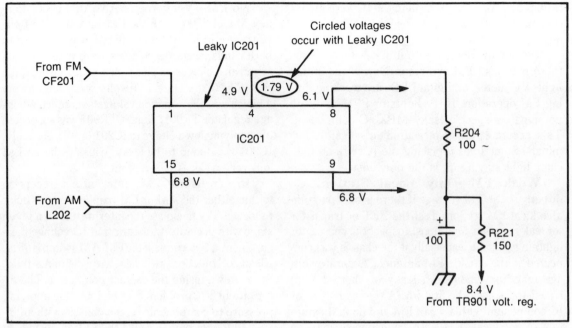

Fig. 5-25. A no FM, very weak AM was found in a J. C. Penney Model 2500 receiver. A leaky IC201 was found with low voltage at pin 4 (1.79V).

AM-FM i-f amp stage. The intermittent matrix MPX IC may produce intermittent reception in either stereo channel.

**Fading FM.** A leaky FM oscillator transistor may cause the FM to fade out after several minutes of operation. Do not overlook a varicap diode connected to the oscillator circuits. Check for a defective padder capacitor mounted on top of the FM tuning capacitor. Monitor the dc voltage applied to the FM circuits. Spray each transistor and IC with coolant after the FM station has faded away to locate a solid-state device. Suspect an AM-FM i-f IC component when the FM fades out and only one AM station is heard.

**FM Hum and Noise.** Check for a leaky MPX IC or dirty preset control in the MPX circuits when the FM is garbled or microphonic. The FM padder capacitor on top of the main FM tuning capacitor may cause a tunable whistle or microphonic noise. A whistling noise on the low end of the FM band may result from improper FM alignment. Suspect a defective voltage regulator circuit when tunable hum is found upon both AM and FM bands.

Intermittent FM hum may be caused by poor shield or grounds in the matrix circuits.

**Stereo Indicator Lights On All the Time.** In many of the AM-FM stereo receivers, the FM stereo light will come on when an FM station is tuned in. If the light does not come on, suspect a bad bulb, LED, or multiplex IC component. Sometimes the stereo indicator light will stay on all the time, indicating a leaky MPX IC. Take accurate voltage measurements of the MPX IC circuit, especially the terminal that connects to the stereo light. A leaky IC102 (MPX) component caused the light to stay on all the time in a Sharp Model SA-5401 (Fig. 5-26).

**FM Tuning Meter Indicator.** The FM tuning meter will operate in proportion to the input voltage of the antenna. Often the meter circuit is tapped off the IC output signal and amplified by several transistors or IC circuits (Fig. 5-27). The i-f signal is then detected and applied to the meter amp transistor. The adjustment of the signal meter should be made at maximum with an FM signal generator.

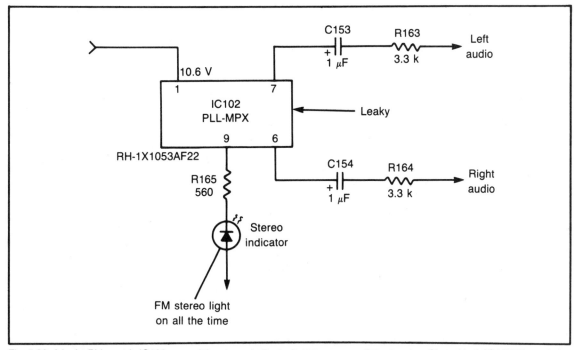

Fig. 5-26. A leaky PLL-matrix IC102 caused the stereo indicator light to stay on all the time in a Sharp Model SA-5401 receiver.

**AM-FM-MPX Receiver Alignment.** Several years back regular AM and FM alignments were very easy. A touch up of the FM chassis might only take a few minutes. Today, with all the various types of receivers and circuits, many different test instruments are needed to do the job right (Fig. 5-28). Each manufacturer's alignment procedure should be followed to their specifications. Always make FM alignments before a multiplex alignment. Besides AM-FM and MPX alignment, you may run

into mute level, signal meter, separation, i-f distortion, auto stop, and threshold alignment.

AM-FM alignment should never be attempted without the correct test equipment. Simply touching up or turning various alignment screws or coil cores should never be made. If you do not have the correct alignment test equipment, take it to someone who does. Most manufacturer servicing depots have the equipment and personnel for receiver alignment. Sometimes AM-FM-MPX alignment is

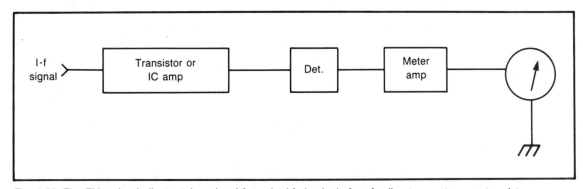

Fig. 5-27. The FM-tuning indicator takes signal from the i-f circuits before feeding to a meter amp transistor.

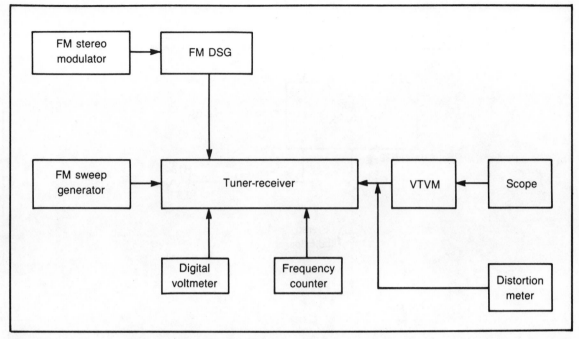

Fig. 5-28. Today several different test instruments are required to completely align the AM-FM-MPX tuner. Do not attempt alignment without them and complete manufacturer alignment procedures.

only needed after replacing the i-f transformer or multiplex coils, or when the receiver is not tracking properly.

## TEN CASE HISTORIES

Although the following troubles cover a wide range of problems in the AM-FM tuner, many of them occur all the time in various tuner and receivers.

**No AM—FM Normal.** The AM band was dead with normal FM reception in a Sanyo DCR100 receiver. Upon checking the schematic, the AM and FM circuits were entirely separate. The AM rf-FET transistor fed into IC2, which serves as converter, i-f, and detector circuits of the AM section. Voltage measurements on all IC terminals were low (Fig. 5-29). Since R51 was running quite warm, pin 11 was cut loose from IC2. Right away the 14.8 voltage source returned to normal. Replacing IC2 (LA1240) restored the AM band.

**No FM—Normal AM.** First voltage measurements were taken in the FM circuits of a Sharp Model SR150. The voltage on each transistor was lower than normal. The 10-volt source had dropped to 9.5 volts. A quick transistor test of each transistor with the DMM indicated the rf-FET amp Q101 was leaky. Another voltage test on Q101 found .55 volts on the S and G terminals (Fig. 5-30). Local stations popped right in after replacing the leaky 2SK49H FET transistor.

**Dead Front End.** The regular signal meter or the FM tuning-meter indicator showed no signs of movement in a Marantz Model 2252 tuner. A quick voltage measurement on the output transistors was normal (41.7V), indicating the main power source was okay. However, the voltage source feeding the AM-FM circuits was only 6.4 volts. The power supply voltage regulator (Q803) was found open. Replacing Q803 with a universal ECG152 replacement fixed the dead AM-FM section.

**No AM or FM.** No voltage was found within the AM or FM circuits of a Pioneer deluxe 1000TA tuner. Tracing the voltage source back to the power supply showed the voltage regulator (2S367) was leaky. The voltage-regulator transistor was replaced with a SK3444 universal replacement.

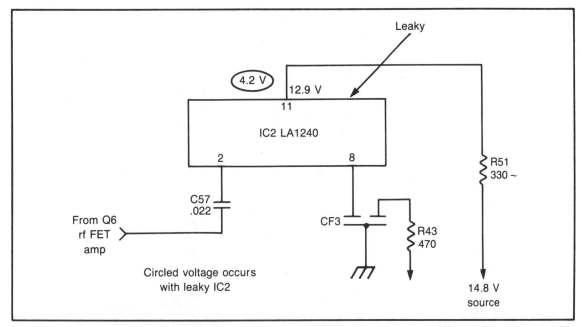

Fig. 5-29. A leaky AM converter, i-f, and detector IC2 in a Sanyo DCR100 receiver caused the no AM and normal FM symptom. Universal transistors and IC components work fine in the sections when original components are not available.

**Rushing FM—AM Okay.** Only a low rushing noise could be heard on the FM bands, but the AM section seemed normal. The voltage measurements on the FM rf and FM converter transistors were about half the supply voltages (3.4V). This

same voltage was applied to the AM circuits and AM stations could be heard over the entire dial (Fig. 5-31). Both FM transistors tested out normal. The voltage source from the voltage regulator amp was only 5.3 volts and should be 9.5 volts. Both

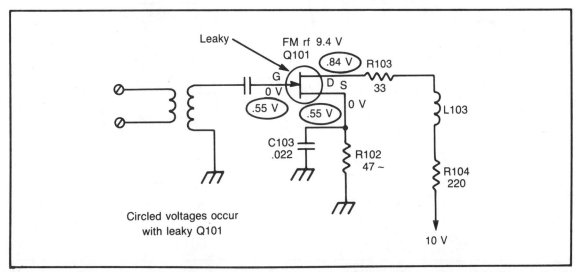

Fig. 5-30. Leakage between terminals G and S of the FM-rf transistor (Q101) caused a no FM, normal AM reception in a Sharp Model SR150. Very low voltage on terminal D indicated a leaky rf transistor.

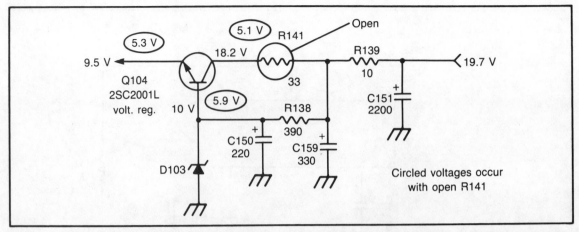

Fig. 5-31. Although the AM reception seemed normal with only a rushing noise on the FM band, low voltage from the voltage regulator (Q104) caused the FM problem in a J. C. Penney Model 1721 receiver. The AM and FM circuits are supplied by Q104, but the FM circuits would not perform with the lower voltage.

Q104 and zener diode D103 tested good. Open resistor (R141) was found and replaced, returning the voltage source to 9.5 volts.

**No FM—Very Weak AM.** Since the i-f sec-

tion is common to both the AM and FM circuits in a Panasonic SE-2250 receiver, voltages were checked at IC201. The AN217 IC serves as both AM-FM i-f amp and AM converter. The IC volt-

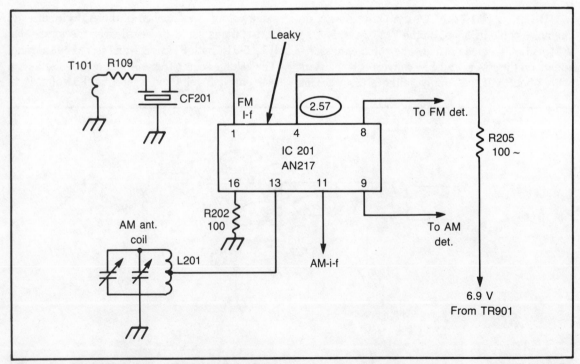

Fig. 5-32. The weak AM, no FM symptom in a Panasonic Model SE-2250 receiver was caused by a leaky AM converter/AM-FM-i-f IC.

124

age source is fed from regulator TR901 (6.9V). The voltage on source pin 4 was quite low (2.57 volts) (Fig. 5-32). Replacing the leaky IC201 with a universal SK3460 IC solved the AM and FM problems.

**AM-FM Distorted on Right Channel.** Since the cassette player in a Sanyo M9975 receiver provided normal music, the i-f and multiplex section was suspected of distortion in the right channel. Only 3.3 volts was found at pin 6 of MPX IC501 (Fig. 5-33). At first, the AN7410 IC was suspected of being leaky, but a poor contact on the radio switch (SW715) turned out to be the culprit.

**Microphonic Squeal.** Sometimes bumping the chassis in a J.C. Penney 3223 AM-FM-MPX stereo receiver would cause a microphonic sound in the speakers. Occasionally a loud squeal could be heard at certain points on the dial. The microphonic condition occurred only in the FM mode. When the large filter capacitor was tapped, the sound would begin. Replacing the padder capacitor CT3 in the oscillator section eliminated the microphonic noise (Fig. 3-34).

**No Signal Lights.** None of the signal lights in a Soundesign M8090 receiver would light up. Although the receiver played perfectly, the LEDs were out. Upon checking the schematic, the driver IC feeding the LEDs were suspected until no voltage source was found at the IC terminal. The 15-volt source was traced back to the power supply (Fig. 5-35). Actually, a ground screw was loose on the chassis, preventing the voltage return to the signal-light circuits.

**No FM Meter Movement.** The FM meter would not move with normal FM reception in a J.C. Penney 2079 modular tuner. The meter movement was checked with the ohmmeter scale of a VOM and indicated continuity. A closer view indicated the meter hand was binding against the warped meter backing material. Instead of replacing the meter, the front plastic cover was removed and the meter hand raised up with the blade of a knife. Sometimes you may find the meter coil open or a broken wire terminal at the rear of the meter.

### TEN DO'S AND DON'TS

1. Do try to replace all FM transistors with the original replacements. The terminal leads are the correct length and they work every time.

2. Do not overlook a broken iron ferrite core inside the AM antenna coil for weak AM reception.

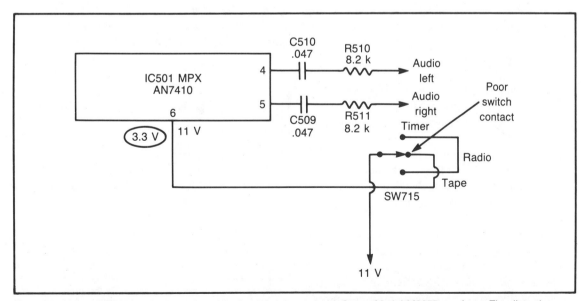

Fig. 5-33. AM and FM distortion were found in the right channel of a Sanyo Model M9975 receiver. The distortion was traced to the matrix system which was caused by a poor radio switch connection.

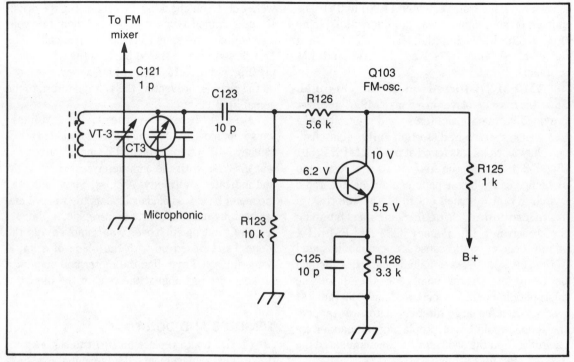

Fig. 5-34. A defective padder capacitor in the tuning circuit of a J. C. Penney Model 3223 caused microphonic reception on the FM band. Replacing CT3 solved the oscillating microphonic sound.

Sometimes they are difficult to see until removed.

3. Don't forget to first spray AM-FM and function switches with cleaning spray, as a good cleanup may immediately solve the dead or intermittent problem.

4. Do not overlook a defective voltage regulator transistor with the intermittent chassis. Some of these transistors may test normal in and out of the circuit. Replace them as they sometimes break down under load.

5. Do take signal in and out tests on IC components in the tuner circuits. Take accurate voltage and scope waveforms. Check all components tied to the IC before replacing it.

6. Don't use a high-wattage soldering iron on matrix or i-f-IC components when replacing them.

7. Do not turn any adjustment screws to improve the receiver reception; you may make it worse. Complete AM-FM-MPX alignment should be done with correct test equipment, following the manufacturer's alignment procedures.

8. Do not throw away open coils or i-f transformers. Most winding connections break right where they connect to the terminal lug. Remove a half-turn of coil and repair it.

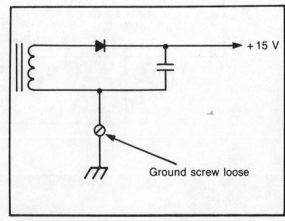

Fig. 5-35. A loose ground screw in the low-voltage power supply circuits produced no signal lights in a Soundesign Model M8090 receiver.

**Table 5-1. AM-FM-MPX Troubleshooting Chart.**

| Symptom | Possible Circuit | Check |
|---|---|---|
| Cannot tune in a station | Rf, oscillator, and mixer stages | All transistors and take critical voltage measurements. |
| | Synthesizer controller | Measure the control voltage applied to the varactor diodes; if missing suspect defective controller processor. |
| No tuning lights or digital channel | Synthesizer controller and memory-driver-digital circuits | Determine if controller is tuning in the stations. Take critical voltages on controller and all digital light circuits. |
| No AM | AM oscillator converter stage | Test AM transistor or IC converter in the circuit. Take critical voltage measurements. |
| Weak AM | AM antenna coil | Check for broken core or bad connections. |
| | AM rf amp | Check FET or rf transistor. Take voltage measurements. Test capacitors tied to AVC or AGC circuits. |
| Distorted AM on strong stations | AGC circuits | Check the resistors and capacitors in the AGC circuit. |
| Noisy AM | Noisy transistor and ICs | Determine if noise is picked up by tuning in a strong local station. Determine if noise is also on FM band. Replace AM converter. |
| No FM, AM normal | FM rf, oscillator, mixer and matrix circuits. | Check voltage source to FM circuits. Determine if i-f circuits use same component in both AM and FM circuits. |
| | Dirty AM-FM switch (clean up) | Test rf, oscillator, and mixer transistors. Take accurate voltage measurements. |
| Weak FM, excessive background noise | FM rf transistor or IC | Test FM rf FET transistor. Take voltage measurements. Replace suspected FM IC. |
| | Misadjustment of tracing or i-f transformer | Complete FM rf-i-f MPX alignment. |
| FM distortion | I-f AGC circuits | Test transistors and take critical voltage measurements on IC components. |
| | Matrix IC | Take critical voltage measurements. Replace matrix IC. |
| Noisy FM | I-f-IC and FM-matrix IC | Spray IC components with coolant and apply heat from heater blower to locate noisy IC. Determine if noise is created in front-end rf, oscillator, and mixer transistors. |
| FM hum | Power supply | Check for dried-up filter capacitor. Will have same hum on AM band. |
| | or | |
| | Voltage regulator circuit | Test voltage regulator for leakage, and check ripple voltage with a scope. |
| No stereo separation | MPX circuits (if stereo light operates normally) | Improper separation adjustment. See if component is touching from other channel in MPX. Check audio-amp circuits. |

127

| | | |
|---|---|---|
| Excessive stereo distortion | MPX IC | Take critical voltage measurements. Replace MPX IC. |
| Stereo light stays on all the time or does not operate | MPX amplifier IC light indicator | Check for proper voltages and for a leaky IC or transistor amp. Check indicator LED or lamp. |

9. Do replace the FM indicator light bulbs or LEDs with the original part number. Remember they are not just another light bulb.

10. Don't forget to replace all shields and common grounds after replacing critical components on top of the chassis. It's very easy to leave off those small shields underneath the PC board.

Table 5-1 lists some additional problems along with their possible causes and suggested troubleshooting procedures.

# Chapter 6

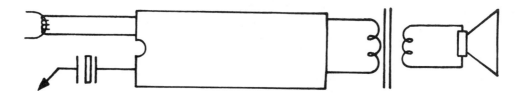

# Repairing the Deluxe Amplifier

THE STEREO AMPLIFIER MAY BE FOUND IN A tuner-amp component, radio receiver, or a separate amplifier with input jacks for a tuner, phono, and cassette player. Some of the new amplifiers have a separate input for the new compact-disc player. The average amplifier power output may be under 20 watts, while the intermediate group may be under 50 watts with the high-power amplifiers over 100 watts (Fig. 6-1). A few super-powered amplifiers may go above 250 watts of power.

The frequency response may vary from 20-20,000 Hz. The output speaker impedance may be 4, 8, or 16 ohms. Several speakers may be switched into the output with a speaker switch assembly. Most new amps have earphone operation.

Since all amplifiers break down sooner or later, the trouble symptoms are about the same. The only difference may be in the higher amperage and wattage of the output components. The high-wattage output system calls for more high-powered transistors and operates at higher voltage and greater amperage than the low-voltage power supply. Of course, these defective components must be re-

placed with the same or higher requirement components. Critical high-powered components must be replaced with the original part numbers.

## THE POWER SUPPLY

You may find higher dc voltage with greater voltage regulation in the separate amplifier. The average output voltage may vary from 24 to 85 volts dc. Several different low-voltage circuits may be located in the power amp (Fig. 6-2). The higher voltages feed the power-output transistors and IC components, while the lower voltage feeds the pre-amp and af circuits. You may find both positive and negative voltage sources in the low-voltage power supplies.

The full-wave low-voltage supply may have very large filter capacitors (Fig. 6-3). The capacitance may vary from 1500 to 4700 $\mu$F in the average amplifier with four separate 10,000 $\mu$F filter capacitors in the high-powered amplifiers. The 50-watt amp may have 12-amp bridge rectifiers, while in the high-powered amps a 30-amp bridge circuit may be found. Amplifiers over 250 watts

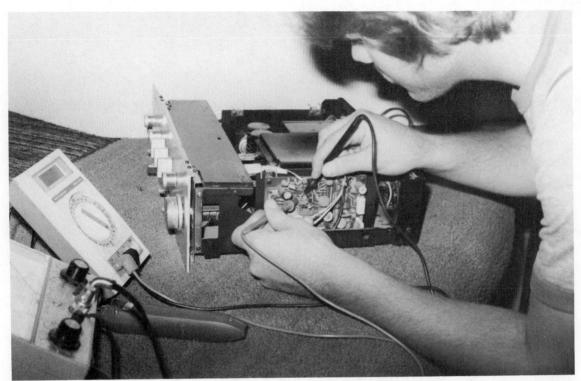

Fig. 6-1. Here the service technician is testing an audio transistor in the circuit with the diode-transistor test of the DMM.

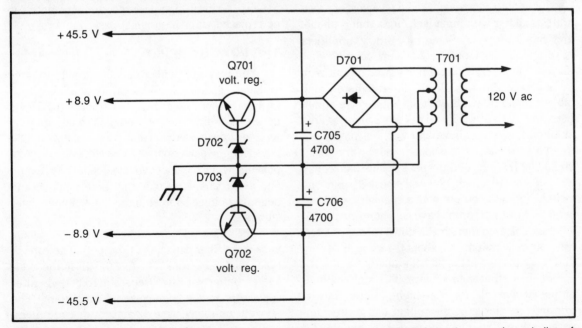

Fig. 6-2. Circuit diagram of a low-voltage power supply with full-wave bridge rectifiers. Note the secondary winding of the power transformer is center-tapped and feeds the negative voltage-regulator circuit.

130

Fig. 6-3. Very large filter capacitors are found in the typical high-powered amplifier (1500 μF to 4700 μF), while in 250-watt amps the filter capacitor may vary from 10,000 to 144,000 μF.

may have electrolytic capacitors up to 144,000 μF. Replacement of these large filter capacitors must be taken into consideration when there are filter hum problems.

**System Dead—Nothing Operates.** Inspect the fuse for blown sign marks or test with the low-ohm scale of the DMM or VOM. Note if the ac solenoid comes on in some models. Next take a voltage measurement at the large filter capacitor or power-output transistor. No voltage may indicate a leaky diode or power transformer. Check each diode with the diode function of the DMM if found separately (Fig. 6-4). Most bridge circuits are found wrapped up in one component. It's best to remove the single bridge-rectifier component from the circuit for accurate leakage tests. Check the on/off switch for burned contacts.

Quickly check the primary winding of the transformer if there are no pilot lights or voltage at the filter capacitors. Leaky audio-output transistors or ICs may destroy the primary winding without fuse protection. Suspect an overloaded circuit, leaky filter capacitors, or a leaky voltage regulator transistor when the LED lights dim and the amp groans when it is plugged into the power line.

**Keeps Blowing Fuses.** Visually inspect the low-voltage power and audio-output circuits for signs of overheated or burned components when the fuse will not hold (Fig. 6-5). Remove B+ fuses to the various circuits to eliminate an overloaded circuit found in some large amplifiers. Cut the circuit at the first large filter capacitor and take ac voltage measurements. If the fuse blows without the external circuits being connected, suspect leaky

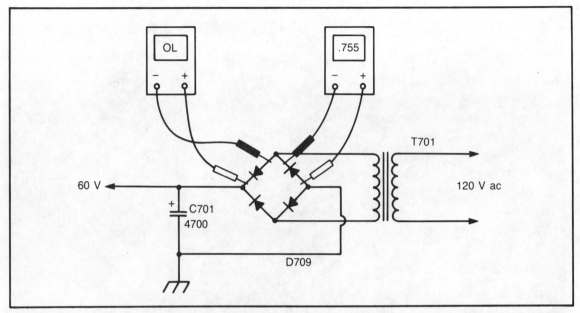

Fig. 6-4. The positive probe of the DMM is connected to the anode terminal with the negative probe at the cathode for a normal diode test. A low measurement in both directions indicates a leaky diode. You may find one or more leaky diodes in one bridge rectifier component.

silicon diodes or power transformer.

Remove the secondary leads from the silicon diode rectifiers and take ac voltage measurements. If the transformer makes a noise with low ac voltage, suspect shorted turns within the transformer. Feel the case of the transformer and notice if it is real warm. Some power transformers will run warm after many hours of use but never too hot to touch. Most overloaded circuits occur in the power output transistor or IC components. Replace the power transformer with the original part number.

**Dead on Both Channels.** Suspect the low-voltage power supply or a dual IC circuit when both channels are dead. Quickly check the voltage at the large filter capacitor. Measure the high dc voltage at the output transistors or IC circuits. Check the low-voltage regulator circuits for leaky transistors or zener diodes if there are no voltages at the output circuits (Fig. 6-6). A large, leaky IC found in the output circuits may cause both channels to be dead. Do not overlook blown speaker fuses.

**Dead Left Channel.** Identify the dead channel with the external audio amp or from the chassis parts layout chart. Check the left-channel

speaker fuse if one is used. Measure the voltage at the audio-output transistors or IC. Compare these voltage measurements with the good channel. Improper or very low voltages may be caused by leaky output transistors or low-voltage power supply circuits. Normal voltages at the audio output stages may indicate a defective driver, af, or pre-amp stages. Note if the left channel VU meter is working, indicating what section of the channel is dead.

The dead or weak audio stage may be hum checked with both channel speakers connected and the volume raised up one-quarter turn. Switch the amp to phono. Place your finger on the center terminal of the phono jack. You should hear a loud hum. Now check the other channel. Do not turn up the volume too high or you may damage the test speaker. Signal-trace the pre-amp and af circuits with the external amp or the audio 1000-Hz signal generator with the speaker or scope as indicator.

Go directly to the audio-output circuits if there are signs of distorted hum in the speaker of the defective channel. Measure the voltage at the collector (body) of each power-output transistor and IC. Compare these voltage measurements with the

Fig. 6-5. Some large amplifiers have each voltage source fused feeding each channel. Suspect leaky output transistors or ICs when the fuse will not hold.

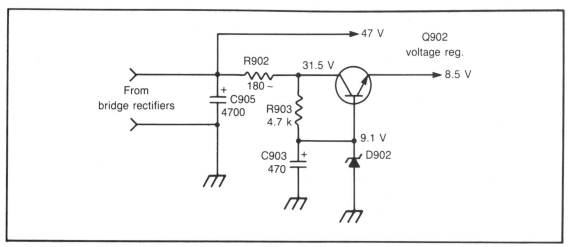

Fig. 6-6. A simple low-voltage power-supply regulator circuit may consist of a transistor and zener diode. Suspect a leaky voltage-regulator transistor when higher voltage is found in the output source. A leaky zener diode may lower the regulated output source.

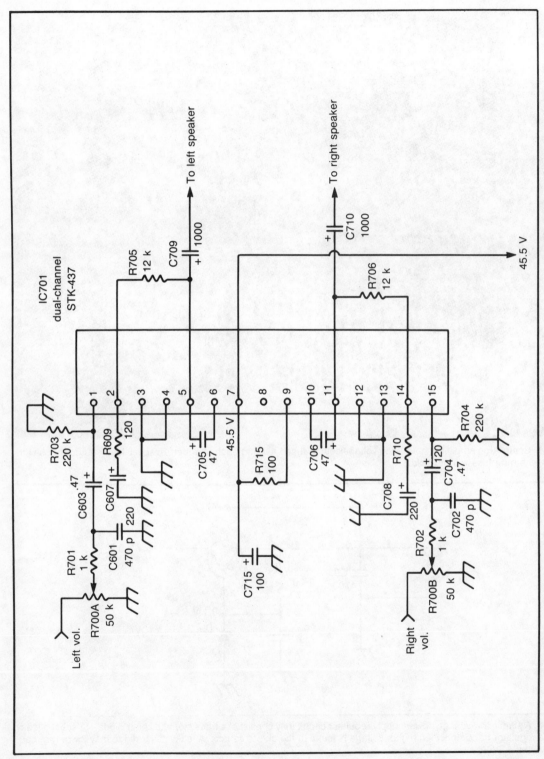

Fig. 6-7. Suspect a defective dual-IC component when one channel is distorted and the other dead. Check the voltage and compare with the normal circuit when trouble occurs in only one stereo channel.

134

normal channel (Fig. 6-7). Check each transistor for leaky or open conditions if there are improper voltage measurements. Remove each transistor from the chassis and test individually when showing signs of leakage in the circuit. Make both open and leakage tests.

Mark down the condition of each transistor. Put back each transistor that tests good. You may find four large output transistors in push-pull operation. Now check the condition of the driver transistors. Check all transistors in directly driven output circuits. Remember, Darlington transistors cannot be checked accurately in the circuit with ohmmeter or DMM tests. Sometimes it's best to replace all directly coupled audio-output transistors when two or more are found leaky or open.

Check all voltages on the suspected audio IC output component with no sound. Low or improper voltages found at the IC terminal may indicate a defective IC. If one channel is dead and the other normal with one IC feeding both channels, replace the defective IC. Check all electrolytic bypass capacitors and resistors connected to the IC terminal. Do not overlook a large speaker coupling capacitor with open conditions (Fig. 6-8).

**Weak Right Channel.** A very weak channel is relatively easy to service compared to a channel that just does not balance up. The weak channel may be located with the audio-signal generator and scope. The external audio amp is ideal in locating a weak or distorted channel. To help locate the defective component, you must have a schematic diagram (Fig. 6-9).

The weak channel may be caused by a leaky transistor or IC circuit. Open or dried up small electrolytic coupling capacitors may cause weak audio. A slight loss of audio in one channel may be difficult to locate. Sometimes the balance control is thrown off just enough to warrant locating the defective component. A change in resistors or coupling and bypass capacitors in the pre-amp stages may throw off the balance control (Fig. 6-10). Signal tracing with a 1000-Hz tone injected at the auxiliary or phono jack of both channels with the scope as indicator may locate the weak stage. Compare the scope waveform at the same point in the circuit as the normal stage.

**Will Not Balance.** Look for a defective coupling capacitor in the pre-amp and af circuits when one channel will not balance up with the other. Small 1, 3.3, 4.7 and 10 $\mu$F electrolytic capacitors cause a lot of balance problems. Check the signal on both sides of the suspected capacitor. Slowly signal-trace each stage until you find the small loss of audio signal. Check the amplifier circuits for balance or level controls and follow the manufacturer's

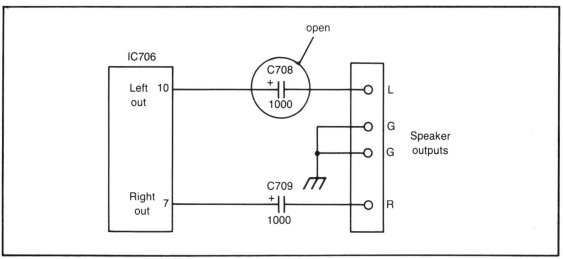

Fig. 6-8. A dead stereo channel may be caused by an open capacitor between transistor or IC and speaker. Signal-trace the circuits with the external audio amp.

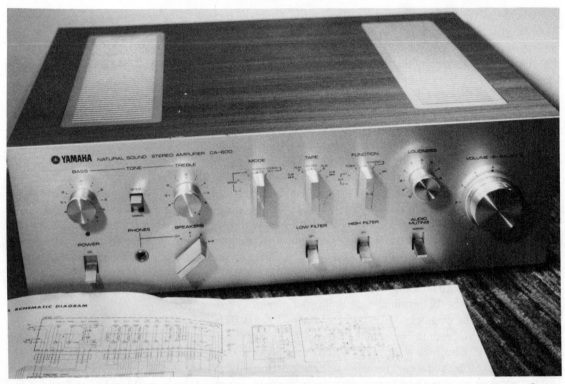

Fig. 6-9. A schematic diagram is a must for locating defective components or taking resistance measurements. Sometimes actual transistors and IC part numbers are found right in the wiring diagram.

literature for correct balance alignment.

**Weak Channel Case History.** The right channel was a little bit weaker than the left and would not balance up in a J.C. Penney Model 3222. The signal was traced to the pre-amp circuits of Q403 and Q404. The right channel was weak compared to the left channel transistors. Both Q403 and Q404 were tested in the circuit and were normal (Fig. 6-11). The signal was scoped with the test tape. Actually, C414 (10 $\mu$F) capacitor was dried up or had lost some of its capacity. Replacing coupling capacitor C414 balanced up both channels.

**Magnetic Pre-amp.** Since the audio signal is much lower in the magnetic pickup compared to a crystal cartridge, one or two stages of audio must be added in the pre-amp circuits. The separate magnetic pre-amp circuits start at the magnetic input jacks, and are switched into the circuit of the pre-amp audio stages (Fig. 6-12). The magnetic amplifiers may be low-level-noise transistors or IC com-

ponents. Often low collector voltages of under 10 volts are found in these circuits.

**Dead Right Channel—Distorted Left Channel.** Here both channels have something wrong with them. Check the circuits which would cause problems in both channels. Improper low-voltage conditions may often cause low audio and distortion in both channels. It's possible to have a leaky or open transistor in the right channel and a leaky transistor in the left channel producing distortion. Likewise, two separate IC output components may be found defective at the same time. Both channels may be defective in the case of a dual-IC in the output circuits (Fig. 6-13). Always check signals in and out with the scope or external amp. A leaky electrolytic bypass capacitor in the dual-IC circuits may cause a dead channel with the other channel distorted.

**Distorted Left Channel.** Excessive distortion found in either channel may result from leaky

136

driver or output transistors and IC components. Weak volume may appear along with distorted audio (Fig. 6-14). Distortion found in both channels may be caused by a leaky dual-IC output or an open filter capacitor in the negative voltage source of a transistorized output circuit. Spray the suspected transistor or IC with coolant when the distortion occurs after the chassis has been on for a few minutes to determine which one is leaky.

Always check the bias resistors when a leaky transistor is found. Remove one end of each resistor for accurate resistance measurements. Look for leaky bias diodes in the base circuits of the audio-output transistors for a small amount of distortion. Again remove one end of the diode and check for leakage. Lower negative voltage in the high-powered amps may cause some signs of distortion.

The distorted stage may be located with the audio-signal generator and scope. The external audio amp may isolate a distorted circuit. Go from base to collector of each transistor or from input to output of each IC component. Replace both audio output and driver transistors when one transistor is found shorted. While the transistors are out of the circuit, check each bias resistor. Compare the voltage and resistance measurements with the good channel after replacement.

**Noisy Right Channel.** The noisy channel may be isolated by turning down the volume control. If the noise quits, the defective component is in the af and pre-amp stages. Check the driver and output stages if the noise is still present. The noisy transistor or part may be located with the scope or external audio amp. Heat and coolant treatments may help in locating the noisy component.

Check the driver and output transistors for a loud popping and cracking noise. Most noise symptoms are caused by transistors and IC circuits. A high-resistance junction in a transistor may cause noise with a lower level of audio in the same channel. The high-resistance junction may be located with the diode-transistor test of the DMM. The normal junction resistance measurements of a good transistor are quite close. For example, a normal

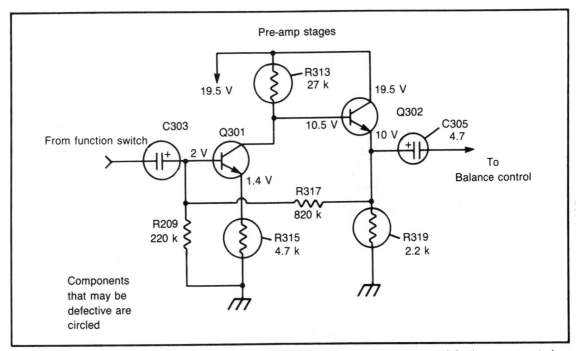

Fig. 6-10. Signal-trace the signal through the pre-amp, af, and audio-output circuits to locate a defective component when the amp will not balance up. Suspect small capacitors and a change in resistance of bias resistor in the case of loss in audio signal.

137

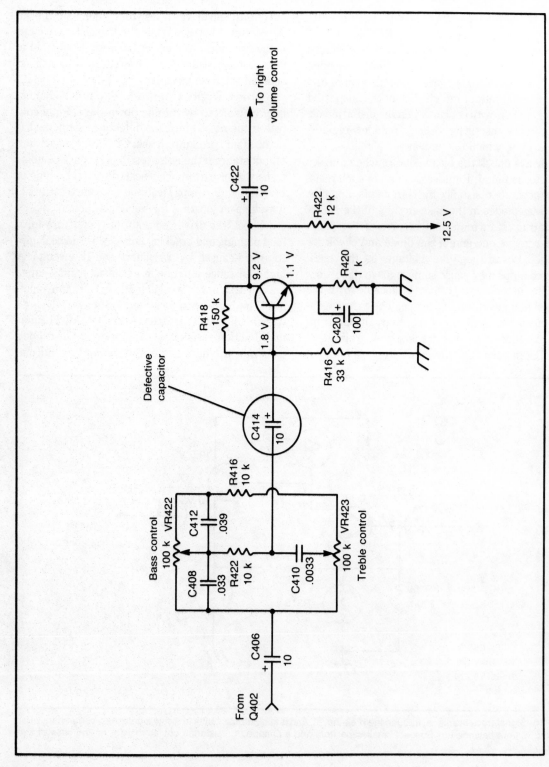

Fig. 6-11. In this J. C. Penney Model 3222, a defective C14 (10 μF) capacitor caused a weak right channel. Actually, the left channel was too loud; after replacing C414, the signal balanced correctly for both channels.

Fig. 6-12. The af and pre-amp stages are located quite close to the audio output transistors. Here is a top photo of a J. C. Penney Model MCS 3226 amplifier.

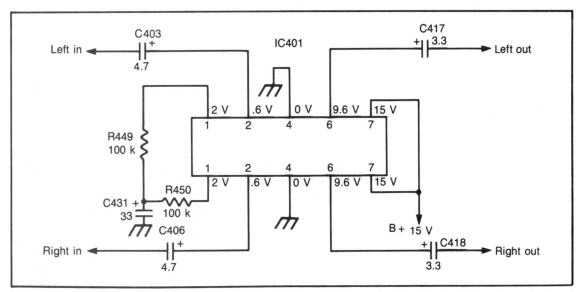

Fig. 6-13. With a dual power IC you may find only one channel or both channels defective. Signal-trace the audio in and out of the suspected IC, then take critical voltage measurements.

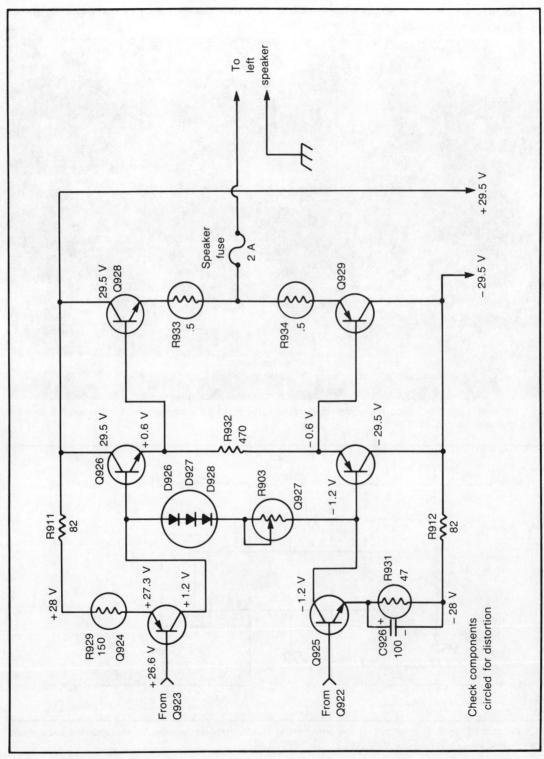

Fig. 6-14. Check the following components in the audio-output circuits for distortion. You may end up replacing four or five transistors with corresponding bias resistors.

af transistor may have a resistance measurement from base to collector of .670 ohms and from base to emitter of .675 ohms. The measurement from base to emitter may increase to .980, indicating a high-resistance junction between these two elements.

Suspect a noisy transistor or IC component when the noise does not appear after the amp has been on from three to four hours. Apply coolant to each transistor until the noise disappears, indicating the noisy transistor. A noisy bias or level control may produce noise in the channel. Sometimes a dirty wiper blade or a change in resistance between wiper and resistance may cause noise. Check for an increase in resistance of the high-value resistors in the base and collector circuits of the af and pre-amp circuits which may cause a hissing noise in the audio. Replace with carbon-film-type resis-

tors if available. Suspect a noisy bypass or coupling capacitor in the af and pre-amp circuits. Look for a loose component or screws grounding the PC board to the chassis if you hear movement or noise from inside the cabinet when it is moved or jarred.

A loud plop or frying noise at the on/off switch turn-on point may be caused by arcing between on/off switch contacts. The sound may stop or continue for several minutes. In either case replace the switch. If the switch must be ordered, try taking the larger switch apart and cleaning it up first. Clean off burned or pitted contacts with a knife, sandpaper, or fingernail file. Wipe off contacts with alcohol and cloth. This temporary repair may keep the amp operating until the new switch arrives.

**Locating Noise in a Sansui Model 2000.** The frying noise was isolated to the audio-output stage by lowering the volume control in the left

Fig. 6-15. Check the various components which might produce hum in the audio circuits. Be careful when clipping or shunting large filter capacitors in the power circuits. Make sure the capacitors are discharged.

channel. The noise would only begin after about four hours of operation. Coolant applied to each af, driver, and output transistor did not locate the noise. The noise was signal-traced to the audio-output transistors with the external audio amp.

Since the output transistors were not readily available, and to prove they were noisy, the two left output transistors were interchanged with the right-channel transistors (2SC793). Simply remove the two mounting screws of each transistor and lift the power transistors. After three hours of operation, the frying noise was now in the right channel, indicating the two output transistors of the left channel should be replaced with the originals. Sometimes a transistor tester may not locate the noisy transistor. Replacement is the only answer.

**Intermittent Left Channel.** Most intermittent conditions are caused by transistors and IC components. Apply heat or coolant on the transistor or IC to make it act up. Small electrolytic-coupling and large speaker capacitors may cause an intermittent audio. Sometimes a defective capacitor or resistor may be found by moving them with a plastic rod or pencil. Dirty contacts in the plugs from the pre-amp to the main chassis may produce intermittent sound.

The intermittent channel may be signal-traced with the scope or external amp to locate the inter-

mittent stage. Play music from either the tuner or phonograph. Divide the circuits in two at the volume control to save time. Of course, monitoring the intermittent takes a lot of time, especially if the amp does not act up for several hours.

**Excessive Hum.** The loud hum problem is much easier to locate than the one with only a slight indication of hum in the sound. Hum with distortion may occur in the power supply or audio-output circuits (Fig. 6-15). A defective or open electrolytic filter capacitor may cause loud hum in both channels. Low hum in both channels may result from a dried-up electrolytic decoupling capacitor (Fig. 6-16). Always clip large filter capacitors into the circuit for hum tests with the power off. Suspect the audio-output circuit with excessive hum in one channel.

A loud hum—weak sound symptom may occur in the audio-output transistors or ICs. Check for leaky and open transistors. Signal-trace the input and output terminal of the power IC component. If normal signal is found at the input and distortion at the output terminal, suspect a leaky IC. Take accurate voltage measurements on each IC terminal. Replace the leaky IC if the voltage measurements are quite close.

Check for burned or overheated bias resistors with poor terminal connections when the hum be-

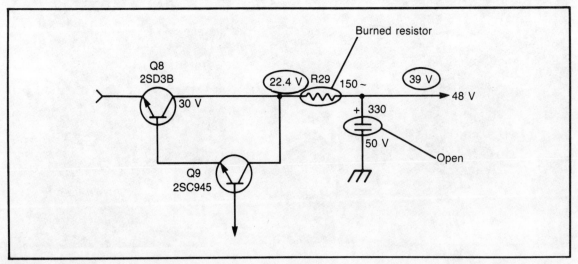

Fig. 6-16. Check for dried up or open decoupling filter capacitors in the voltage-regulator circuits or in the pre-amp and af stages if there is only a slight amount of hum.

gins after several minutes of operation. Double-check variable bias controls. Inspect the PC board for burned areas around transistors and electrolytic capacitors. Note if black or white material is leaking out of the filter capacitors. Replace filter or decoupling capacitors that are warm to the touch.

Loose shields or poor board grounds may cause intermittent sound or motorboating. Push up and down on the chassis to see if the hum comes and goes. Poor connections and ground wires of cable plugs and harness may produce pickup hum. Suspect a dried-up decoupling filter capacitor if there is motorboating on both channels. A defective audio-output transistor may produce a motorboating symptom. Low hum levels and motorboating stages may be located with the external audio amp.

**Signal Tracing.** The audio circuits may be signal-traced with the scope and external audio amp as indicators. Use the cassette tape player with a 1 kHz tone cassette connected to the audio amp. A dead, weak, or distorted stage may be quickly located. Take the external audio amp with test leads and signal-trace from stage to stage to locate the defective component. Of course, any external amp may be used, but here is a circuit that can be placed right in a speaker cabinet.

You may purchase a small amplifier already mounted on a PC board or build your own (Fig. 6-17). The chassis can be mounted in a small speaker enclosure picked up for a few dollars at various electronic outlets. Select one with an 8-ohm speaker at least four or six inches in size for normal sound. Many of the parts may be found in the junk box. This little external amp may be used in signal-tracing radio, phono, and cassette player circuits besides the regular audio amplifier.

**Smoking Amp.** Where there is smoke there are burned bias resistors, overheated power transformers, and transistors in the audio amp. Burned or smoking bias resistors result from leaky transistors in the audio-output circuits. You may find burned voltage-dropping resistors caused by leaky or shorted filter and bypass capacitors. A smoking power transformer may occur if there are shorted or leaky output transistors or diode rectifiers. Sometimes lightning damage or line power outage

may destroy the power transformer.

Expensive repairs may be needed if the power transformer must be replaced along with other components. Power transformers are rather expensive. Determine what caused the transformer damage. If the bridge diode rectifier becomes leaky or shorted, knocking out the transformer, the additional component cost is not worth it. But if several power-output transistors damaged the power transformer, the repair may be costly. In fact, you may find four or six audio transistors open or leaky in the output circuits in addition to burned bias resistors and a transformer.

**Power Output Transistor Replacement.** Try to replace each power output transistor with the original. If not available, replace with universal replacements. Cross reference the defective transistor number with those found in manufacturer's transistor replacement guides. RCA, GE, Sylvania, Mallory, and Workman have universal replacement guides.

If the power-output transistor burns out after replacement, suspect a defective driver transistor or bias resistors. Recheck those bias resistors. It's always best to replace four or five of the transistors in the driver and output stages. Sometimes an intermittent transistor will not act up under test but will break down under load. Note if the transistors are running red hot after replacement. Excessive idling current may destroy the output transistor. Adjust the variable-bias resistor for correct current and voltage settings by the manufacturer. Check to see if the operating voltage is too high compared to the normal channel. Always keep speakers connected to each channel while servicing the amplifier. Replace the speaker fuse, if blown, before power is applied to the chassis.

Always replace the mica insulator found between transistor and heat sink. Some of these transistors in push-pull operation may have the transistor collector (metal body) bolted right to the heat sink. Apply silicone grease on transistor body and heat sink or on both sides of the mica insulator. Be careful not to crack or break the insulator. If the corners are torn or broken off the insulator, throw it away and get another. Clear silicone grease

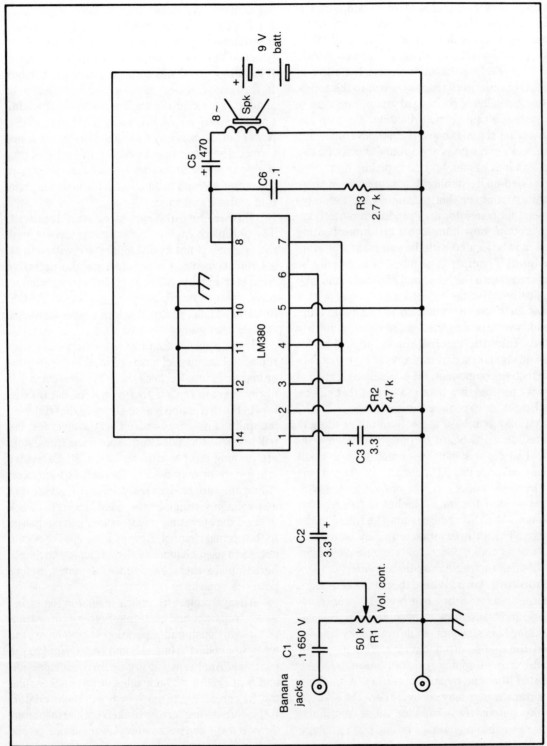

Fig. 6-17. A simple schematic diagram of an audio amp you can build to signal-trace audio circuits. The little amplifier may be placed in a small speaker enclosure with an 8-ohm speaker.

is easiest to work with since it does not stain hands or clothes.

**Darlington Transistors.** The Darlington transistor may be used in a driver, balance, or power-output stage. These transistors may have two directly coupled transistors internally operating in parallel. In high-power-output circuits, the Darlington transistors may have diode and bias resistors inside the metal case. You may find either npn or pnp types.

Actually the Darlington transistor looks just like any other transistor with three leads or terminals, but they are very difficult to test with the DMM or on some transistor testers. The different ohm tests may be compared to a known good one in the other stereo channel. Signal-trace the audio up to the suspected Darlington transistor and replace it. The suspected Darlington output transistor may be subbed with one in the good channel. Use the original part number when replacing Darlington transistors.

**IC Power Output Replacement.** Be careful when unsoldering IC terminals to prevent damage to other components and PC wiring. Use solder-wick material to pick up the excess solder. Some smaller IC power-output components may have extra shields over the wiring area. Remove and replace all shields to prevent hum pickup. The power IC is rather easy to replace. Apply silicone grease to the back of the IC that touches the heat sink. Bolt the IC in place (Fig. 6-18). Solder each terminal with a low-wattage soldering iron.

**Poor Bass.** The treble and bass controls are often found after the pre-amp stages in the audio circuits. With stereo channels the bass control has two controls in one. The bass is controlled in both

Fig. 6-18. The large power ICs either bolt to a large single heat sink or to a metal chassis. You may find one large dual power IC or two separate ones.

145

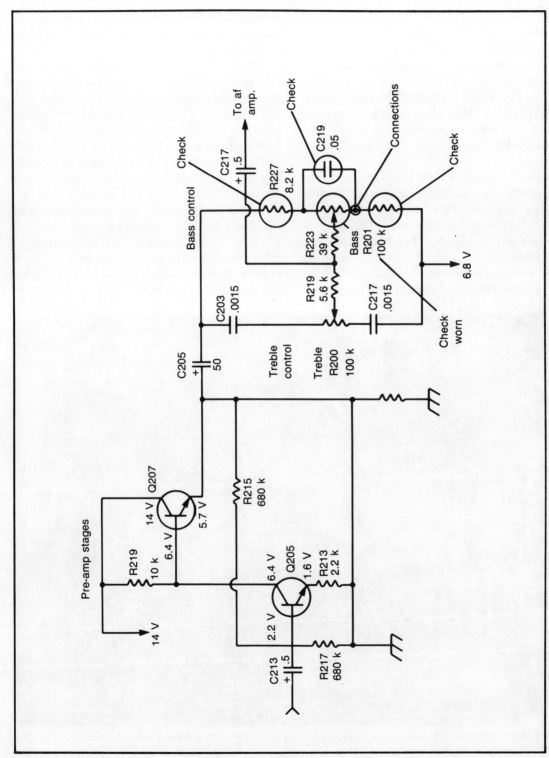

Fig. 6-19. Check the following components when the bass control has no effect on the music. Sometimes a broken connection or wire may prevent the bass tones from being controlled by the bass control.

channels when the control is rotated (Fig. 6-19). Check for a broken wiper blade or connecting wire to the center bass terminal when no change of bass is found in the speaker. Lower the treble control and now turn the bass control. Check for an open electrolytic capacitor, bypass capacitor, or small resistor in the bass circuits if the treble control affects the music.

**Cannot Lower Volume.** Suspect a broken control or wire connection if the volume cannot be lowered in one channel with the other channel normal. Check for an open ground wire on the control terminals. Sometimes the dual volume and tone controls grounds are connected together. Inspect the wire or soldered terminals for a badly soldered connection.

**Keeps Destroying the Speaker.** Excessive volume may blow the voice coil right out of the woofer speaker. Too much volume may destroy the speaker. Insufficient wattage speakers may be damaged by a very high power-output amplifier.

Speakers may be damaged when operating directly from the power output transistors or IC circuits. A shorted IC or transistor may place excessive voltage at the speaker terminals, burning out the voice coil. Some speakers are protected with a speaker fuse, preventing damage to the speaker (Fig. 6-20). If the fuse blows and is replaced with a larger fuse or wrapped with tin foil, the speaker now has no protection. Always replace the speaker fuse with the same amperage as the original.

In many of the speaker output circuits, a large electrolytic coupling capacitor is connected between the speaker and output transistors. Here the transistor voltage is isolated from the speaker voice coil. With larger high-powered amplifiers the speaker output is connected through a fuse or resistor to the output transistors or IC component (Fig. 6-21). Of

Speaker fuses

Fig. 6-20. Check the speaker fuse when one channel is dead. Often too much volume applied to the speakers knocks out the fuses. Check the fuse terminal for B+ voltage, indicating a leaky transistor or IC component.

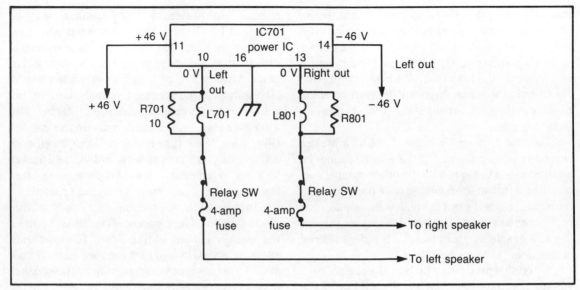

Fig. 6-21. A resistor, fuse, or relay contacts may be in series with the power IC or transistor output to the speakers for protection. A dirty relay contact may produce a noisy or dead speaker channel.

course, zero voltage is found at these terminals. If the IC or transistors become leaky, higher voltages may be applied to the voice coil, knocking out the expensive speakers unless the speaker fuse opens. Always check the voltage at the speaker output terminals when a voice coil is damaged. Repair the leaky output stage or you may quickly burn out another expensive speaker.

**Blown Components.** Sometimes it is very difficult to explain why various components blow up. Electrolytic capacitors may blow due to a buildup of gas inside the plastic containers which become leaky and overheat. Small pieces of tin foil and insulation from the blown capacitor may be found inside the amplifier. This was the case in a J.C. Penney MCS series Model 3233 amp. A 470 $\mu$F capacitor was found with only the terminal connections left and pieces scattered all over the chassis (Fig. 6-22). Q601 was found leaky and replaced. No doubt higher dc voltage was applied to C602, causing it to blow its top.

**Lighted Power Indicators.** Like the LED tuning lights, some audio amplifiers had LED power-level indicators (Fig. 6-23). The level meter circuits may connect to the audio-output speaker circuits. Often each channel has its own IC driver with corresponding LEDs. The LEDs and IC components are mounted on a separate PC board (Fig. 6-24).

The peak or power level meter may be serviced like any other audio meter circuit. Signal-trace the sound from speaker circuit to the input terminal of the level meter IC (Fig. 6-25). If the audio signal is going into the IC but is not applied to the LEDs, suspect a defective IC. Measure the dc voltage source (pin 9). Check the voltage at each LED pin number of the IC. Suspect a defective LED if only one is out.

**Loudness Control.** You may find a loudness control circuit in the audio-amp input circuits in some models. Usually the loudness switch is a DPDT variety placed between the balance and volume controls (Fig. 6-26). When switched on, part of the signal is paralleled across the top of the volume control. In the off position, two small resistors are placed in the circuit. The small resistors and capacitors may vary in resistance and capacity but serve the same purpose. Suspect a dirty loudness switch or broken wire from the volume control when the loudness switch has no effect on the audio.

**Audio Output Resistance Checks.** After

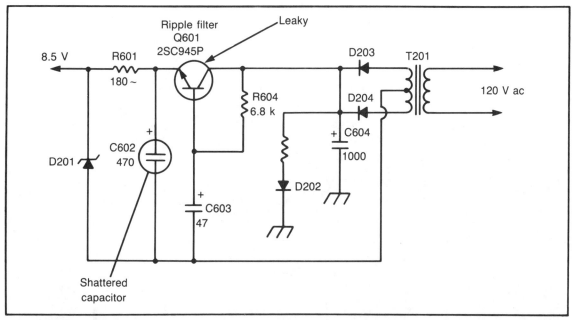

Fig. 6-22. C602 was found blown apart in a J. C. Penney Model MCS 3233. Replacing both Q601 and C602 solved the defective regulator circuit.

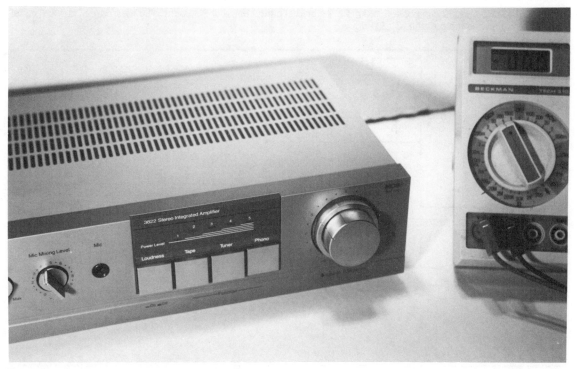

Fig. 6-23. A lot of the solid-state integrated amplifiers have power level ICs on the front side of the panel. Actually, the ends of the square LEDs poke through the metal front panel.

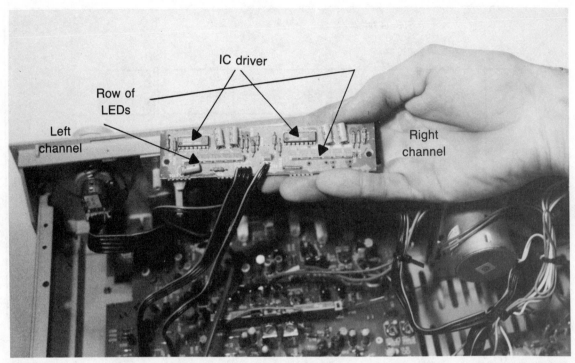

Fig. 6-24. The LEDs and IC components are mounted on a separate piece of PC board. The audio signal may be signal-traced right up to the input of the IC LED driver.

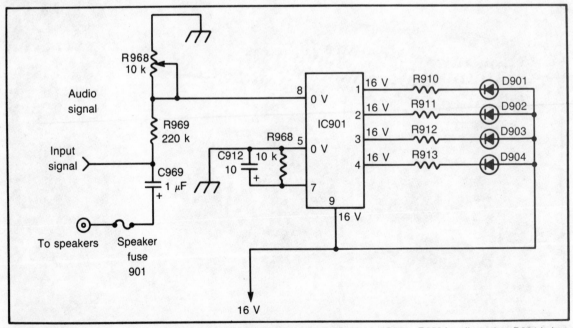

Fig. 6-25. Note a portion of the audio is tapped off the speaker output circuits to IC901. R968 is adjusted so D901 is just lit at normal sound. Suspect a defective LED when only one bulb is out.

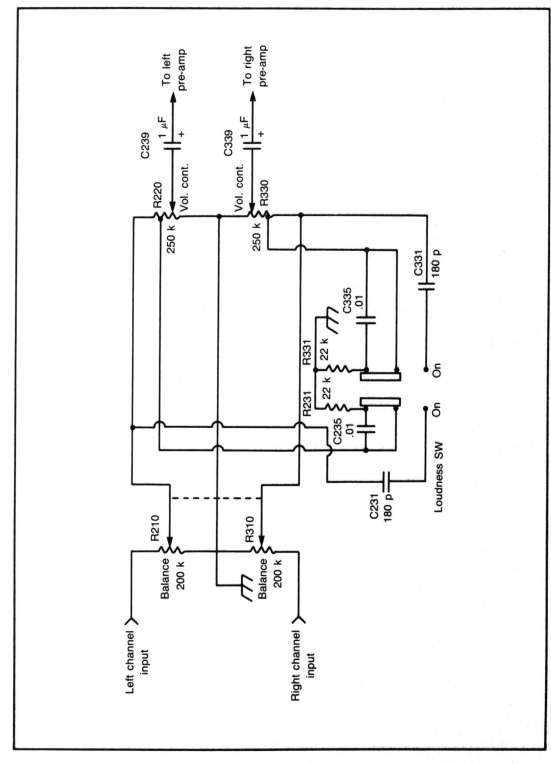

Fig. 6-26. The loudness control is usually located between the balance and volume controls. Actually, the control switches resistance or capacitance in or out to raise or lower the amount of volume.

replacing audio-output transistors or IC components, take a resistance measurement from each terminal to ground. Compare the same resistance measurements between the ones just replaced and the good channel. This may take a few minutes, but can be done rather rapidly with the DMM. Take one terminal measurement and compare this with the same terminal in the normal channel. These resistance checks should be within a few ohms of one another.

You may locate a poorly soldered connection, a shorted connection, or a defective component in the circuit. A lot of times the burned or open bias resistors were actually defective in the first place. If you forgot to check out the new transistor replacement before installation, the leaky transistor will show up in the measurements. However, you have located a defective component connection before firing up the amplifier and damaging another part. Resistance and voltage comparison tests in the audio-output circuits with the normal channel are quite valuable in amplifier servicing.

**Audio Adjustments.** Idler current, power meter, and peak level meter adjustments should be made according to the manufacturer's specifications. Since most idling current adjustments are made across the emitter terminals of the output transistor, the voltage and current requirements are different in each manufacturer's output circuits.

Idling current is taken in milliamperes when no audio signal is present in the circuit. The same may hold true for power and meter adjustments. Idling current and bias adjustments should be made after replacing high-powered output transistors.

## CASE HISTORIES

Here are ten audio problems that were found in different sound amplifiers. They are listed here in the hope that they will illustrate how the defective component was located. The audio problem discussed may be the same or similar to the one you now have on your service bench.

**Keeps Blowing Fuses.** The fuse would blow as soon as it was replaced in a Realistic STA-740 deluxe stereo amp. Since the low voltage diodes and power circuits seemed normal, the power-output transistors were tested. Output transistors D896, B776 and driver transistors D600K were found leaky in the right channel. All bias resistors were checked while the transistors were out of the chassis. One 4.7-ohm bias resistor was found open and replaced. Universal transistors were used for replacement. D896 was replaced with a ECG36, B776 with a ECG37, and D600K with a ECG373 replacement.

**Dead—No Right Channel.** The left channel was normal in a Sanyo 2050 model with a dead right channel. The audio signal at the output tran-

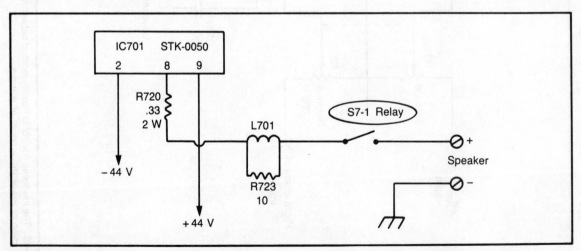

Fig. 6-27. A dead channel in a Sanyo Model 2050 was caused by dirty speaker relay controls of S7-1. The contacts were cleaned up with cleaning fluid. Check R720 and L701 when the woofer speaker cone is damaged.

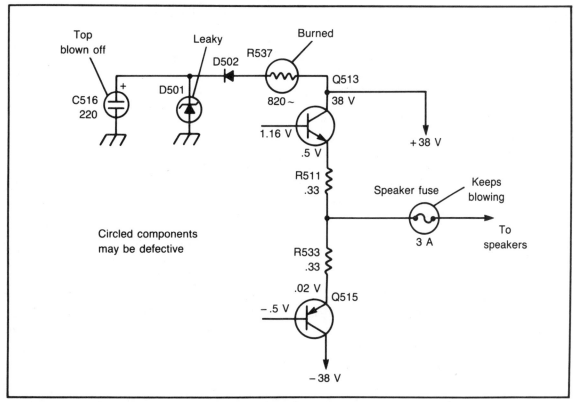

Fig. 6-28. The fuse kept blowing in a J. C. Penney Model 3235. Replacing R537, D501, and C516 solved the speaker fuse problem.

sistors were the same volume on both channels with the external audio amp. Upon checking the circuit, L801, S7-2 and speaker terminal connections were suspected. The signal was normal up to S7-2 (Fig. 6-27). A dirty relay contact S7-1 was cleaned, restoring the right speaker.

**Dead Left Channel.** The fuse would open in the left channel of a Pioneer Model SX-1000 TW. Right away a burned .7-ohm bias resistor was spotted. Both 25G897 output transistors were replaced with a universal SK3535 replacement. All other transistors and bias resistors were checked in the same output circuit. Since 75 volts was measured at the power output transistor, replacement with either high voltage types or originals was necessary.

**Intermittent Left Channel.** Besides the intermittent left channel, a low noise could be heard in a AKAI Model CR-80 T. The intermittent signal was monitored at the input terminal of the left

output IC. When the speaker cut out the signal was normal at the input terminal. The input sound was compared to the normal right channel. Replacing the STK-011 IC output with a universal SK3152 replacement solved the intermittent left channel.

**Noisy Left Channel.** After operating for three hours, a low frying noise was heard in the left channel of a Sansui Model 2000. The noisy channel was isolated by turning down the volume control. The signal was the same with the volume control turned down, indicating the noisy component was in the output circuits. Starting at TR801, the external amp noise was traced right up to the left output transistors. Both 2SC793 output transistors were replaced, eliminating the noisy left channel.

**Keeps Blowing Speaker Fuse.** Sometimes the speaker fuse will blow if too much volume is applied to the speakers. The 3-amp fuse was re-

153

placed and again blew out in a J.C. Penney Model 3235. All eight transistors within the left channel tested normal. A quick check of the circuits found R537 burned with the top of C516 blown off. Upon checking the circuit, D501 was found leaky (Fig. 6-28). After replacing all three components the left channel audio was restored.

**Low-Level Hum.** A slight hum could be heard in a J.C. Penney Model 3835. The customer had complained of smoke coming out of the amplifier. A visual inspection of the chassis did not turn up anything. The voltages measured at the IC output were +36.1V and −40.1V. The two voltages should be the same with opposite polarity. Finally, arcing seemed to occur at the bottom of the large filter capacitor (6800 μF, 45V). I removed the bottom cover and found the capacitor arcing between the terminals and PC board. The capacitor was removed and part of the burned PC board was cut out. Replacing the large filter capacitor and repairing the PC wiring solved the low hum problem.

**Weak Volume Left Channel.** The signal was traced from the volume control to the pre-amp circuits in a J.C. Penney Model 3230 with weak volume in the left channel. Q202 and Q204 were checked in the circuit with Q204 found leaky between the base and emitter. Voltage measurements on Q202 were quite high compared to the schematic (Fig. 6-29). Replacing Q204 with a GE-20 universal replacement restored the weak channel and returned the voltages to normal.

**No Volume, Distortion.** Very little volume was found in the left channel of a Sansui Model 5000X. There was no voltage at the left channel output transistor. Eighty volts was found at the right channel transistors. The missing voltage was traced back to an open 4-amp fuse (F.002). Since the left channel was weak and had distortion, the power-output stages were checked first. Replacing the left channel B+ fuse solved the problem.

**Left Channel Dead—Distorted Right Channel.** Both channels were found defective in

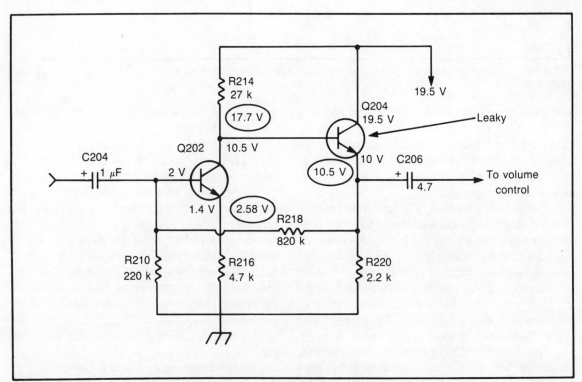

Fig. 6-29. A leaky pre-amp transistor (Q204) in a J. C. Penney's Model 3230 caused a weak left channel. Higher than normal voltages were found on Q202 since it was directly coupled to Q204.

a Sanyo DXT-5004 amplifier with two separate IC output circuits. The symptoms pointed to a defective low-voltage power source. Normal voltages were found in the low-voltage power supply. After signal-tracing both channels, each separate power-output IC was replaced. Here the power IC in the left channel was open and the power IC in the right channel was leaky. Both ICs were replaced with the original part number (ICLA4051P). Occasionally you may find defective components in both stereo channels.

## TWELVE DO'S AND DON'TS

1. Do not place too large an ac line fuse in the amp or you may damage the primary winding of the power transformer.

2. Do not insert too large a speaker fuse or wrap the defective one with tin foil. A leaky transistor or IC in a directly coupled (dc) output circuit may place high dc voltage on the voice coil of the speaker and burn it out.

3. Do check all transistors in the power-output circuits for leakage both in and out of the circuit. Replace both output transistors when one is found defective.

4. Be sure to test the new transistor replacement before mounting. It may take even more time to diagnose the same problem the second time around, aside from the frustration.

5. Do double-check each transistor replacement for correct terminal connections before soldering up. Check both top and bottom sides of the PC board.

6. Do use a low-wattage soldering iron when soldering the IC and transistor terminals. Inspect each terminal for a good, soldered connection.

7. Do replace the heat sink before trying out the amplifier after transistor or IC replacement. You may damage the replaced component within minutes.

8. Do be careful when shunting filter capacitors in the power-supply circuits. Clip them in with the volume off. Always discharge the capacitor. Make sure you have the right capacitance and voltage.

9. Do not forget to have a speaker or a load resistor connected to the speaker output terminal while working on the amplifier. You may damage the output transistors or IC with the volume turned up.

10. Do use the normal stereo channel as a reference point when signal-tracing and doing voltage and resistance measurements.

11. Do take comparable resistance measurements between transistor terminals of output transistor and ground. Compare these measurements with the normal channels. You may have burned or open bias resistors when the resistance measurements are way off.

12. Don't assume right off that the defective component will be difficult to locate. First look for the obvious. Usually burned resistors, leaky or blown capacitors, and other similar problems can be spotted right away.

# Chapter 7

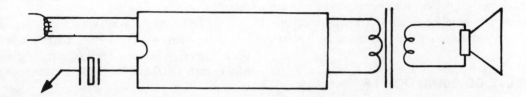

# Auto Stereo-Cassette Repairs

OPERATING THE AUTO CASSETTE PLAYER HAS changed drastically in the past five years. The new cassette receivers may have digital tuning with a quartz frequency-synthesis processor or varactor diode (Fig. 7-1). The new receivers stay perfectly tuned to the exact frequency without station drift. Some of the new radios may have provisions for the new AM stereo broadcast reception.

Several preset station memory button selections and seek and scan buttons make for easier tuning. The scan tuning system is great for finding what is playing on every station, while the seek tuning system tunes up or down the broadcast band, stopping at the first desirable station. A digital display responds to the tuning system.

The auto cassette may have auto-reverse, tape music search, and Dolby noise-reduction circuits. With auto-reverse, you may listen to both sides of the tape without stopping the player. With automatic music search, you may fast forward or rewind automatically to the beginning of a song at the push of a button. The Dolby noise-reduction system is very effective in removing tape hiss over a wide range of frequencies.

Some of the latest added features are automatic radio play, which automatically plays the radio while the cassette tape deck is in fast-forward or rewind modes. Some have the ability to accept an add-on alarm module that honks the horn when the radio is being ripped off. Some of the new car radios have compact disk (CD) inputs to accommodate auto CD players.

Today the regular car stereo player may have up to 15 watts of power output compared to 2 to 5 watts in the early models. You may add on component amplifiers from 15 to 75 watts per channel with each speaker system that will withstand 80 watts of power. The normal speaker response ranges from 35 to 20,000 Hz, with exceptional speaker systems ranging from 28 to 25,000 Hz. A two-way high-powered radio may have four built-in amplifiers to drive four separate speakers or a switch to drive two speakers with greater power output.

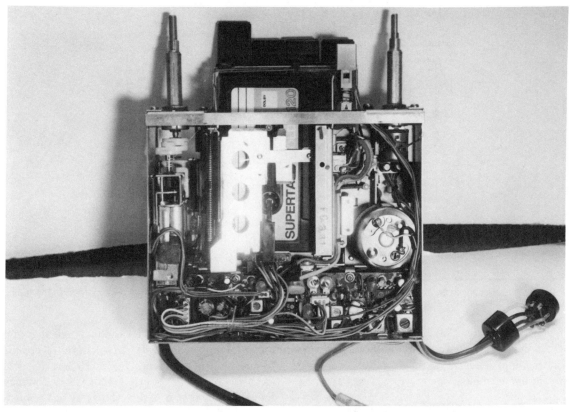

Fig. 7-1. A manual tuner with permeability-tuned coils in a compact AM-FM-MPX cassette player.

## ELECTRONICALLY TUNED RADIOS

In the electronically tuned radios you may find a quartz-locked tuner and frequency processor with varactor-diode-tuned circuits. The frequency-controlled circuit, like those found in many tuners, selects the station frequency by providing a tuning voltage to the varactor diodes in the rf, mixer, and oscillator circuits (Fig. 7-2). In the standard car radio the permeability-tuned coils are tuned manually.

Check the variable varactor-diode voltage when stations cannot be tuned in. If the voltage does not change at the diode, suspect a defective IC processor. Take critical voltage and resistance measurements on the controller IC. Sometimes the frequency controller processor must be replaced to cure the automatic-tuning problem. Follow each manufacturer's service procedures for electronically tuned receivers.

The FM-AM electronic-tuning-control processor may contain a frequency counter system which provides channel and band selection. The same IC may control the logic sequence of memory, manual, up-and-down scanning, mute, and DX-LO functions. These IC processors may have up to 42 working terminals. You may find a separate voltage regulation IC for the electronic tuning system (Fig. 7-3). A separate digital display IC may control the clock and frequency systems.

Extreme care must be taken when handling LSI (large-scale integrated circuits), CMOS, and variable-capacity diodes. The LSI IC may come in a piece of conductive urethane foam to prevent static electricity or electrostatic field damage. Do not touch the LSI IC terminals. Hold the IC by the ends with forefinger and thumb. Make sure the soldering iron is at the same ground potential as the

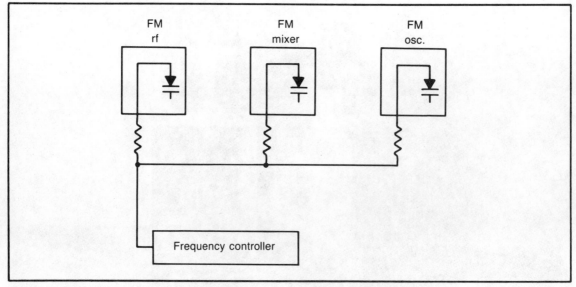

Fig. 7-2. The frequency controller controls the station selection for search, seek, and push-button operation. The tuning voltage is applied to the varactor diode in the FM rf, mixer, and oscillator circuits.

technician's body. Some manufacturers suggest changing all three variable-capacitor diodes when one is found defective, as they come as a complete set in one envelope.

## PERMEABILITY-TUNED CIRCUITS

The early car radio had separate AM and FM front-end circuits that were tuned manually with permeability-tuned coils for each rf, oscillator, and mixer stages (Fig. 7-4). In modern electronic frequency-controlled receivers both AM and FM front-end tuning are controlled together. You may find a dial pointer or a digital display in the manual car stereo player along with a digital clock assembly. The digital display is controlled by the clock and frequency-IC component.

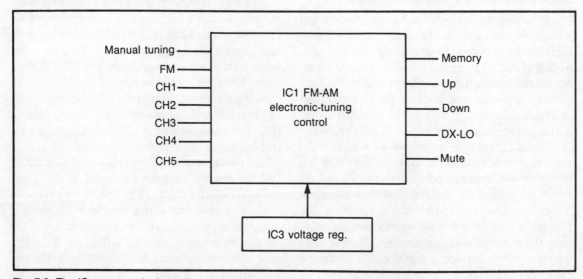

Fig. 7-3. The IC processor in the tuning-control circuit controls many different circuits.

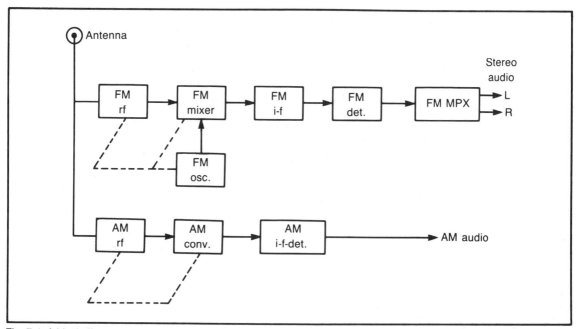

Fig. 7-4. A block diagram of the different FM and AM circuits. In this model, the FM and AM circuits are not tied together until the audio stages.

A local DX switch may be found in some models (Fig. 7-5). In DX reception the antenna is switched directly into the FM and AM circuits. For local reception R1 and R2 are switched into the circuits. Suspect a dirty switch control when only local stations are received. Another DX-LO switch assembly may be controlled by a transistor circuit (Fig. 7-6).

**FM Front-End Circuit.** An FET or regular rf transistor may be found in the FM rf stage. The front and output circuits are permeability tuned by L101 and L103 (Fig. 7-7). C8 couples the FM rf signal to the base terminal of the mixer transistor, TR2. The oscillator frequency from TR3 is capacity coupled by C11 to the mixer circuit. The FM i-f stages are transformer coupled to the collector terminal of TR2 (Fig. 7-8).

**I-f and FM i-f-MPX Circuits.** I-f transformer T1 couples the 10.5-MHz i-f frequency through a ceramic filter network (CF201) to the base terminal of Q101 (Fig. 7-9). Another ceramic filter network (CF202) is found in the collector terminal of Q101. IC101 acts as FM i-f and stereo multiplex circuits. The right and left stereo channels

are taken from pins 11 and 12 of IC101.

**AM IC Circuits.** The AM rf-converter stages may consist either of transistors or one IC component (Fig. 7-10). IC201 combines the rf, converter, and i-f stages (Fig.7-11). L101, L102 ,and L103 tune the rf and converter circuits. The AM i-f transformer, T102, transformer couples the 10.5-MHz signal to ceramic filter CR101. Another ceramic i-f filter network (CF102) ties to the IC terminals 10, 12, and 14. The AM output signal is taken from terminal 15 and feeds to the AM detector diodes which are capacity coupled to the right and left af audio amps.

Isolate the AM circuits when no AM is found within the receiver. Clean up the AM-FM switch in case of poor contacts. Take critical voltage measurements on the AM IC terminals. Make sure the voltages are correct on terminals 4, 7, 8, 14, and 19. Very low supply voltage at pin 19 may indicate a leaky IC101.

The rf and converter transistors in the AM circuits may be tested in the circuit with a transistor tester. Critical collector and emitter voltages may indicate a leaky or open transistor. The front-end

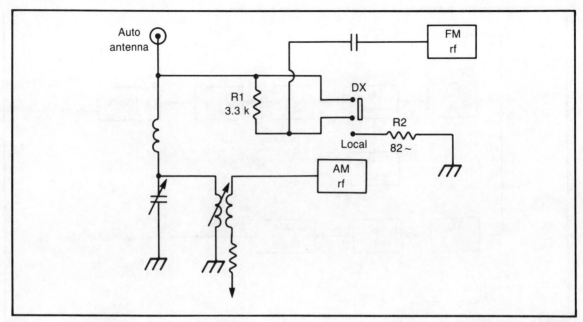

Fig. 7-5. The local DX switch connects two resistors in series at the local reception mode. Both resistors are switched out of the AM and FM antenna circuits during DX reception.

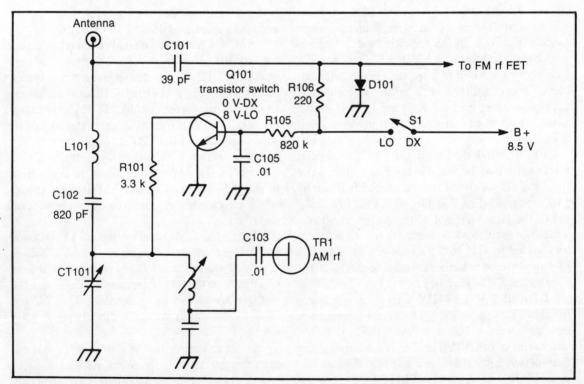

Fig. 7-6. Here transistor Q101 acts as a switch in Dx and local modes. Local AM and FM reception is in operation when dc voltage is switched to the base of Q101.

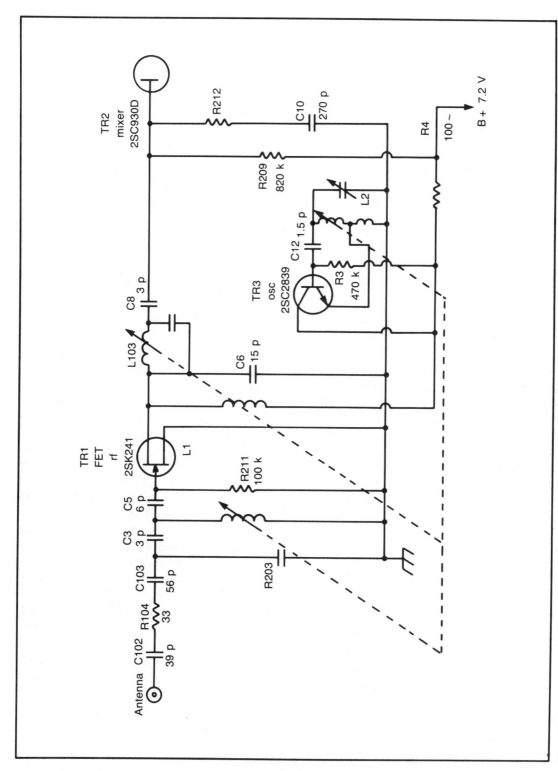

Fig. 7-7. Permeability-tuned coils cover the entire FM band in a manual-tuning operation. The tuning coils are found in the base and collector circuits of rf FET TR1 with oscillator tuning in the base circuit of TR3.

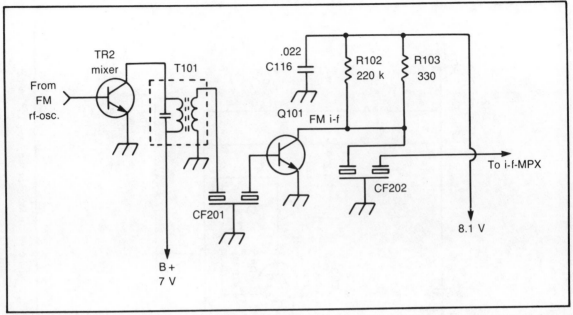

Fig. 7-8. In the new car receivers you may find ceramic, frequency-tuned circuits in the i-f stages instead of transformer coupling.

AM circuits may be signal-traced with a noise-injection tester or AM signal generator.

**No AM—FM Normal.** Go directly to the AM rf and converter stages if there is normal FM reception but no AM. Sometimes when the collector terminal is touched with a meter probe during voltage measurements, a local station may be heard. Look for a defective rf transistor or torn AM coil connection. Improper voltage at the rf transistor may be caused by a dirty AM switch or burned voltage-dropping resistor. Often the rf transistor may break down under load but otherwise tests normal. Measure the emitter voltage, which may be quite low under normal operation. No voltage may indicate an open transistor or emitter resistor. Suspect an open transistor with no forward bias voltage between emitter and base terminals.

**Dead on AM.** When the voltmeter test probe touched the collector terminal in a Sanyo FT1490A car radio, a local station could be heard at 1400 kHz. The collector voltage was low and the same voltage was found at both base and emitter terminals (Fig. 7-12). Replacing the leaky rf amp transistor (Q104) with an SK3124 universal replacement fixed the dead AM problem.

**Intermittent AM.** Determine if the radio is intermittent on both AM and FM. Try to isolate which AM stage is intermittent using voltage tests. Check for poor antenna-coil connections at the AM antenna jack. Poorly soldered connections at the coil or ground eyelet terminals may cause intermittent reception. Simply moving the AM-FM board assembly may turn up a poorly soldered connection. Try moving the i-f coils to check for intermittent connections. Sometimes rf and converter transistors may have good beta readings in test but show low-level leakage between the emitter and collector, indicating a possible intermittent condition.

**FM Problems.** Note if the AM and cassette play operations are normal. Go directly to the FM rf-FET transistor if there is weak FM reception. A dirty local DX switch or open switch transistor may cause weak FM reception (Fig. 7-13). Poor FM board connections may produce intermittent reception. Do not overlook a defective MPX IC or circuit in the case of poor FM stereo reception. Check the dc power source if both AM and FM are dead.

## THE AUDIO CIRCUITS

Today most audio functions in the cassette

162

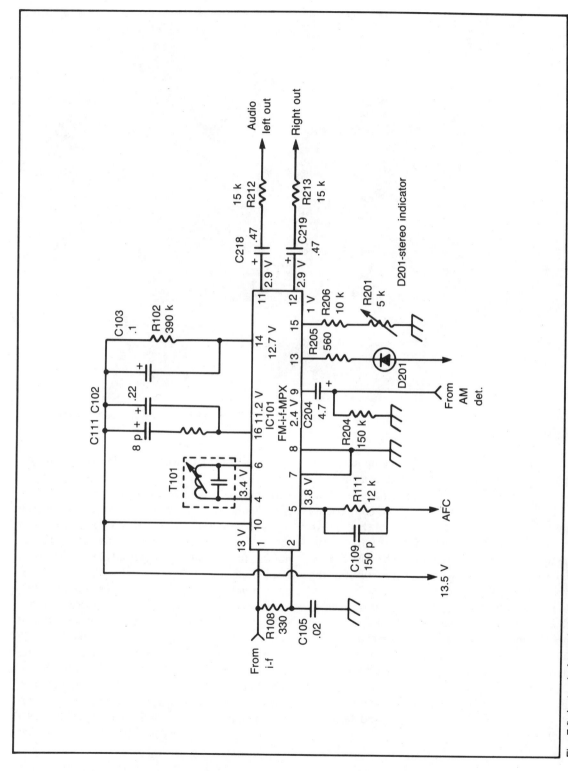

Fig. 7-9. Instead of transistors, the MPX circuits may consist of one IC component with an FM stereo-indicator LED.

Fig. 7-10. Note how small the permeability-tuned coils are in the AM-FM front-end circuit of a manually tuned car radio and cassette player.

player have been taken over by IC components. In small low-wattage audio-output circuits a single IC may take care of both audio-output channels, while in higher powered outputs separate IC components may be found in each stereo channel (Fig. 7-14). Transistor or IC components may be found in the pre-amp tape deck audio circuits. The AM-FM audio circuits may be switched in before or after the pre-amp circuits (Fig. 7-15).

**Dead Right Channel.** Note if the dead channel occurs in both radio and cassette modes. Signal-trace the audio circuits with the external audio amp (Fig. 7-16). The dead or weak channel may be located with the audio amplifier. Inspect the audio-IC output for overheating or damaged areas. You may find a red hot, leaky output-IC component. Do not overlook poor switching contacts and defective coupling capacitors.

**Dead Left Channel Case History.** The left channel was dead in a Pontiac 22FT451 tape player with normal radio and right-channel reception. Since both AM and FM reception was normal, the pre-amp tape-deck circuits were signal-traced with the audio amp. The first pre-amp transistor (Q1) signal was fairly weak and was dead at Q2 (Fig. 7-17). Both transistors tested normal in the circuit. Abnormal voltage measurements were found at Q2. Q2 was again checked for leakage. Replacing a shorted electrolytic capacitor in the low-voltage supply (8.65 V) fixed the dead left channel.

**Weak Left Channel.** Compare the weak audio signal and the normal right channel with the external audio amp. A 1-kHz cassette test tape and scope may quickly locate the weak stage. Overheated af, driver transistors, and IC components may isolate a weak circuit. Burned bias or emitter

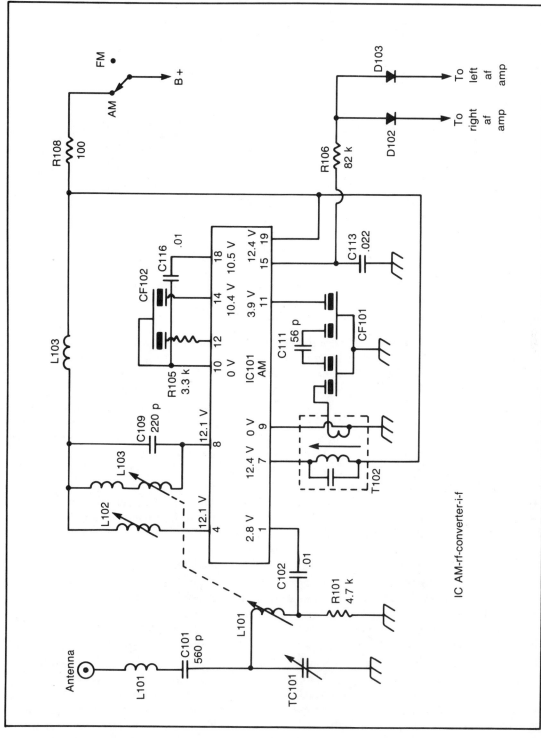

Fig. 7-11. You may find only three IC components along with a power-output transistor in some of the new compact car radios. Here IC101 takes care of all the AM front-end circuits.

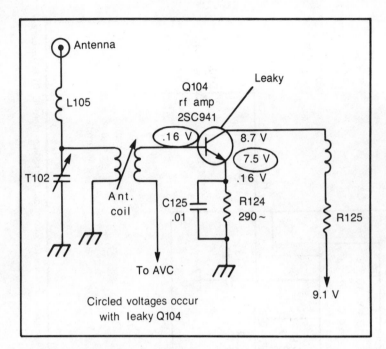

Antenna

Q104
rf amp
2SC941

Leaky

L105

.16 V          8.7 V

7.5 V

.16 V

T102

Ant.
coil

C125
.01

R124
290 ~

R125

To AVC

9.1 V

Circled voltages occur
with leaky Q104

Fig. 7-12. A leaky rf transistor (Q104) in a Sanyo FT1490A radio caused a dead AM problem. Sometimes touching the collector terminal of the rf AM transistor may bring in a local station.

resistors may cause a weak left channel. Check the signal on both sides of an electrolytic coupling or speaker capacitor. Signal-trace the audio signal in and out of a suspected audio IC. Do not overlook a possible open volume control.

**Weak Left Channel Case History.** The left channel was very weak and distorted in a Pioneer KP500 cassette player. The left channel output was isolated and signal-traced with the external audio amp. Replacing the left audio output IC (AN214Q) with a universal ECG1058 replacement fixed the weak and distorted left channel.

**Distorted Right Channel.** Excessive distortion often occurs in the audio-output circuit. Signal-trace the distortion with the scope or external amp. Intermittent distortion may be caused by a leaky driver transistor or output-IC component. Sometimes you may find one power IC in the output for both channels. One channel may be normal with the other distorted. Replace the audio IC component.

The right channel was distorted with a normal left channel in a Delco Model 21XFM-1 (Fig 7-18). The signal was found to be normal at pin 3 of IC U5 with the external audio amp. Normal audio signal was found on terminal 1 and 4 of the audio output IC, U7. Be very careful in signal-tracing and

connecting speakers to some of the Delco auto radios because the speaker return wire is above ground. You may damage the output IC if one side of a speaker is connected to ground. Replacing DM133 solved the distorted right channel.

**Intermittent Left Channel.** Sometimes intermittent sound problems are difficult to locate. Determine if the intermittent audio is only in the cassette player or both radio and player. Suspect poor or broken tape-head connections if intermittent is only on the tape player. Flex the tape-head cables. You may find one channel dead and the other intermittent if there are poor tape-head connections.

Isolate the intermittent audio to one or both audio channels. A broken or erratic volume control may cause intermittent audio. Check for intermittent speakers and base coupling capacitors. Power-output transistors and IC components may appear intermittent after warm up (Fig. 7-19). Feel the body and note if red hot. Poor or dirty bias controls may cause intermittent hum and audio.

**Intermittent Audio Case History.** Sometimes the audio was weak and intermittent in a Ford D6TA-18806 AA receiver. The audio signal was traced up to the af amp IC (Fig. 7-20). Both pins

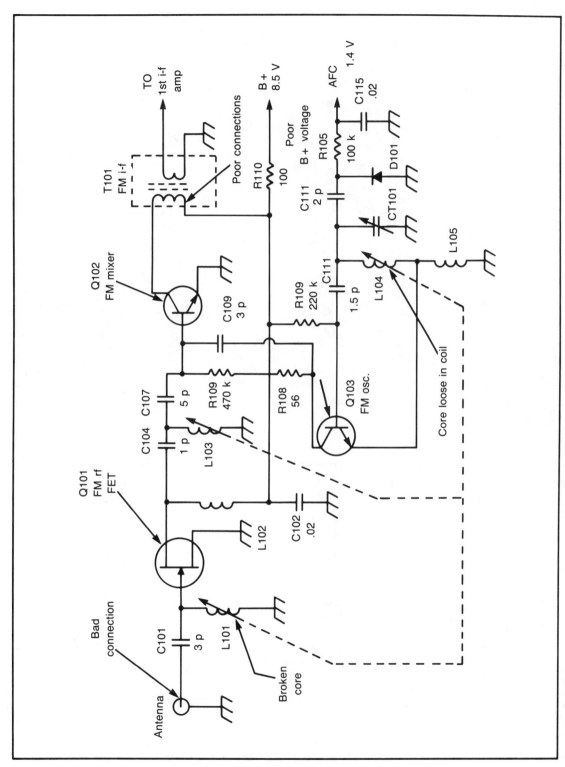

Fig. 7-13. Check the indicated component if there is poor FM reception in the car receiver.

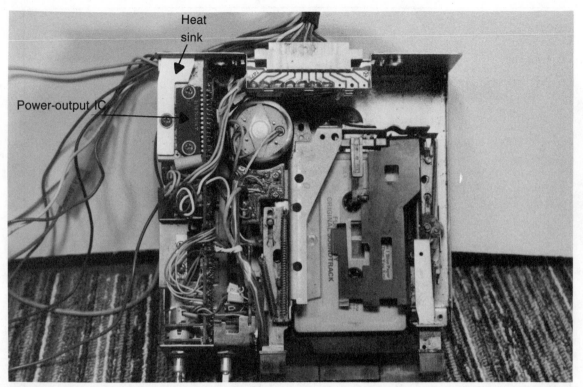

Fig. 7-14. Note the heavy heat sink of the power-output IC in this car cassette player. Silicone grease should be placed on the metal back area of the power IC.

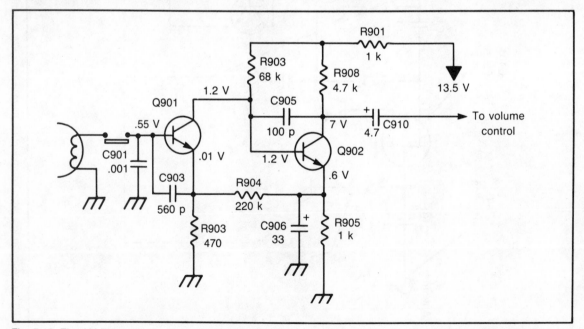

Fig. 7-15. The AM-FM audio circuit may be switched into the pre-amp tape or after the cassette tape circuits.

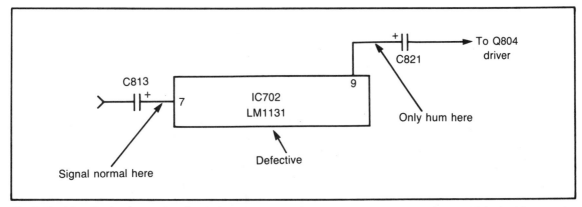

Fig. 7-16. All audio circuits may be effectively signal-traced with the external audio amp to locate a defective IC or transistor. In this diagram of a Sanyo FTV90 player, the signal was normal at pin 7 with only a hum at pin 9.

6 and 4 were monitored at N3. Only a hum could be heard on pin 4 when the radio became intermittent. N3 was replaced with the original part number (3K5-0011-04).

**Noisy Channel.** Remove the outside antenna lead-in to determine if the noise is being picked up or is inside the radio chassis. Suspect a noisy transistor or IC component if the noise is still present.

Turn down the volume control and listen for the frying noise in the speaker. Is the frying noise in both or just one channel?

Cold spray and head applications may turn up a noisy transistor or IC component. The noise may be signal-traced with the scope or external amp. When taking voltage measurements on the collector terminal, a noisy transistor may cause the me-

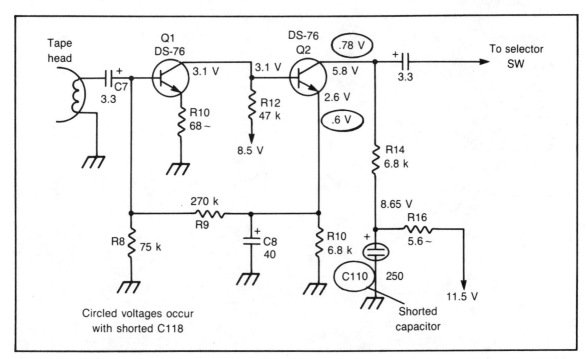

Fig. 7-17. A dead right channel in a Pontiac Model 22FT451 was caused by a shorted decoupling capacitor (C110) of the tape pre-amp transistor.

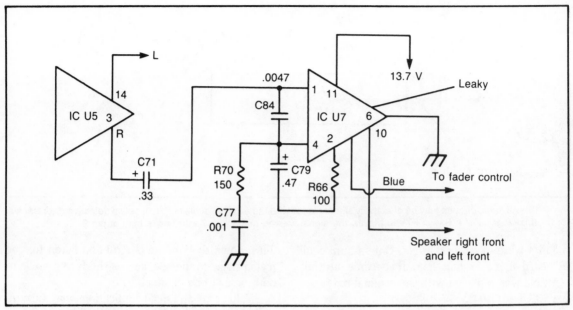

Fig. 7-18 A leaky IC U7 in a Delco Model 21XFM1 caused excessive distortion in the right channel. Make sure both speakers and the test speaker are connected above ground, otherwise they may be damaged.

Fig. 7-19. A leaky IC or transistor may appear red hot after a few minutes of operation. The IC or transistor may become intermittent after being overheated; otherwise the IC may be damaged.

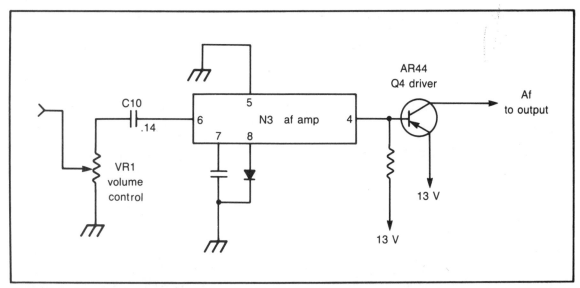

Fig. 7-20. An intermittent pre-amp IC (N3) in a Ford Model D6TA-18806AA receiver caused weak and intermittent symptoms. N3 was replaced with the original part number (3K5-0011-04).

Fig. 7-21. A dried up or open decoupling filter capacitor may cause motorboating sounds in the speaker. Shunt a new one across each one until the defective one is located.

ter hand to rapidly move off the VOM. Suspect a noisy power-output transistor or IC when the noise starts several minutes after warm up.

A loud howling noise may be caused by a power-output IC component. The rf, converter, and af transistors may produce microphonic noises. Check the output transistor and power IC for motorboating noise. Do not overlook a possible dried-up decoupling capacitor (Fig. 7-21). Improper grounding of transistors or IC heat sinks may produce motorboating sounds.

**Loud Hum Right Channel.** Excessive hum found on both channels may be caused by a filter capacitor in the low-voltage power-supply circuit. A leaky zener voltage-regulator diode may produce hum in the various circuits. Low-level hum may be caused by open or dried-up decoupling electrolytic capacitors. Hum in one speaker may indicate a leaky output transistor or IC component. Check the

IC for symptoms of overheating.

When the output transistor or IC becomes shorted, dc voltage may often be found on the speaker terminals. Check for dc voltage at the speaker with the cone pushed in one direction. A loud hum may occur in the new Delco car players when one side of the speaker is connected to ground. Remember that the return and live channel terminals in these radios have low-voltage. You may destroy the output transistor by connecting one speaker to ground. You may find several audio-output transistors in radios with several separate amplifier stages (Fig. 7-22).

## THE CASSETTE PLAYER

The auto player may have only one tape head but may still have a four or six-wire hookup. In some models with reversed tape decks the tape head is switched in and out of the circuits. The

Output transistors          Output transistors

Fig. 7-22. In the quad-8 or receivers with several separate amplifiers you may see a row of power-output transistors.

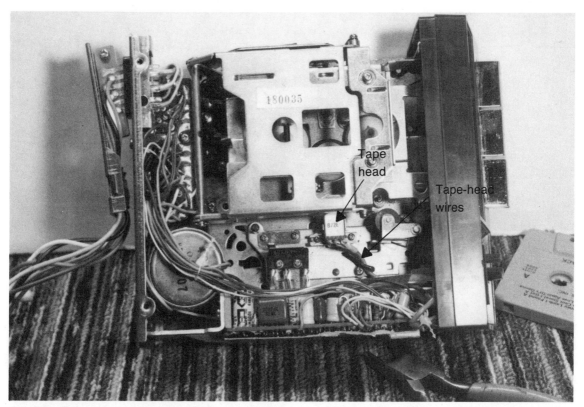

Tape head

Tape-head wires

Fig. 7-23. The tape-head cable wires often break off right at the tape head. You may hear a low rushing noise if there are open tape head wires in one channel.

defective tape head may be dirty, out of line, worn, or magnetized. Check for a worn or magnetized tape head when high-frequency reproduction is poor.

Clean the suspected tape head with alcohol and cloth. Magnetic head cleaner may be purchased at most stores that sell magnetic tape or players. Make sure the brown tape oxide is not over the tape head openings. Do not use a sharp screwdriver blade to remove hard-packed oxide on the tape head. Use the end of a pencil eraser or plastic rod. A dirty tape head may cause weak, distorted, or no sound in one stereo channel. Do not overlook a defective cassette.

Inspect the tape head terminals for broken wire connections (Fig. 7-23). Sometimes the wires may break right at the tape head or where they connect to the switch assembly. Simply flex each wire with the end of a pen or pencil while the tape is playing

(Fig. 7-24). Solder each broken wire back with a small, low-wattage soldering iron.

Crosstalk or garbled music may be caused by improper tape-head alignment. Locate the azimuth screw alongside the tape head. The azimuth alignment may be made with a cassette inserted which contains piano or string music. Turn the azimuth screw until the high-frequency reproduction is the loudest and clearest. Tape-head adjustments should never be made close to the end of the tape.

When a test tape is available, adjust the azimuth screw for maximum output at speaker or with a scope as indicator. Adjust for maximum meter indication of the VTVM with a cassette test tape (Fig. 7-25). A 6.3-kHz test tape and ac voltmeter may be used for maximum azimuth screw adjustments. Try to adjust so both channels are matched at the highest output on the meter.

**Dead, No Tape Rotation.** Measure the dc

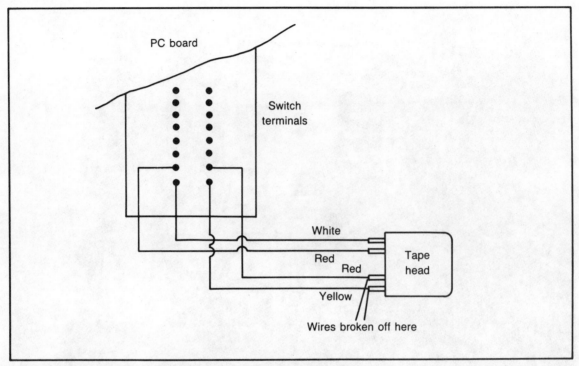

Fig. 7-24. Flex the tape head cable to see if the sound goes up and down when the cassette is playing.  Check for cable or wire continuity with the low-ohm scale of the VOM or DMM.

voltage at the motor terminals with no tape motion. If 12.5 volts or more is found at the motor terminals, suspect a defective motor or frozen bearings. A frozen capstan/flywheel bearing may cause the motor to stop. Usually the motor pulley will still spin inside the small belt despite the frozen capstan bearing. Very low voltage at the motor may be caused by a defective voltage source caused by a leaky zener diode. Check for a broken or dirty switch if there is no voltage at the motor. A dead

motor may result from an open isolation resistor or diode in the motor power source (Fig. 7-26). A broken belt with motor operating prevents tape rotation.

**Drag and Slow Speed.** Improper lubrication and dry bearings may cause the cassette to drag or run slow. Check for excess tape wrapped around the pressure-roller bearings. A dry flywheel/capstan, spindle, or turntable and idler pulley bearings may cause the tape to run slow (Fig. 7-27). Too

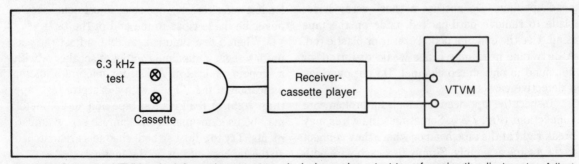

Fig. 7-25. Connect a VTVM to the left speaker output terminal when using a test tape for azimuth adjustments.  Adjust the azimuth screw for maximum reading on the VTVM.

174

Fig. 7-26. Measure the voltage at the motor terminals to determine if the motor is defective.  No voltage may indicate an open resistor, diode, or switch contacts in the motor circuit.

much lubrication and oil spilled upon the motor belt may produce erratic speeds. Do not overlook a defective motor for erratic tape movement.

**Runs Too Fast.** Suspect excess tape built up on capstan drive area for fast tape speed. A defective motor may also cause fast tape speeds. Check the motor circuits for a speed control adjustment. Sometimes the speed can be adjusted with a small speed adjustment screw at the end of the motor. The correct speed may be checked with a 3-kHz test cassette and frequency counter connected to the left speaker output terminals. If the frequency is above 3 kHz on the frequency counter, the player is running too fast. Likewise, if the reading is under 3 kHz, the tape player is operating too slow.

**Pulling of Tape.** Tape may spill out of the cassette when the take-up reel is erratic or sluggish in operation (Fig. 7-28). A worn or irregular pressure roller may cause the tape to pull out and wrap around the pressure-roller bearings. Inspect the turntable or reel assembly for a missing "C" washer. The black plastic hub may let the turntable pull up and slow down, letting tape spill out. Readjustment of the take-up reel tension may be needed at the take-up turntable.

**Keeps Switching Directions.** In automatic-reverse car tape players, the tape may automatically change directions from a defective switch, a broken switch wire, or dirty commutator rings. In some models a round magnet may be attached to the bottom of the turntable. As it rotates, the magnetic switch underneath the magnet opens and closes, which triggers the automatic-sensing circuit (Fig. 7-29). When the turntable does not turn, the switch remains in one position and the relay energizes, causing the motor to reverse directions erratically (Fig. 7-30).

In other automatic-reverse tape circuits a com-

Fig. 7-27. Slow speeds may be caused by a loose motor drive belt. Check the capstan and motor pulley for oil spots.

mutator may be built on the top side of the take-up reel. Here two small wire-like tongs engage the metal commutator rings, causing a switching action (Fig. 7-31). If the metal commutator or tong contacts become dirty, the switching action ceases and causes the auto-reverse circuits to erratically switch the direction of the small motor. Before digging into the auto-reverse circuits, clean up the commutator rings and tongs with alcohol and cleaning stick. Make sure the turntable is moving and the tongs are seating properly. A broken belt or drive wheel may not turn the reel assembly and cause the solenoid to switch directions.

Suspect a broken tape-head wire or improper head adjustment when the cassette reverses directions and plays normal in one direction but sounds terrible in the reverse direction. Clean up the tape head, then check head alignment. A slipping belt

in a Sanyo Model FT1490A would not change directions when the cassette had reached the tape end. Replace the belt if too large. A cleanup of belt and pulley may be all that is needed.

You may find two separate capstan/flywheels in the automatic reverse tape players (Fig. 7-32). Often two sets of pressure roller assemblies are needed to pull the tape in both directions. To get at the tape player, the front assembly and radio boards sometimes must be pulled up (Fig. 7-33). Just replacing a broken belt may require moving the receiver boards to get at the bottom side of the tape player. In the latest auto-cassette players LEDs are used to indicate in what direction the tape is moving (Fig. 7-34).

## EQUALIZER COMPONENTS

An equalizer-booster unit may be connected to

Fig. 7-28. Pulling of tape may be caused by an erratic or stopped take-up reel. Check the rubber drive areas for slippage.

the speaker or pre-amp output terminals for more control and power. The equalizer gives the operator much greater control over how the music sounds (Fig. 7-35). You may add more bass or higher tones by moving several equalizer frequency controls up or down. The equalizer unit connects directly to the speaker output or pre-amp output terminals of the cassette tape player.

**External Amplifiers.** For greater radio-player power output, a separate amplifier may be connected to the pre-amp or speaker output terminals. The amplifier component may feature speaker protection relays, built-in power noise filtering, bass drive filter and automatic on/off features (Fig. 7-36). The component amp may add from 15 to 125 watts per channel with a 20 to 20 kHz frequency response. Heavy-duty speakers must be installed to absorb the added power.

**Cable Hookup.** Extreme care should be

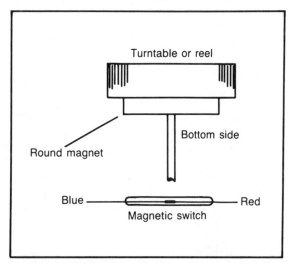

Fig. 7-29. The automatic-reverse procedure may be activated by a magnet attached to the bottom of the turntable or reel. A stationary magnetic switch under the turntable operates the automatic-reverse circuits.

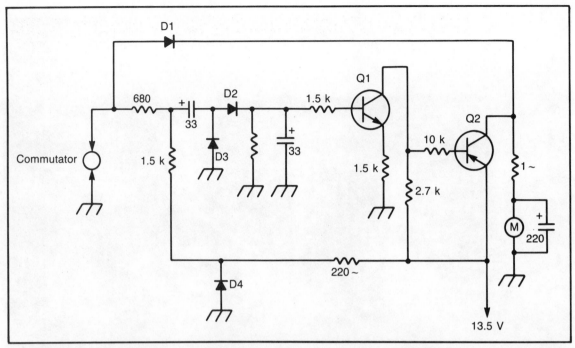

Fig. 7-30. Intermittent switching of a commutator ring on the take-up reel operates the automatic-reverse sensing circuits. Dirty commutator contacts may cause the player to keep reversing and not play the tape.

Fig. 7-31. In this tape player two wire metal tongs combine switching actions at the take-up reel to produce automatic reverse. When the tape ends, the reel stops triggering the automatic-reverse circuits.

Fig. 7-32. Two different flywheels with two separate pressure-roller assemblies are used in auto-reverse cassette players.

taken when wiring or connecting the speaker wires to the cassette player. Always follow the manufacturer's hookup chart. Often the chart is glued to the back or top side of the metal cabinet (Fig. 7-37). If not, check the service literature. Never tie all speaker wires together when only two speakers are used. Be careful in connecting speakers to ungrounded circuits. All speaker outputs should be connected to a speaker to prevent damage to the output transistors or IC components.

## TEN CASE HISTORIES

The following problems all occurred in auto radio-cassette players. Some are simple while others are more complicated. Sometimes the simpler the problem, the more difficult it is to find, because we overlook the obvious problem that is right in front of our nose. Always start with the simplest

working hypothesis, then work up to the most complex.

**Weak FM—Normal AM.** The AM was normal with very weak FM in a Sanyo FT-C4 cassette player. Right away the front end FM stages were checked and tested good. Since both AM and FM were switched into the MPX circuits, the defective component had to be in the FM circuits. While signal-tracing with the scope, C208 was found to be open (Fig. 7-38).

**Stations Fade Out.** The audio would completely fade out in a Chevy Model 986771 after the radio had operated for several minutes. The audio signal was monitored at the volume control and when the signal went down the audio was still present at the volume control. Voltage on the collector terminal was fairly high (10.7V). When the probe was applied to the emitter probe, the radio came

Fig. 7-33. You may have to remove the radio section along with controls to get at the tape player. This is necessary to just change the drive belt in compact radio-cassette players.

alive (Fig. 7-39). Bias resistor (R2) was erratic and was replaced.

**Intermittent Right Channel.** In a Craig Model 3135 tape player, the right channel was in-termittent. When in the intermittent condition, the audio signal was traced to the tone and balance control (Fig. 7-40). No signal was found on the positive terminal of C210. A closer inspection found the

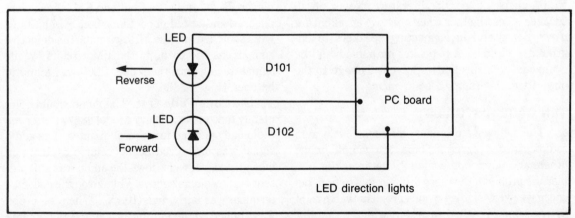

Fig. 7-34. Lighted LEDs are found in the auto-reverse circuits, indicating what direction the tape is playing in the latest car tape players.

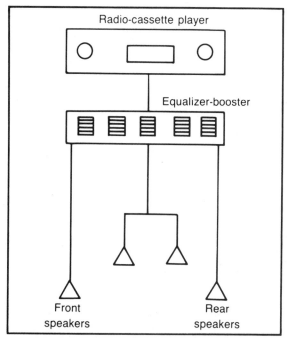

Fig. 7-35. The equalizer-booster system is installed between cassette player and speakers. Follow the manufacturer's hook-up procedure.

of the left channel of a Craig Model T618 player when the volume was turned up. The output IC2 was running fairly warm. Although IC2 provided power output for both channels, replacing it with a TA7227 IC fixed the noisy left channel.

**Noisy Car Receiver.** When the volume control was turned down, the noise would disappear in a Chrysler Model 3501235. The noise was still present when the antenna plug was removed, indicating the noisy component was in the front end of the receiver. Water rings were found on the rf and oscillator sections. The noise would come and go when the rf trimmer capacitor was pressed down with the rubber eraser of a pencil. The noise was stopped by releasing the tuning tension of the rf padder capacitor. The padder capacitor was replaced with the original part number, 3596333.

**Turn On—Pops and Cracks.** The tape player was very noisy when first turned on in a Craig Model T621. After playing for several minutes, the music would quiet down a little. With higher "A" voltage applied, the player would really act up. Signal-tracing the noise with the external amp to the power output IC turned up a noisy power IC. UPC 1185H was replaced with an ECG1293 universal replacement.

**Intermittent Right Channel.** Only the tape player was found to be intermittent in the right

capacitor terminal lead broken going to the first af amp.

**No Sound, Loud Howl.** The right channel was fairly normal with only a loud howl coming out

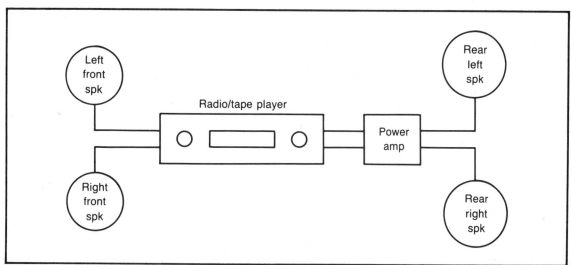

Fig. 7-36. A high-powered separate amp may be installed between speakers and cassette player. The power output may be up to 125 watts per channel in some installations.

181

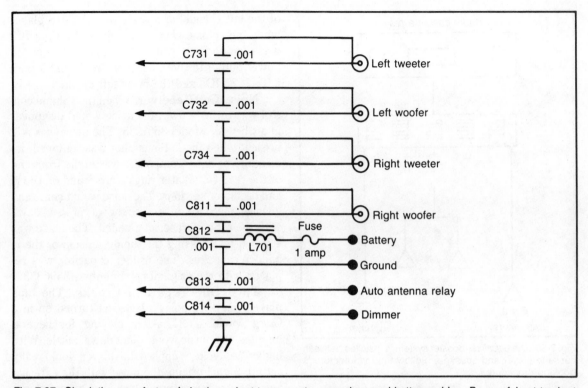

Fig. 7-37. Check the manufacturer's hook-up chart to connect up speakers and battery cables. Be careful not to short out speaker terminals.

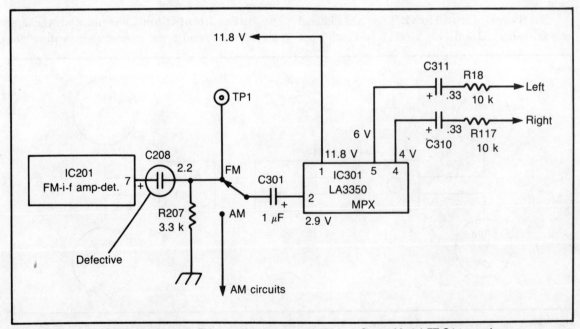

Fig. 7-38. An open C208 caused weak FM reception but normal AM in a Sanyo Model FT-C4 tape player.

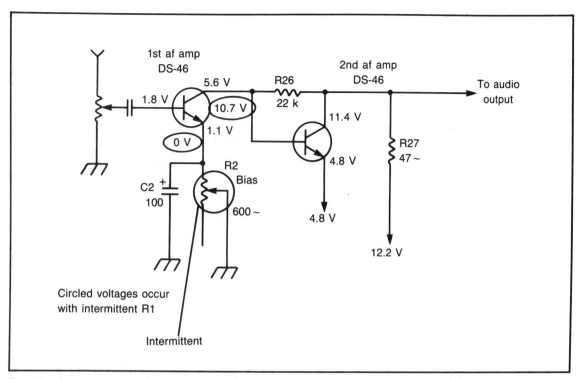

Fig. 7-39. Stations would fade out in a Chevy Model 986771 radio because of defective bias control R2.

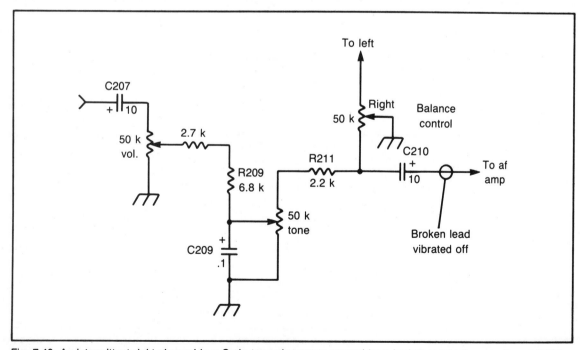

Fig. 7-40. An intermittent right channel in a Craig tape player was caused by a broken terminal connection at C210.

183

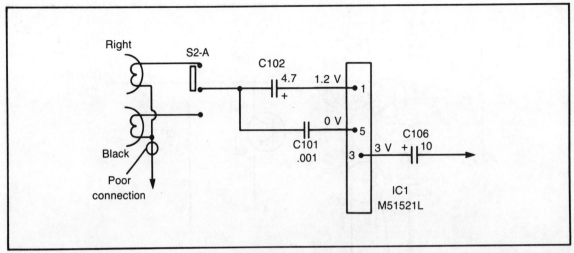

Fig. 7-41. The common black ground connection of the right tape head had a poor connection in a Sanyo Model FT642 cassette player, producing an intermittent right channel.

channel of a Sanyo ET642 cassette player. The signal was found to be intermittent at pin 3 of the preamp IC (Fig. 7-41). Switch S2-A and the tape-head windings had good continuity. A closer inspection revealed that a broken black lead to the ground side of the tape head was just lying against the tape-head terminal.

**Loud Hum in Left Channel.** The right channel was normal in a Sanyo FTC 26 player with a loud hum in the left channel. The volume control

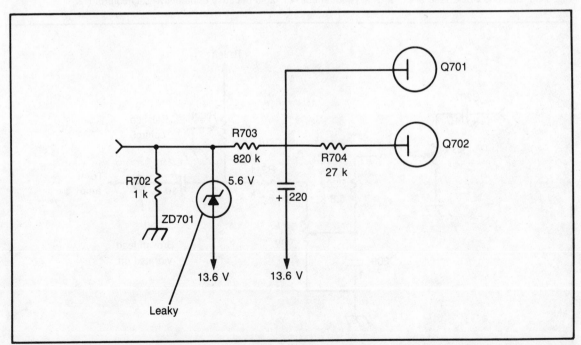

Fig. 7-42. Leaky diode ZD701 caused a dead motor regulation circuit in a Ford Model DAF-19A168AB radio cassette player. Replacing the 5.6-volt zener diode solved the dead motor problem.

**Table 7-1. Auto Stereo Cassette Troubleshooting Chart.**

| Symptoms | Possible Causes | Repairs |
|---|---|---|
| Radio dead—tape does not move—No dial light | Blown fuse; poor ground; bad "A" lead | Check fuse; check voltage; inspect "A" lead. |
| Tape does not move | Listen for motor running, defective switch, defective motor | Measure voltage at motor terminals; replace defective motor. |
| Motor rotates—no tape sound | Frozen capstan or reel; frozen pinch roller; broken belt | Rotate capstan by hand; try a good cleanup and lubrication; replace belt. |
| Pilot lights, no sound from radio or tape | Improper voltage IC or transistors | Check voltage source; check voltage at transistor and ICs. Test transistor with DMM; replace if defective. |
| Left channel dead | Defective speaker; defective pre-amp; defective output | Shunt another speaker. Check voltage at pre-amp and output. Test transistors; replace defective IC or transistors. |
| Weak right channel | Coupling capacitors, defective IC, defective transistors | Signal-trace audio signal with scope and external amp. Take voltage measurements; replace leaky IC and leaky or open transistor. |
| Radio normal—no cassette action | Defective switch; defective tape head; broken belt; defective motor | Check switch and tape-head continuity with low-ohm scale of DMM or VOM; replace belt and motor if defective. |
| Excessive wow and drag | Belt slippage; poor take-up; loose belt; binding pinch roller; defective cassette | Clean up all moving parts. Readjust take-up tension. Inspect pinch roller for excess tape wrapped around bearing. |
| Fast tape speed | Defective pinch roller; defective motor; excess tape around capstan | Inspect and replace pinch roller. Clean up pinch roller. Replace defective motor. Check for excess tape on capstan. |
| Noisy rotation | Defective motor; squeaky pinch roller; squeaky idler or turntable; squeaky flywheel capstan | Replace noisy motor; clean up and lubricate all moving parts. |
| Distorted sound | Dirty tape head, high-frequency distortion; pre-amp IC or transistors, output amp IC or transistors | Clean up tape head. Readjust azimuth screw on tape head. Signal-trace distortion with scope and external amp. Replace leaky transistors or ICs. |
| Cassette player normal—no radio | Dirty tape-radio switch; defective antenna; defective transistor or ICs | Clean up tape switch. Inspect antenna and jack. Take voltages and do in-circuit tests of transistors and ICs; replace if defective. |

| Symptoms | Possible Causes | Repairs |
|---|---|---|
| No AM or FM | Defective controller; improper voltage to IC processor; defective power circuit | Check voltage to IC; replace leaky IC processor if voltages are very low. Measure tuning voltage at varactor diodes; check power-supply voltage source. |
| No AM—FM normal | Defective rf transistor; defective converter transistor; defective AM IC, dirty AM-FM switch. | Test transistors in circuit. Take voltage measurements and replace defective transistor or ICs. Clean up AM-FM switch. |
| No FM—AM good | Defective FET transistor; defective oscillator transistor; defective mixer transistor; defective FM IC; dirty AM-FM switch | Check transistors in-circuit; replace if leaky or open. Replace FM IC. Clean up switch. |
| Microphonic noises on AM-FM | First af or pre-amp transistors; rf FET transistor; IC output | Signal-trace noise with external amp. Replace defective transistor; replace noisy IC. |
| Motor-boating | Af transistor; output transistor; output IC; decoupling electrolytic capacitor; bad grounds on IC output of heat sink | Replace noisy transistors; replace output transistors; replace IC. Shunt each decoupling capacitor and replace if defective. Check for good heat sink-to-chassis ground with ohmmeter. |

had no effect upon the hum level. The left channel output IC was running red hot. These two IC output channel ICs are located on separate heat sinks. Replacing the UPC1230H IC output solved the left channel hum problem.

**No Tape Motion.** The motor would not rotate in a Ford DAF-19A168AB radio-player. Upon checking voltages in the motor-control circuits, no voltage was found across zener diode ZD701 (Fig. 7-42). ZD701 was found to be leaky. Replacing the 5.6-volt zener diode solved the tape-motor motion problem.

**Keeps Reversing.** The tape would not move

because the auto-reverse circuits would keep reversing the tape direction in a Craig Model 3510. A small, round belt was found broken and lying in the bottom of the player. In this model, if the belt is off the turntable containing the commutator, the auto-reverse solenoid keeps energizing and the play direction lights flash off and on. After clean up, a new belt solved the constant reversing problem in the tape player.

Table 7-1 lists some additional problems along with their possible causes and suggested troubleshooting procedures.

# Chapter 8

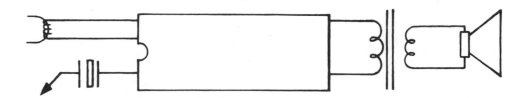

# Turntable Repairs and Maintenance

A GOOD TURNTABLE WITH A QUALITY PHONO cartridge provides easy-listening music. The turntable with a high signal-to-noise ratio and phono cartridge with a wide frequency response probably provides the best sound. The signal-to-noise ratio indicates how quiet the turntable rotates so the cartridge will not pick up vibrations or rumbling sounds. The high-quality phono cartridge with wide frequency response reproduces all the sounds recorded on the record (Fig. 8-1).

## TYPES OF TURNTABLES

The fully automatic turntable operates with only one button which may include repeat and pitch control, auto anti-skate, complete sitdown, and shut off features. The semi-automatic changer requires you to manually start the tone arm, although it will pick up the arm and return it at the end of the record. The semi-automatic turntable may have auto return and shut off, reject control, auto anti-skate, and belt drive with synchronous ac motor.

The new linear-tracking tone arm moves later-

ally across the record with no tracking-angle errors. The motor-driven tone arm moves across the record with automatic shut-off features. Some of the linear-tracking tone arms may select portions of the record using automatic set-down features. Actually, the linear-tracking tone arm just plays the record as it was originally cut.

The upright or vertical-mounted turntable may provide dual-side playing with automatic turn-on, shut-off, and single-play operations. Variable speed control and front loading features are usually included on the upright turntable.

The turntable may be driven by an idler wheel, belt, or direct-drive mechanism. In the older manual and automatic turntables, the turntable was rotated by a friction motor pulley that rotated an idler wheel that then rotated the turntable. The large platter turntable was often rotated by a large belt around the motor pulley. With a heavy, machined platter, room or motor vibrations are not transmitted in the sound. In the direct-drive turntables, the motor shaft is actually the record spindle assembly. The direct-drive turntables have accurate

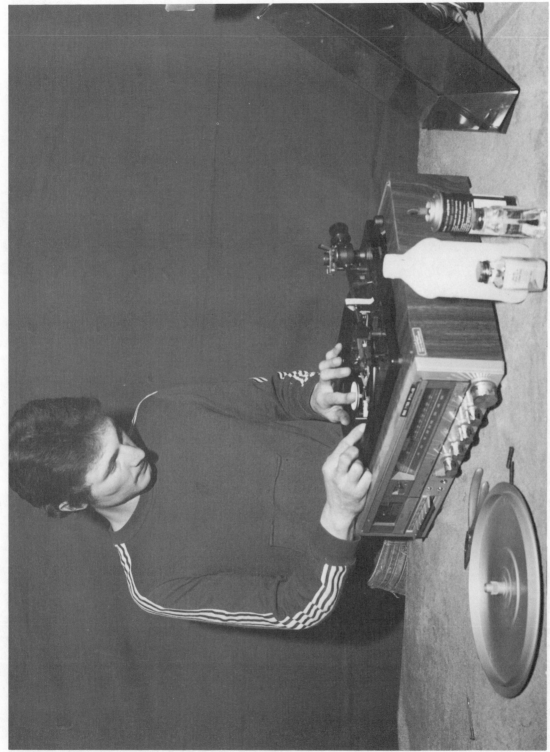

Fig. 8-1. A good cleanup of the idler wheel turntable and motor pulley may solve a slow speed problem in the automatic turntable. Clean all surfaces with alcohol and cloth.

speed regulation but are prone to motor vibration sounds.

## THE AUTOMATIC CHANGER

The automatic turntable may play 78, 45, or 33⅓ RPM records. Some of the latest turntables may have only two speeds, 33⅓ and 45 RPM (Fig. 8-2). The correct speed and record size is usually selected by controls on the top side of the changer. A cue stick raises the arm so certain music selections may be played. The tone-arm adjustment applies more or less tone-arm weight upon the stylus and record. All records are loaded on top of the center spindle and held in place with a keeper arm.

**Dead, No Rotation.** Listen for the motor rotating under the turntable. Suspect a defective ac switch, cord, or motor if there is no motor rota-

tion. The motor switch is engaged when the reject or start lever is pressed. Check the ac switch contacts with the low-ohm scale of the ohmmeter if the lever is moving the switch assembly (Fig. 8-3).

Take a continuity ohm measurement across the motor terminals. Sometimes the motor terminals are found right on the coil assembly. If not, trace the motor wires to the switch and turntable plug. Inspect the motor coil assembly for brown or burned marks, indicating the motor is running too warm.

Note if the motor is making a humming noise. The motor bearings may be frozen, preventing rotation of the armature. Place the tip of a screwdriver blade against the motor metal assembly and see if it vibrates. A vibration noise indicates the motor is receiving ac voltage but has a frozen shaft bearing (Fig. 8-4). Remove the motor mounting

Fig. 8-2. Standard 3-speed record changer with 33, 45 and 78 RPM speeds. Some of the latest turntables have only 33 and 45 RPM speeds.

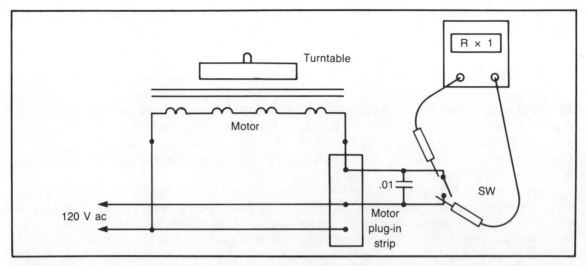

Fig. 8-3. The ac switch and motor field coil should be checked with the low-ohm range of the VOM or DMM if there is no motor action.

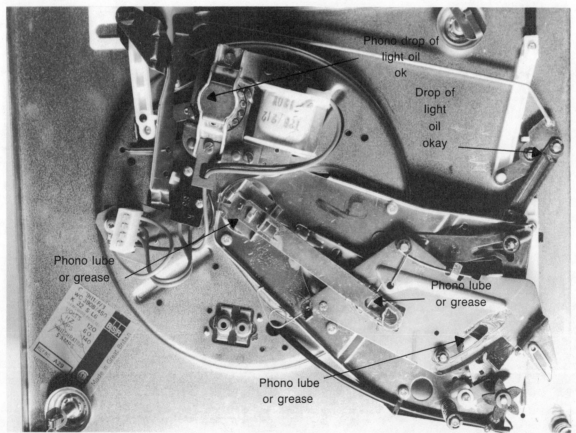

Fig. 8-4. Recommended lubrication points on the bottom of the changer. A frozen motor may be caused by dry armature bearings.

bolts and drop the motor down. Disassemble the motor and clean out each bearing with cleaning fluid. Wash out the shaft bearing areas before assembling the motor.

The motor may be dead if the arm lever does not engage the on/off switch. Check for a missing "C" washer. Suspect a defective switch or binding-arm lever is the motor runs all the time. Check the price of a replacement motor since a new motor assembly may cost half the price of the whole turntable, if the motor is found defective.

**Speed Problems.** A worn idler wheel or gummed up motor bearing may cause slow speeds. Remove the idler wheel and inspect the rubber drive area. Look for small pieces of rubber around the motor pulley and idler wheel, indicating the idler wheel should be replaced. Apply a dab of phono lube upon the idler wheel shaft before installing a new wheel (Fig. 8-5).

Check the turntable bearings for dried-up grease or dirt down inside the bearing area. Clean off the bearings and turntable hub with alcohol and cloth. Lubricate bearings and hub with phono lube grease. Only a dab will do.

Excess oil on idler wheel or motor pulley may produce slow speeds. Clean off with alcohol and cleaning stick. An overheated or shorted motor may cause slow speeds. The turntable may accidentally be left on all day or night and overheat, producing frozen motor bearings.

**Improper or Erratic Speeds.** Check the turntable bearings for hair or foreign material that could produce incorrect speeds. Very jerky music may result when the idler wheel operates part way on the 45 RPM part of the spindle in the 33⅓ RPM mode. Readjust the idler wheel adjustment screw so the idler wheel runs on the center area of the spindle in each speed setting (Fig. 8-6). If the ad-

Fig. 8-5. A worn or cracked idler wheel may produce slow speeds. Try cleaning up the idler wheel and bearings. A drop of light oil or phono lube on the idler wheel bearing may help.

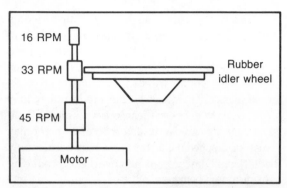

16 RPM

33 RPM

45 RPM

Motor

Rubber idler wheel

Fig. 8-6. The idler wheel assembly should be adjusted so that the wheel rides in the center area of the set-speed assembly. Locate the idler wheel screw or bend the idler wheel assembly back into level position.

justment is way off, you may find only one speed on the turntable.

When the 33⅓ RPM speed is too fast, suspect the idler wheel is running on the 45 RPM part of the spindle. A screw out of the speed lever arm or a gummed up plastic selector assembly will not let the turntable change speeds. Check for old and gummed up grease around the spring lift area.

**Will Not Shut Off.** Inspect the record arm keeper for dry or gummed parts which will not let the keeper fall down and so will shut off after the last record is played. Note if the rubber washer at the end of the arm keeper is out of position and keeps the arm up so the motor will not shut off. If the arm keeper is loose and will not stay in place, check for a loose set screw. A frozen or dry shut-off assembly may prevent the player from shutting down. Check that a bent arm shaft at the bottom side of the tone-arm assembly is not striking or applying enough pressure against the trip lever of the cam assembly.

Fig. 8-7. Here the head shell tone-arm assembly can be completely removed with a turn nut at the rear of assembly. Sometimes the tone arm is lifted on the record to start the turntable.

**Tone Arm Will Not Set Down.** Improper adjustment of the height screw may prevent the arm from setting down properly on the record. Check to see if the cue stick is up instead of down. In some changers a plunger-type assembly is found under the tone arm at the pivot point. A dry or frozen plunger assembly may prevent the arm from setting down. Clean up and apply a coat of grease on plunger assembly.

**Records Do Not Fall.** Make sure the spindle assembly is seated properly. Note that the trip lever at the top of spindle comes up high enough to move the record off of the spindle. If not, see if the trip assembly at the bottom of the spindle assembly is bent out of line under the turntable. A bent arm keeper may not apply enough pressure against records to move them down the center spindle post. Check for a bent spindle assembly, and replace if sluggish or erratic in operation.

## THE SEMI-AUTOMATIC TURNTABLE

Often with automatic shut off the tone arm is lifted upon the turntable to start the motor rotating at the end of the record in a semi-automatic turntable (Fig. 8-7). A heavy or machined platter is belt or directly driven in these turntables. The tone arm may have a removable head/shell cartridge assembly. Usually there is a counterweight

at the end of the tone arm for proper stylus pressure.

Vertical tracking force (VTF) is the amount of pressure applied to the record by the stylus and tone-arm assembly. If the VTF is set too low, high-frequency signals are distorted and attenuated. When it is set too high, low-frequency signals are distorted. The vertical tracking adjustment is made by rotating the counterweight at the end of the tone arm. Rotate the counter balance until the correct weight (in grams) is applied as specified by the manufacturer.

The automatic or semi-automatic turntable may have additional features such as anti-skate control, cueing lever, speed select, and stop button. The anti-skate bias control compensates for the inward lateral pressure imposed on the tone arm by the rotation of the record grooves. The anti-skate control should be set to the same gram setting as the cartridge stylus pressure.

In some turntables you may find an electronic speed control with 60-Hz strobe markings. The markings are found at the outside edge of the heavy platter (Fig. 8-8). A pitch control is rotated until the strobe lines appear to stand still in either 33⅓ or 45 RPM speeds. If the platter is rotating too slowly, the dots will appear in a counterclockwise direction. When rotating too fast, the dots will appear to be

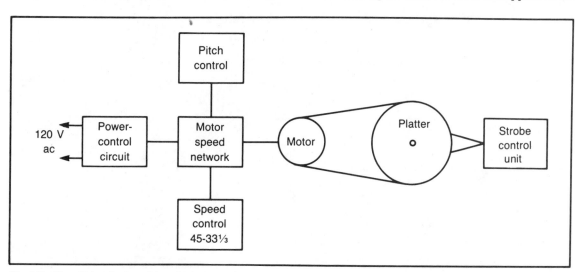

Fig. 8-8. The pitch adjustment is set to govern the correct speed of the strobe control. A neon bulb illuminates the dots or lines at the edge of the platter.

moving in the clockwise direction.

The cartridge is usually a magnetic type with easy replacement. The new p-mount type arm allows the cartridge to be plugged in without changing pickup wires. These moving-magnet or coil-type cartridges have a wide frequency response range from 10 to 35,000 Hz. Of course, many of the p-mount type cartridges are rather expensive to replace.

**Dead—No Movement.** Often the large belt is off the turntable when there is no platter movement. Note if the motor is running. Remove the large turntable and check for a loose belt. In some models the belt may be replaced by lifting the rubber mat and reaching through the slots in the heavy turntable (Fig. 8-9). Sometimes when the speed is changed, the belt is lifted or lowered to a different spot on the motor pulley and the belt will fly off.

Check the belt for oily areas. Clean off with alcohol and cloth. Hold the belt with left thumb through the cutout provided on the platter. Place the belt on the rib of the platter and motor pulley.

Measure the belt for correct length if the belt is too loose or broken. Hold the pieces together to measure for the length of belt. Lay the belt alongside a ruler to get the correct length. Select a belt ¼-inch shorter than the measured length (Fig. 8-10). These drive belts can be picked up at most electronic music and stereo stores.

Suspect a defective motor, micro-switch, or broken ac cord when the motor will not rotate (Fig. 8-11). Check the switch and motor for continuity with the low-ohm scale of the DMM. Rotate the motor pulley to see if the motor bearings are frozen. Check for 120 Vac at the motor terminals with the micro-switch in on position.

Fig. 8-9. Remove the rubber mat and rotate the platter until you can see the motor pulley. Note if the belt is off. The belt may be replaced on the motor pulley through one of these slotted areas.

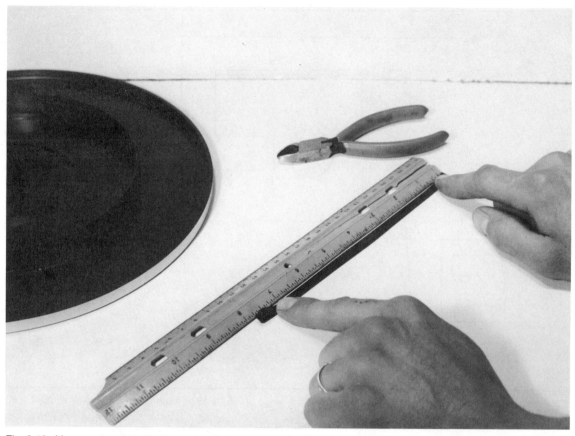

Fig. 8-10. Measure the old belt with a ruler. Select a new belt with the same thickness and width but ¼ inch shorter than the measured belt.

**Improper Speeds.** Inspect the belt and motor pulley for oil spots. Clean off the belt and pulley with alcohol and cloth. Dirt on the motor pulley or belt may produce wow, flutter, and rumble. Determine if the belt is too loose and replace the belt. A dry or gummed up turntable bearing may cause slow speeds.

**Erratic Shutoff.** Remove the platter and note if the small trip lever is bent out of line. Bring the tone arm across to see if the trip lever will strike the hub of the turntable. Inspect the trip lever for a gummed up or frozen bearing on the cam assembly (Fig. 8-12). When the record has finished playing, the arm lever places pressure against the trip lever which in turn strikes the platter hub, causing the tone arm to return and shut off the motor.

**Correct Arm Adjustment.** Most arm screw return adjustments are found at the bottom of the tone-arm assembly. Securing or fine-adjustment screws are turned to make arm-return adjustments. Adjust the screw so the auto-return mechanism triggers within a range of 57 to 65 millimeters or according to the manufacturer's specifications.

**Motor Speed Controls.** The 33⅓ and 45 RPM speed may be selected by switching resistance into the leg of the motor assembly (Fig. 8-13). The dc turntable motor operates from a dc bridge-rectifier circuit. Check for dc voltages (under 16 volts) at the large filter capacitor. Inspect the speed select switch (SW1) for dirty contacts if the motor is erratic or does not change speeds. A worn, variable-resistor pitch control (R102) may cause erratic or no 45 RPM speed.

A speed-control circuit with a neon lamp strobe

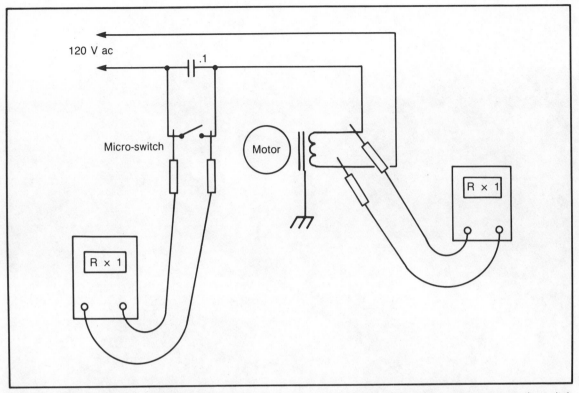

Fig. 8-11. Check the switch and motor field with the R X 1 range of the DMM. If there is no measurement, the switch or motor is open and must be replaced.

and pitch control resistor had no 33⅓ speed in a J.C. Penney Model 6500 belt-driven turntable (Fig. 8-14). The 45 RPM speed was normal and could be controlled with VR101. If the changeover switch was pulled to one side, the 33⅓ RPM speed would start to work. The rotary switch was sprayed with cleaning fluid and restored the 33⅓ RPM speed. Several coats of spray were needed before the switch contacts were clean enough to operate properly.

**Directly Driven Turntables.** In a direct-driven turntable, the record spindle is actually part of the motor shaft. Most direct-drive motors are either a dc servo or quartz-locked type which keeps perfectly accurate speed. The motors are dc types that are controlled from a dc power supply. The speed-control circuits may consist of a bridge-rectifier circuit, speed compensation, driver and speed detection, or strobe-type circuits. In Fig. 8-15, a Hall IC determines the correct speed of the

speed detection unit which is amplified and sent to the rectifier circuit which applies voltage to the separate motor windings.

Just about every turntable manufacturer has a different servo-motor speed circuit. You may find IC components in the latest direct-driven motor-speed circuits. The low-voltage bridge-rectifier circuit supplies voltage to regulator transistors Q1 and Q2 (Fig. 8-16). A 21.6- and 22.8-volt supply provides voltage to IC101.

IC101 delivers a BFG method (back-electromotive-force frequency generator) that is generated in the drive-coil winding of the motor to determine the speed of the turntable (terminals 8, 9, and 10). In addition to employing a trapezoidal wave-generating circuit, a pulse-generating circuit, and a sampling integration circuit, the BFG output frequency is converted to a voltage which maintains the rotation speed of the turntable. The operation control circuit functions as a control output voltage

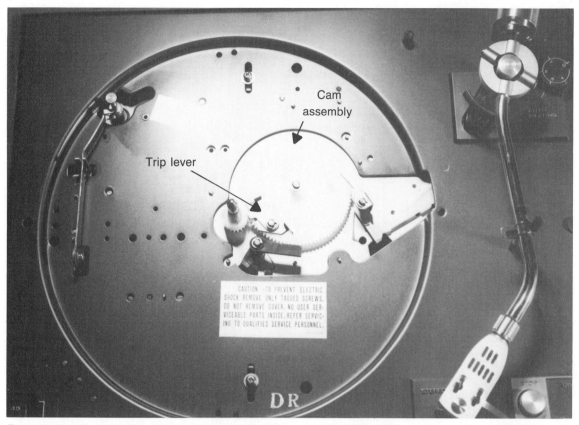

Fig. 8-12. Check for a broken trip lever on the cam assembly when the tone arm will not reject at the end of the record.

control, keeping the rotation speed of the platter constant (pin 22).

The operational amplifier in the active filter provides ideal filter operation (pin 20). As a result, the signal-to-noise ratio is high but with a very low wow and flutter level.

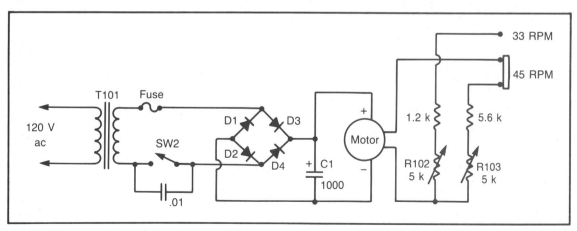

Fig. 8-13. The speed of the dc phono motor is determined by inserting resistance into the legs of the motor or by changing the voltage applied to the motor windings.

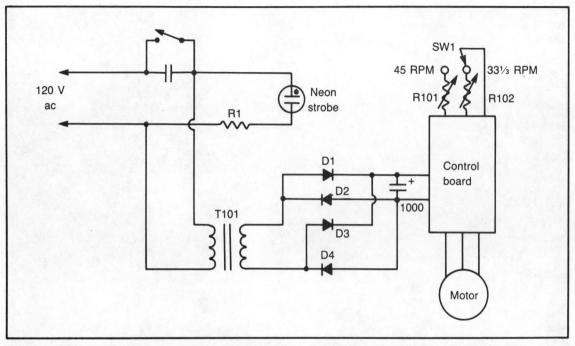

Fig. 8-14. Different speeds are selected with SW1 and pitch controls R101 and R102. The correct speed is set with a neon strobe light.

Prompt starting of the motor is accomplished by a large-capacity power transistor in the integrated circuit, which has a high starting-torque circuit. Smooth motor rotation results from three differential switching circuits by means of the signal from the position signal coil and start circuit of the power transistor on pins 12, 13, and 14. There are several different motor windings found in this particular direct-drive circuitry.

R4 and R3 vary the 45 and 33⅓ RPM speeds with the help of a neon lamp strobe and turntable. SW2 switches in the 33⅓ or 45 RPM speeds or turns the turntable off. Accurate voltage measurements on IC101 may indicate a leaky or open IC when the motor is erratic in operation. Improper supply voltage at Q1 and Q2 may indicate a leaky or open regulated power transistor. Check the bridge rectifiers for leaky conditions when T1 becomes warm or there is improper dc output voltage. Some manufacturers request that should the servo motor or components need replacement, the whole PC board assembly should be replaced along with the motor.

## LINEAR-TRACKING TURNTABLES

The linear high-tech tracking tone arm plays records as flawlessly as they were recorded with virtually no tracking-angle error. The tone arm operates with a worm-type gear system to move the arm across the radius of the record. The tone arm will automatically set down at the beginning of the record or at any point you may choose. After the record is finished playing, the arm comes over the start/rest position and shuts off the turntable. Of course, only one record is played at a time (Fig. 8-17).

In some linear turntables an optical sensor locates each track, and any one track or all the programs may be played in any sequence. Just pushing a button automatically advances to the next song or music. You may select the repeat mode to play a side up to eight times in a row.

In addition to automatic shut-off and auto repeat, many linear-tracking turntables are belt or direct driven with electronic strobe speed adjustments. Automatic muting, silicone damping, and cueing controls are added features. Almost all

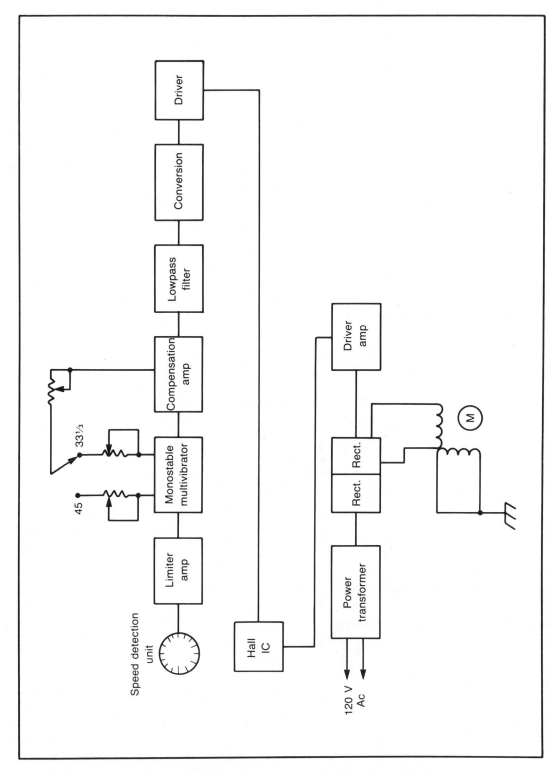

Fig. 8-15. A more complicated motor speed circuit is used in directly driven motors. Here the Hall IC selects the correct speed signal from the speed reduction circuits to the drive amp and servo motor.

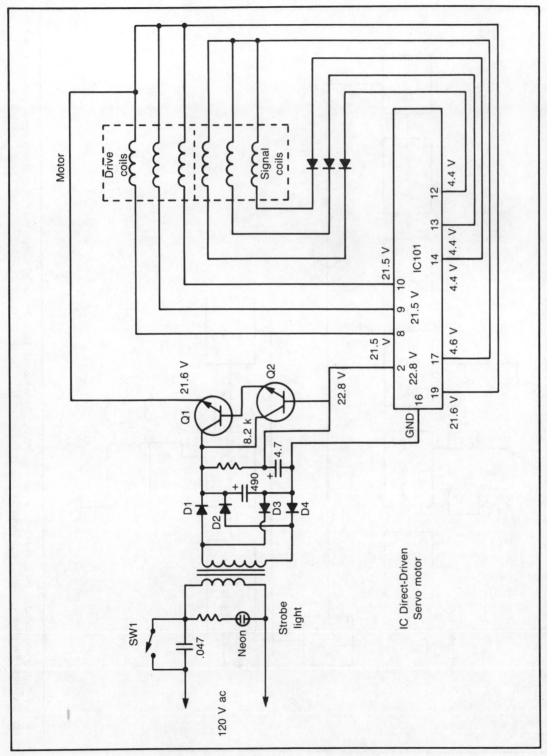

Fig. 8-16. The bridge rectifier circuit supplies two voltage sources to voltage regulator transistors Q1 and Q2. The drive and signal coils are controlled by IC101.

Fig. 8-17. A Realistic Model LAB-2100 linear-tracking automatic turntable. The tone arm is geared to travel horizontally with the record.

linear-tracking turntables have die-cast aluminum platters. Accurate vertical tracking and anti-skate adjustments are also located on the base of the turntables.

## Radio Shack Model LAB-2100

The linear-tracking automatic turntable may have a separate PC board with the various IC and transistor components that control the turntable operation. A separate power supply, signal-processing circuit, sub-motor operating circuit, and the main motor circuits are found on a separate board (Fig. 8-18). The tone-arm sensor, strobe indicator, tracking sensor, solenoid, and up and down signal are controlled from the various circuits.

A critical microprocessor is the MP-2001,

which is the heart of the operation control circuits (Fig. 8-19). The various switches are tied directly to the processor IC. Take critical voltage measurements on the IC when one or more functions do not operate. Check the various switches for good contacts. A dirty speed switch may cause improper rotation. Check the MP-2001 and the sub-motor control for poor or erratic tracking.

You may find several different power-supply sources within the linear-tracking turntable (Fig. 8-20). Here the positive (+) and negative (−) 15-volt source supplies voltage to IC102, the sub-motor drive and the solenoid. The positive and negative 5-volt source connects to the logic circuits, while the 22-volt source supplies power for the main motor.

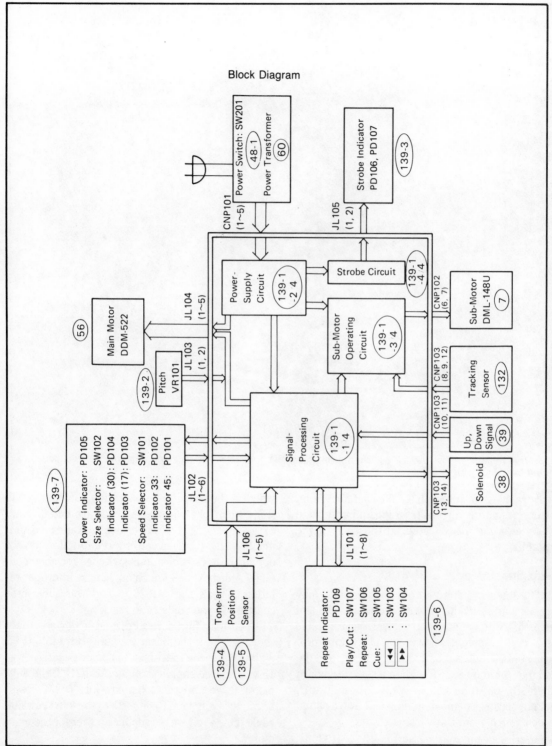

Block Diagram

Fig. 8-18. In contrast to other turntables, the linear-tracking unit is controlled by a signal-processing IC circuit (courtesy of Radio Shack).

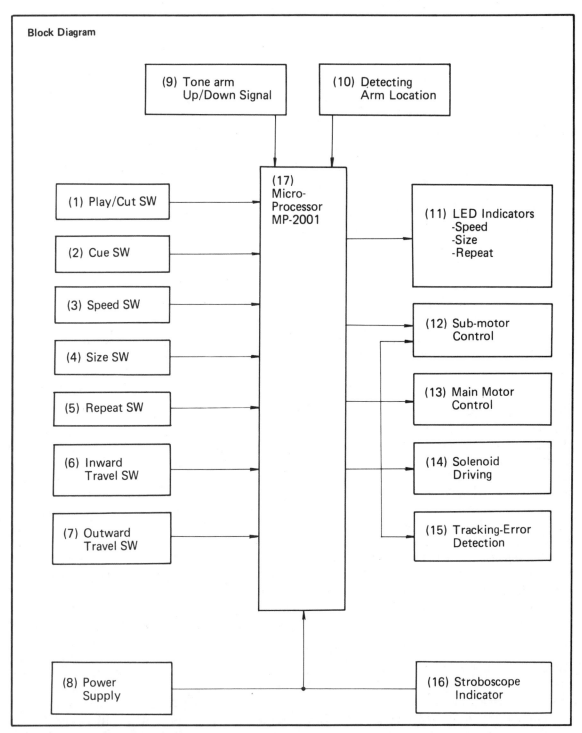

**Block Diagram**

(9) Tone arm Up/Down Signal

(10) Detecting Arm Location

(17) Micro-Processor MP-2001

(1) Play/Cut SW

(2) Cue SW

(3) Speed SW

(4) Size SW

(5) Repeat SW

(6) Inward Travel SW

(7) Outward Travel SW

(8) Power Supply

(11) LED Indicators -Speed -Size -Repeat

(12) Sub-motor Control

(13) Main Motor Control

(14) Solenoid Driving

(15) Tracking-Error Detection

(16) Stroboscope Indicator

Fig. 8-19. Microprocessor M2-2001 controls most of the functions of the control circuits. Note the various switches are tied to the microprocessor.

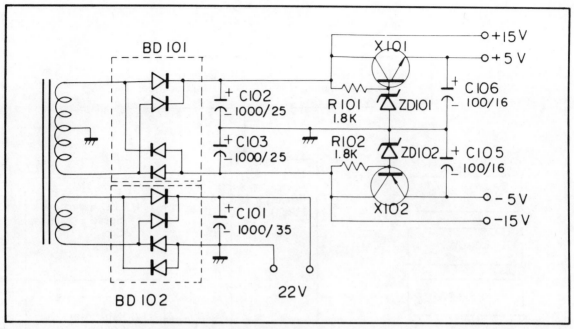

Fig. 8-20. Here several different voltages are used to operate the various circuits in a linear-tracking turntable. Always check the supply voltages when there is no movement of the tone arm.

A low or improper 5- or 15-volt source may be caused by regulator transistors X101 and X102. Check zener diodes ZD101 and ZD102 for leakage. When a regulator transistor becomes leaky, often the corresponding zener diodes are damaged. No 5- or 15-volt source may be caused by a shorted or leaky bridge rectifier, (BD101). Check BD102 for improper voltage (22V) at the main motor terminals.

**Tone Arm Does Not Move.** Inspect the sensor assembly with no tone-arm movement. Measure the voltage applied to the sensor PCB assembly. A defective sub-motor may prevent the arm from moving. Measure the voltage at the motor terminals (Fig. 8-21). Check the submotor driver transistors for open or leaky conditions. Inspect the play/cut switch for defective or dirty contacts. Note if the linear-tracking carrier mechanism is stiff or will not move. Rotate the drum pulley and note if the guide bar assembly is deformed, dented, or nicked, preventing movement of the tone arm.

**Tone Arm Does Not Descend to Disc.** Check the contacts of the up leaf switch. Often the leaf-switch contacts are closed when the power switch is off and the tone arm is up. Measure the voltage across the leaf switch. A defective solenoid may cause the tone arm to remain in the up position. Sometimes improper adjustment of the solenoid lift mechanism prevents the tone arm from descending.

**Start and Stop Problems.** Improper starting may result from a jammed worm gear or a defective electronic servo-control circuit. If the arm does not start to move, make sure voltage is applied to the motor tracking circuits. Inspect the belt and motor-drive assembly in the belt-driven models. Replace with a new belt (Fig. 8-22).

Suspect foreign material in the worm-gear assembly or a defective speed-control circuit when the arm stops in the middle of a section (Fig. 8-23). Check the sequence in repeat mode. See if the arm will start up or reject to the shut-off position. Note if the small motor belt or drive mechanism is off the tracking motor. Take quick voltage and resistance measurements on IC and transistor components in the variable motor speed control circuits.

## VERTICAL MOUNT/UPRIGHT TURNTABLES

Although there are only a few upright or vertically mounted turntables on the market, the record player may play both sides of the record (Fig. 8-24). The dual-play disc turntable plays both A and B sides and is automatic. The player has automatic turn-on and shut-off with front loading features (Fig. 8-25). Like the semi-automatic turntable, a variable speed control is found on most models.

Check the switch and motor for a no-start symptom. A jammed or binding mechanism may prevent the turntable from starting up. Since the turntable weight is on the center hub area, check for adequate lubrication of the turntable bearing. Aside from the above considerations, the upright turntable may be serviced in the same manner as any record player.

## TURNTABLE CARE

After repairs are made on the defective turntable assembly, inspect all moving components for correct lubrication. All cams and sliding levers should have a touch of light grease applied to the working areas. Inspect the turntable bearings for gummed up or hardened grease bearings. Remove the bearing ring of the automatic turntable, wash out the old grease, and apply a coat of light phono lube.

Check the motor for dry bearings. A squeaking motor may need only a squirt of light oil. In older open-type motors, remove the motor assembly and the armature. Wash out the bearings with alcohol or silicone shield lubricant. Do not overlook gummed-up motor shafts. Lubricate bearings with a light oil. Do not over oil or over grease any moving bearing. The oil may drip down or land on the motor belt or rotating turntable, causing slow-speed problems. Wipe off excess oil with alcohol and cleaning stick.

All turntables seem to collect dust, especially if there is no dust cover for the turntable. Wash off all dust and dirt with a window-cleaning spray. Spray the cleaning fluid on the tone arm, turntable, and mounted surfaces. Get down into the small areas with a brush. Be careful not to hit or damage the stylus or cartridge. Removing dirt and grease from the top of the turntable assembly makes it not only perform better, but makes it shine like new.

## CARTRIDGE AND STYLUS REPLACEMENT

A dirty stylus or needle may cause distortion or fuzzy music. Excessive dirt between stylus and cartridge may produce tinny and weak sounds. First clean out around the stylus with a small brush. Look at the stylus under a magnifying glass to determine if the point is worn or chipped. Always replace the stylus with a diamond needle. The chipped diamond stylus may cause scratchy music and gouge out the recording.

To remove the defective stylus, drop the cartridge down, straighten the stylus clip upward, and then pull outward (Fig. 8-26). Some needles are removed by pulling straight out. The stylus may slip under a keeper metal piece to hold it in position. When removing the stylus be careful that the small saddle attached to the crystal or moving metal vane is not broken.

A defective cartridge may cause excessive distortion and mushy music. Very low or no volume may be produced by a defective or broken cartridge. It sometimes happens that the music volume can be fairly normal but without clear vocal recordings. This can also be caused by a defective cartridge. Excessive motorboating sounds may also result from a defective cartridge. Replace if in doubt.

Check the continuity of all magnetic cartridges with the low ohmmeter scale (Fig. 8-27). Both left and right channels should be equal in resistance. The open or shorted winding should be replaced with a new cartridge. Often the cartridge terminal clip leads come off the right channel, and red ( + ) and green ( − ) with white ( + ) and blue ( − ) or black off the left channel.

Intermittent or erratic phono reception may be caused by broken wires or loose clips on the cartridge. Check each connection at the cartridge terminals. Hum may be present with a broken negative or black ground wire. Measure the con-

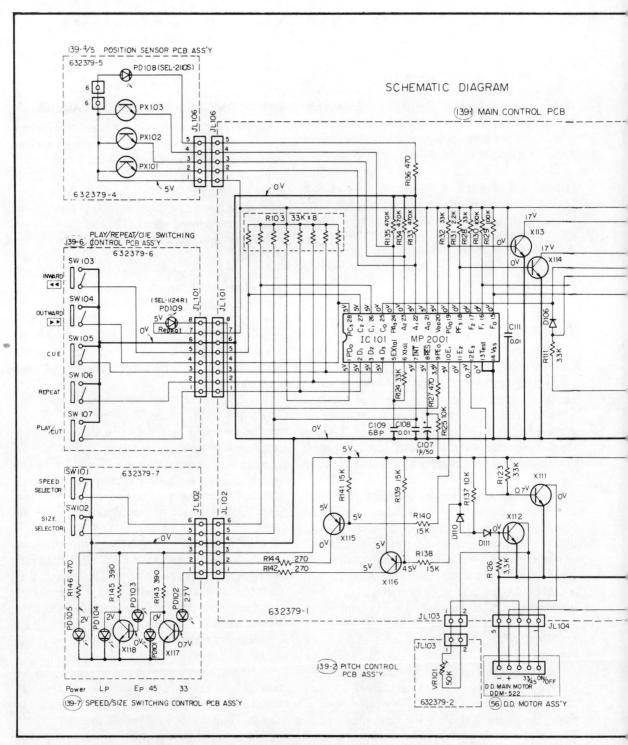

Fig. 8-21. A complete circuit diagram of the Radio Shack Model LAB-2100 linear-tracking turntable.

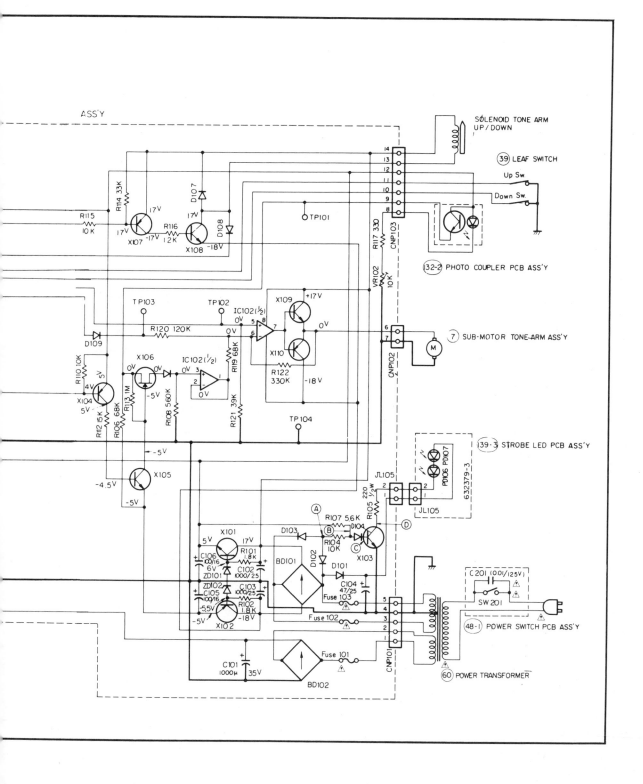

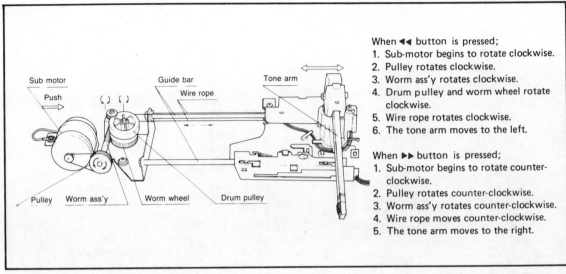

When ◄◄ button is pressed;
1. Sub-motor begins to rotate clockwise.
2. Pulley rotates clockwise.
3. Worm ass'y rotates clockwise.
4. Drum pulley and worm wheel rotate clockwise.
5. Wire rope rotates clockwise.
6. The tone arm moves to the left.

When ►► button is pressed;
1. Sub-motor begins to rotate counter-clockwise.
2. Pulley rotates counter-clockwise.
3. Worm ass'y rotates counter-clockwise.
4. Wire rope moves counter-clockwise.
5. The tone arm moves to the right.

Fig. 8-22. Check the sub-motor and motor drive belt when there is no tone-arm movement. Inspect the worm wheel and drum pulley for broken or damaged plastic gear teeth.

tinuity of each channel with the ohmmeter where the female phono plugs are found on the turntable. This test will detect an open magnetic cartridge or broken wire lead. Crystal cartridges should have infinite resistance.

Remove the head-shell mounted cartridge by loosening the small mounting screws. In models with the cartridge incorporated with the head-shell, it is recommended that the two be replaced together. The head-shell attached to the tone arm should not be inclined to the right or left. If necessary, loosen the screws attached to the tone arm or unscrew the cartridge head from tone arm. Make sure the stylus is normal to the record surface.

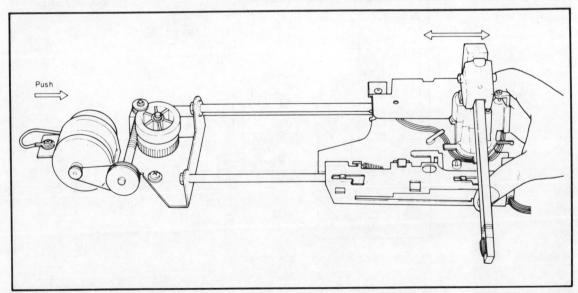

Fig. 8-23. Try to push the tone-arm assembly on the guide bar with the pulley off. Rotate the worm-gear assembly and note if the tone-arm assembly moves easily and smoothly.

Fig. 8-24. The upright turntable may be found in the AM-FM-MPX cassette player.

Fig. 8-25. Both sides of the record can be selected in this Sharp Model UZ3000.

Fig. 8-26. The stylus is removed from the clip area at the rear of the cartridge. A clip at the front of the cartridge holds the cartridge in position.

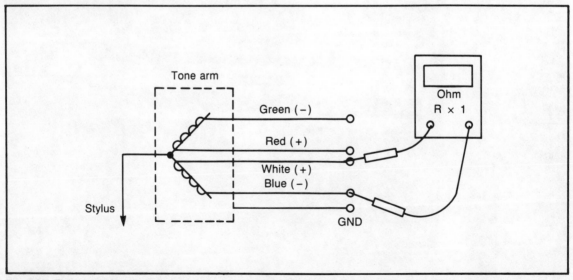

Fig. 8-27. The magnetic coils in the cartridge may be checked with the R X 1 scale of the VOM or DMM. Both left and right coils should be the same resistance. Crystal cartridges have infinite resistance measurements.

**Table 8-1. Troubleshooting Chart for Automatic and Semi-Automatic Turntables.**

| Symptoms | Possible Trouble | Repair |
|---|---|---|
| Turntable does not rotate | No power to motor | Check ac switch and ac voltage at motor terminals. |
| | Defective motor | Take continuity tests for open motor winding. |
| | Idler pulley not engaging motor shaft | Note if small spring is missing. Lubricate idler arm. |
| | Idler pulley not rotating | Clean up entire idler wheel, turntable rim and motor-drive shaft surfaces. |
| Turntable rotates but no arm movement | Tone arm poor height adjustment | Adjust screw for correct height. |
| | Actuating spring loose or missing | Check for missing spring. |
| Turntable stops after playing | Idler pulley | Clean off idler pulley with alcohol and cloth. If still slow speed, replace idler pulley. |
| | Insufficient idler pulley spring | Check tension and cut off a wind or two and refasten. |
| Slow turntable speed | Idler wheel | Replace if slow after cleanup. |
| | Turntable bearings | Clean up and wash out bearings. Lubricate with light grease or phono lube. |
| | Turntable rim | Clean off rim surfaces with alcohol and cloth. Resurface with liquid rosin. |
| | Motor bearings | Remove motor and wash out motor bearings. Lubricate with light oil. |
| Record fails to drop | Spindle | Reseat spindle in center of turntable. |
| | Bent spindle | Replace spindle. |
| | Missing spring on feed lever link | Replace; look in bottom of changer for loose spring. |
| Tone arm drops too far in on record | Tone-arm set-down | Readjust tone-arm set-down screw so arm falls at the beginning of record. |
| Tone arm does not track across record | Excess dirt | Clean off stylus with a small brush. |
| | Worn stylus | Remove stylus and check for worn or cracked point under magnifying glass. |
| | Pick-up leads tight | Check for slack pick-up leads at the rear of tone arm. |
| | Changer not level | Level the changer. |
| | Only on one record | Record is defective—check with another new one. |
| | Wrong setting of anti-skate compensation | Reduce anti-skate setting. |

| Symptoms | Possible Trouble | Repair |
|----------|------------------|--------|
| | Sticking actuating-point assembly | Clean up and lubricate with light oil. Replace if bent and defective. |
| Will not recycle at end of record | Dry tripping pawl assembly, improper stylus set down | Clean up and lubricate; correct set-down must be right in some changes. Make sure set-down is not in too far at the start of the record. |
| More than one record drops | Holes too large in records | Check for large hole—replace record. |
| | Control arm not down on records | Check setting of control arms. |
| | Small lever on spindle up | Check to see if small lever inside spindle is down. Sometimes when whole stack of records is loaded the small lever is up and should be down. |
| Will not shut off after last record | Defective switch | Note if switch is being tripped. |
| | Arm keeper up | Check to see if arm keeper goes down after the last record. |
| | Bent switch lever | Note if switch lever is in line to trip the switch when the last record is shut off. |
| Turntable will not start | No power | Check ac switch contacts—note if motor is rotating. |
| | Belt off | If motor is rotating, suspect the belt is off. |
| Belt will not stay on | Loose or oily | Inspect belt for oily spots. Clean up belt and turntable rim with alcohol and cloth. Replace belt after cleanup. |
| Slow or erratic speed | Grease or oil on drive surfaces | Clean off with alcohol and cloth. |
| | Warped records | Note if one or more records are warped. |
| | Defective speed system | Check for defective servo-motor or speed indicator system. |
| | Motor | After testing speed indicator circuits, suspect a defective servo direct motor. Check for correct voltage at the motor. |
| | Erratic speed at 45 RPM | Check 45 RPM speed switch and speed-adjustment control. Replace speed adjustment control if erratic. |
| | Improper motor voltage | Measure for accurate voltage at motor according to the schematic. Note if voltage can be adjusted. If not, check diodes and power supply. |
| | Correct motor voltage | Remove power-supply leads. Inject correct dc voltage from external power source and note how motor rotates. |
| | Motor | Replace servo motor if it does not operate with correct external voltage. |
| | Servo PCB | Check components upon PCB board if motor operates correctly. Repair or replace PCB board assembly. |

Some cartridges are held in position with a front metal clip. Pull down on the clip and the cartridge will release.

The new p-mounted cartridges plug right into the cartridge mount and are easy to replace. The stylus may be bonded, nude, micro, or linear with a bi-radial or elliptical shape. Prices range from $19.95 to $250.00.

Try to replace both cartridges and stylus with the originals. Select a cartridge with the same voltage and frequency response when replacing with an unusual component. Take the old cartridge and stylus to a record or music store or to where you originally purchased the player, along with the model number of the turntable for correct replacements. Remember, there are hundreds of different stylus and cartridges on the market.

Table 8-1 lists some additional problems along with their possible causes and suggested troubleshooting procedures.

# Chapter 9

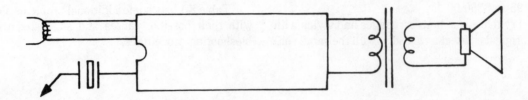

# Servicing the Compact Disc Player

THE COMPACT DISC PLAYER HAS MADE GREAT strides toward wide acceptance in the last few years. Although the disc player is relatively new, adequate disc recordings can now be found in most music and shopping-mall stores (Fig. 9-1). The noise-free discs eliminate the clicks, hiss, wow, and scratching noises that are found in ordinary records. With a laser beam pickup for the music, the discs should last for a very long time if stored properly.

## SPECIFIC MODELS AVAILABLE

There are many different types of disc players on the market. Most have controls for play, reverse, fast-forward, pause, reset, and stop. Others may have numerical pad program selections and music-search buttons. Several have infrared remote controls.

**Onkyo Model DX-200.** This compact disc player has an optical pickup with a semiconductor-laser pickup. The quantization is 16-bit linear with two channels of stereo. The frequency response is 2 Hz to 20 kHz ± 0.5 dB with a dynamic range of

over 96 dB. The total harmonic distortion is less than 0.003% (1 kHz) with channel separation of 93 dB at 1 kHz. The sound-to-noise ratio (S/N) is over 96 dB with unmeasurable wow or flutter. The sound output is 2.0 volts.

**RCA Model MCD-141.** An objective lens drive pickup with an optical-source semiconductor laser with a wavelength of 780 nanometers is found in this compact disc player. There are two channels of audio with a frequency response of 5 Hz to 20 kHz ± 0.5 dB. The signal-to-noise ratio is 90 dB with a dynamic range of 90 dB. The harmonic distortion is less than 0.004% at 1 kHz with channel separation of 90 dB (1 kHz). Wow and flutter are below measurable limits at ± 0.001% w peak distortion. The output signal voltage is 2.0 volts. The signal format has a sampling frequency of 44.1 kHz with a 16-bit linear channel.

**Yamaha Model CD-3.** The optical pickup is a three-beam laser with a compact-disc digital-audio-system format. The frequency response is 3 Hz to 20 kHz with less than .002% of harmonic distortion. The sound-to-noise ratio (S/N) is a flat 98

Fig. 9-1. The modern compact disc player is itself fairly compact. Note how small the compact disc is compared to a regular record. This is a Sanyo Model CP500.

dB with a dynamic range better than 96 dB. Wow and flutter are unmeasurable. Channel separation is better than 90 dB (1 kHz) with a 2.0-volt audio-output signal. A headphone IC output circuit is used with an 8-ohm impedance.

## SAFETY PRECAUTIONS AND THE LASER PICK-UP

Like any electronic product, safety precautions must be taken when working on the compact disc player or before returning the unit to the customer. Always unplug the power cord before removing or reinstalling any component, circuit board, module, or any other instrument assembly. Pull the ac cord while shunting electrolytic capacitors in the circuits. Always clip them in with the power off.

Do not spray chemicals on or near the compact disc player such as tuner sprays used on the TV chassis. Do not use cleaning sprays or cold spray

on LSI or critical IC components. To clean electrical or electronic contacts, use a pipe cleaner, cotton-type stick or comparable swab with 10% acetone and 90% isopropyl alcohol. In most models lubrication of contacts is not required.

Be careful when defeating plug/socket B+ voltage interlocks without checking the schematic diagrams. When replacing ICs or transistors, make sure the heat sinks are in place before firing up the unit. Make sure the ground connection of the test instrument is connected before applying the positive probe of the instrument.

**Laser Warning Labels.** You will find a laser warning label on or close to the laser head pickup assembly. When servicing, do not make eye contact with the laser exit (Fig. 9-2). If it is necessary to confirm laser beam emission, be sure to observe from a distance of more than 30 centimeters from the surface of the objective lens or the optical pick-

Fig. 9-2. The laser head assembly reads the bits and flat spots on the compact disc. The head pickup is located underneath the disc.

up block. Do not stare constantly at the laser beam at any time. Always avoid direct eye exposure to the beam.

In many models, do not attempt to operate the instrument without the disc clamp properly in position. (The disc clamp is found on top of the laser pick-up assembly.) Do not attempt to operate the player and place any foreign object (fingers, mirror, test-probe tools, etc.) between the laser-assembly objective lens and the disc clamp. Do not allow the laser beam to come in contact with the skin. When replacing the laser assembly, make certain the assembly is in the exact spot before attempting to test or operate the player. Do not attempt to adjust the laser gain controls by any method other than those described in the service manual. Misadjustment may increase the laser radiation beyond acceptable limits.

**Precautions in Servicing.** When servicing or making required adjustments, do not put too much pressure on the laser pick-up block assembly. Be careful when placing the PC board chassis on the service bench that no metal objects are under the player with the power cord plugged in. Ground the metal part of the soldering iron with a large test clip to prevent static electricity or leakage from the soldering iron from damaging LSI or IC processors, or use an anti-static soldering device (Fig. 9-3). Be careful not to leave blobs of solder or nuts and bolts inside the chassis. Use a wrist grounding strap when making tests or working on the compact disc player.

Some manufacturers request that a conductive sheet be placed under the disc player while servicing because laser diode and LSI processors are so sensitive to static electricity, surge current, etc. All

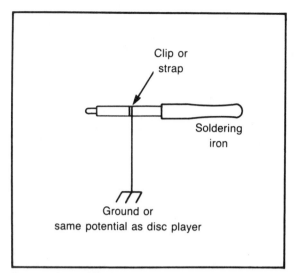

Fig. 9-3. Make sure the soldering iron and all test instruments are grounded when repairing a compact disc player. Critical LSI and microprocessors may be damaged by ungrounded equipment.

test equipment and tools should be so grounded that their dc level is the same as the power source. To prevent static electricity when the air is dry, wear synthetic fiber clothes when servicing a compact disc player.

## TEST INSTRUMENTS FOR THE COMPACT DISC PLAYER

Except for the test disc and laser meter testers, most of the following test instruments are now found upon the electronic technician's service bench.

1. DMM or VTVM
2. Oscilloscope
3. Frequency counter
4. Audio oscillator
5. Test discs
6. Laser power meter

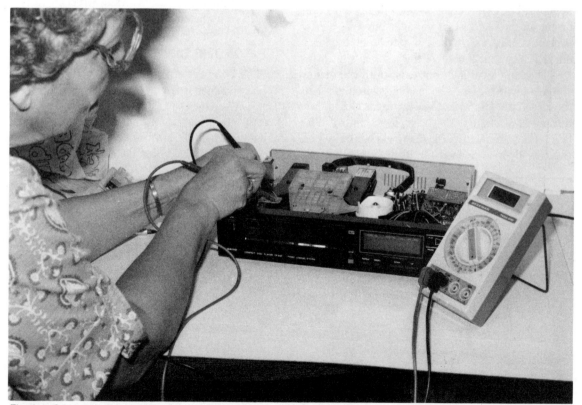

Fig. 9-4. Critical diodes, transistors, and IC components can be checked with a small DMM. Here a disc LED diode is checked with the diode test.

217

The DMM, VTVM, and scope are required test instruments in servicing the compact disc chassis (Fig. 9-4). Critical voltage, resistance, and voltage adjustments are made with either the DMM or VTVM. The scope is a must item for quickly isolating critical waveform test points. The frequency counter is used to check the phase-locked loop (PLL) circuits. For audio-output checks employ the audio oscillator. The test disc is rotated when isolating tests and waveform tests are made. A laser beam meter may be used to check the output and laser beam emission.

## INTERLOCK OPERATION

Since direct eye or skin contact with the laser beam must be avoided, an interlock operation circuit is equipped to prevent unnecessary laser output. The laser output may be controlled by the IC processor or in conjunction with several IC components. The laser output is controlled by injection or cut off of the constant voltage source at the IC processor (Fig. 9-5). When at high level, the laser emits a beam; at low level the laser is shut off.

The high level does not exist until the player is loaded with a disc. The loading switch is set to the closed position when the disc tray is closed, furnishing full voltage to the laser power control. The laser emits a beam after the play switch is on. When the tray door is opened for loading, the loading

switch returns to the low level and cuts off the supply voltage to the laser to protect the operator.

In some models, there is a photo transistor and LED to turn on the IC processor when a disc is not loaded (Fig. 9-6). The LED will provide light to the photo transistor without the disc in position, and the IC101 processor will cut off operation of the laser beam. When the disc is in place, the LED light is cut off from the IC101, and IC101 turns on the laser (Fig. 9-7). The open and close switch and all interlock switches should not be defeated while servicing the compact disc player.

## BLOCK DIAGRAMS

One of the simplest methods to show how the different circuits and components are tied together is the block diagram (Fig. 9-8). The block diagram is very helpful in isolating which section the defective component is in. After isolating the defective section, with the block diagram, proceed to the defective circuit and make critical tests.

## CARE OF THE DISC

The compact disc should last many years if properly handled with correct care. Always hold the discs by the edges so as not to soil the surface with fingerprints or oil from the hand (Fig. 9-9). Be careful not to scratch the surface of the discs, especially on the shiny metal side. Do not attach tape or write

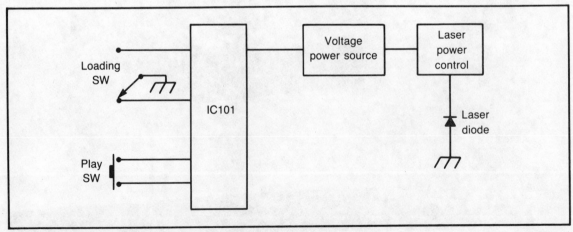

Fig. 9-5. The laser beam is controlled by an interlock system to prevent injury to the operator when loading. At high level the laser diode emits a beam, but at low level it is cut off.

Fig. 9-6. The pen indicates an LED that cuts off the laser beam when no disc is in position to play.

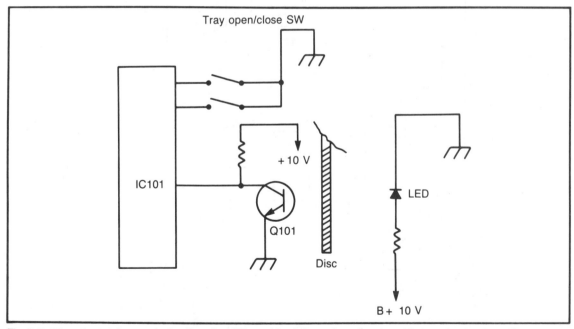

Fig. 9-7. When the tray is open for loading, the LED provides light to photo transistor (Q101), shutting down IC101. When loaded, the disc prevents the LED light from striking Q101 and turning on the laser beam.

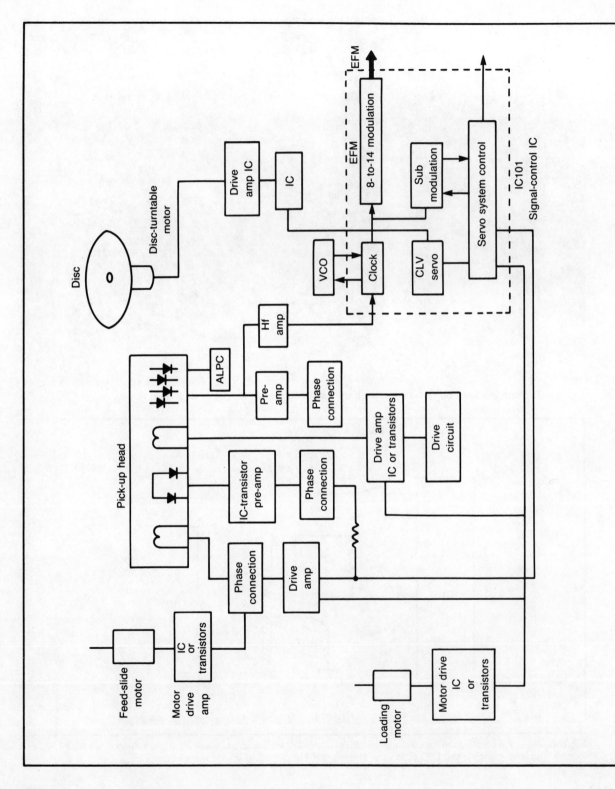

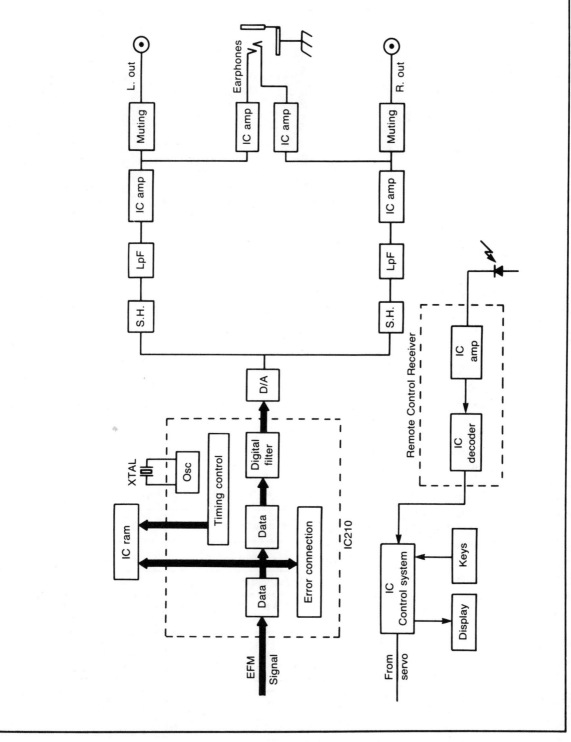

Fig. 9-8. This block diagram shows how all the components are connected together in a compact disc player. Just by looking at the block diagram you may be able to isolate what section is causing the trouble.

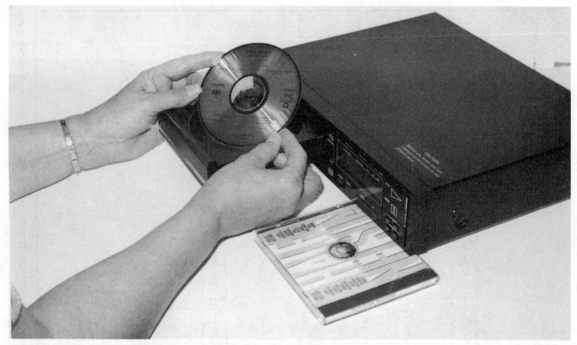

Fig. 9-9. Handle the compact disc at the outside edges when loading. The disc can be grasped with finger in the center hole and thumb on the outside edge for easy handling.

on the label side of the disc. Do not warp or bend the disc. Keep record-cleaning sprays away from the disc. Use water to wipe off the disc and clean outward from the hole in the center. Before playing a disc, wipe off the playing surface with a soft cloth to remove dust or smudges. Remember, the side with the rainbow or shiny reflection is the side containing the audio recording. Insert the disc with the label on top (Fig. 9-10).

Keep each disc in the container it comes in. Never leave a disc in the player. Store the disc in a cabinet away from sunlight, dust, high heat, very cold temperatures, and humidity. Never leave a disc in the car in the summertime. When a disc is brought into the house in the winter, dew may form on the disc. The dew can prevent the laser pickup from reading the correct data contained in the pits on the disc surface. Let the compact disc player warm up for several minutes if moisture or humidity is a problem within the room. A dirty or smudged disc may start to play, misstep, and then shut off.

**Test Discs.** Just about every compact-disc manufacturer has a different test disc for making critical adjustments on the player (Table 9-1). A lot of the players are aligned with a Sony 3YEDS-7 and 4YEDS-18, or with Phillips 410056-2 and 400079-2 test discs. In most cases, adjustments are not needed until the laser pick-up assembly has been replaced.

**Table 9-1. Various Test Discs.**

| Manufacturer | Test disc |
|---|---|
| Akai | AT-751370 |
| Mitsubishi | 350 HS |
| Sylvania & Magnavox | 4822-397-30085<br>4822-397-30096 |
| Phillips | 410056-2<br>400079-2 |
| Quasar | SZZP1014F |
| Sony | 3YEDS-7<br>4YEDS-18 |

Fig. 9-10. Do not put tape or any kind of label on the top or bottom side of the compact disc.

## THE LASER DIODE PICK-UP ASSEMBLY

Laser diodes are so sensitive to static electricity or surge current that they may be damaged or destroyed while working around or installing a new pick-up assembly. Some manufacturers issue warnings about using circuit testers or scope probes on the laser terminals. Others use a voltage test with a resistor in series with the laser for correct laser adjustments. Many recommend that the whole laser diode assembly be replaced instead of the diodes (Fig. 9-11). If the laser diode pick-up assembly must be replaced, all adjustments and alignment procedures should be made on the disc player.

The laser-diode pick-up assembly may consist of one, three, or four diodes. In Fig. 9-12, the laser-diode assembly consists of a four-element photodiode, monitor photo-diode, laser diodes, laser protection diode, focus servo coil, and tracking-servo coil. The laser-diode assembly is mounted under-neath the compact disc and the beam shines upward against the shiny or bottom side of the disc. Do not look at the laser beam if the pressure-lever plate or assembly is removed in servicing with the power switch on. The eyes should be at least 30 centimeters away from the laser beam.

**Laser-Diode Power-Meter Check.** The laser-diode beam may be seen when the disc player is in operation. The radiative output power of the laser may be checked by slipping a laser power meter over the optical lens where the beam hits the compact disc (Table 9-2). This output measurement is made at a distance of 1.8 millimeter from the objective lens surface of the optical or diode pick-up assembly. If the power meter shows less than 0.1 milliwatt, then the laser diode should be replaced. A normal laser diode should be around 0.4 milliwatt. Follow the manufacturer's measurement procedures when using the laser power meter. Ta-

Fig. 9-11. The laser pick-up head emits a beam that strikes the compact disc. The pickup starts at the center of the disc and proceeds toward the outer edge.

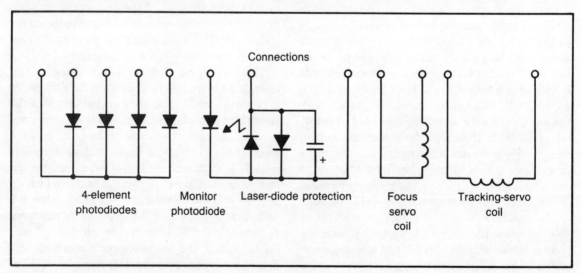

Fig. 9-12. Here twelve different connections are tied to the laser pick-up head. The laser diode pick-up assembly may consist of 1, 3, or 4 laser diodes.

**Table 9-2. Semiconductor Makes of Aluminum (Al)-Gallium (Ga)-Arsenide (As) Laser Diodes.**

| | Mitsubishi Model DP107 Laser diode properties |
|---|---|
| Material | Ga-Al-As |
| Wavelength | 765-795 nm (25° C) |
| Laser Output | Continuous wave max 0.4 mW |
| | Onkyo Model DX200 Laser diode properties |
| Material | Ga As/Ga AlAs |
| Wavelength | 780 nm |
| Laser Output | Continuous wave max 0.4 mW |
| | Yamaha Model DC3 Laser diode properties |
| Material | Ga Al-As |
| Wavelength | 760-800 nm (25° C) |
| Laser Output | Continuous wave max 0.5 mW |

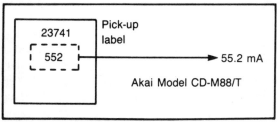

Fig. 9-13. To determine the operating current of the laser pick-up head, check for a pick-up label listing the current value. This Akai Model CD-M88/T has a 55.2 mA operating current.

ble 9-2 shows several makes of laser diodes along with their specifications and maximum rated output.

**Checking the Electric Current.** The laser may be checked by measuring the electric current of the laser diodes. The output current of the laser is usually specified on the labels on the laser pickup. The laser current of an Akai Model CD-M88/T is 55.2 milliampere (Fig. 9-13). The current is checked by connecting a millivoltmeter between test point 2 and test point 3 on the servo PC board (Fig. 9-14). The electric current of the laser equals the voltage divided by 10. If the electric current exceeds 10% of the recommended value (in this case 60.7 milliampere) the laser pickup should be replaced.

In the RCA MCD141 Model disc player, the output current may be checked by measuring the voltage across R209 (Fig. 9-15). The current ranges from 40 to 80 milliamperes (0.48 to 0.96 volts across R209). If the current is over 120 milliampere (1.44 volts across R209), the laser diode may be defective. If the laser current increases rapidly, this indicates the laser assembly should be replaced.

**The Laser Circuit.** The laser pick-up circuit is quite common in all of the disc players (Fig. 9-16). In some models you may find the ALPC transistorized or diode circuit also mounted within the pick-up head assembly. The four laser diodes connect to an rf amplifier and the ALPC diodes to the

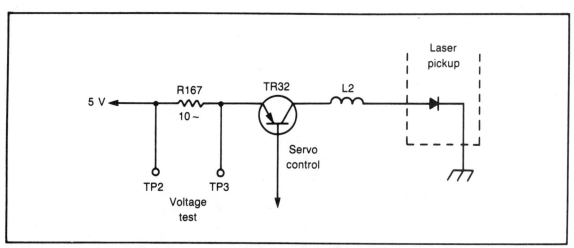

Fig. 9-14. The current may be checked on any compact disc player by measuring the voltage across a small resistor in the emitter circuit. Replace the laser pickup if the current is 10% higher than normal.

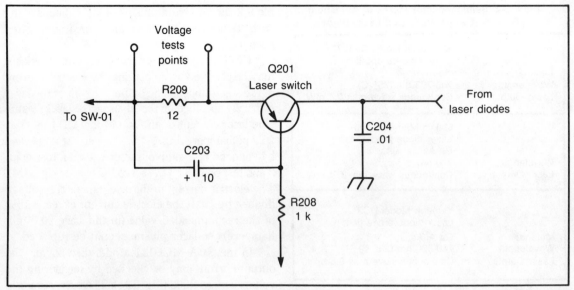

Fig. 9-15. The voltage is measured across R209 in an RCA Model MCD141 to determine the operating current. Most laser diode currents range from 40 to 80 mA.

APC circuit (Fig. 9-17). The focus and tracking coils of the pick-up head feed into a focus-tracking coil drive section.

**Cleaning the Laser Lens.** If the optical lens of the laser pick-up assembly has become dusty, stained, or tarnished, you must use extreme care during cleanup. Use a cotton swab or lens-cleaning paper to wipe off the lens area. The lens may be cleaned with photo-lens cleaning products. The disc drawer, flapper, or disc-changer assembly may have to be removed to get at the optical lens. A dirty optical lens may cause weak or poor sound and poor focus.

**Removing and Replacing the Pick-up Head Assembly.** After determining the laser pickup is defective, the disc drawer, flapper or disc

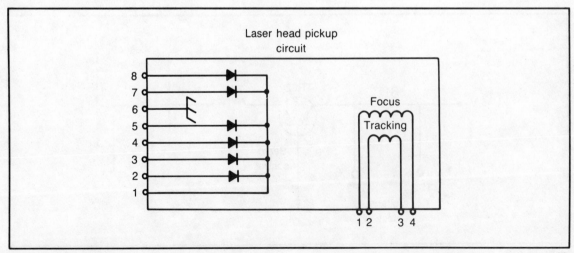

Fig. 9-16. The laser pick-up head assembly is common in all compact disc players. Always replace the laser pickup with the original part number.

226

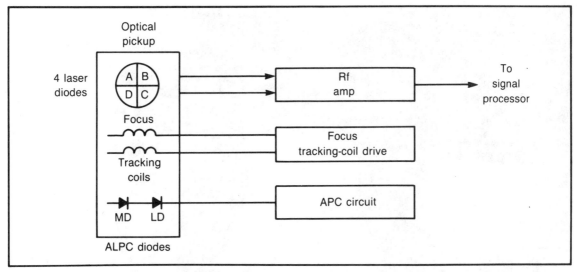

Fig. 9-17. The output from the laser diode is very weak and is amplified by an rf amp. The focus and tracking coils are driven by a focus drive IC or transistors.

changer assembly must be removed in some models (Fig. 9-18). In others, only a few mounting screws hold the pick-up assembly in position. Always follow the manufacturer's removal and replacement procedures. Laser-head pick-up alignment and adjustments must be made after installing a new pickup.

Usually the pick-up assembly replacement comes in a conductive envelope. A conductive rubber protection may be found over the laser diodes. The new head should be kept away from strong magnets or static electricity. The laser connection may have a metal shorting bar or ground clip wire to protect the diodes in shipping and installation. In some models the laser terminals are soldered in a short circuit to protect the diodes. The metal bar or clip must be removed after installation and making wire connections.

## FOCUS ERROR CIRCUIT

The focus error circuit is designed so as to detect changes in the distance to the disc from the pick-up head and makes sure the laser beam spot is kept in proper focus on the reflecting surface of the disc. The beam from the laser pickup must remain focused on the surface to accurately read the information. When the focus on the pits becomes blurred, the focus servo functions to move the objective lens up and down to correct the focus. The error-amp circuit corrects any errors and maintains a perfectly focused beam.

## TRACKING—SERVO CIRCUITS

The laser pickup must track the groove of pits at all times. The tracking-error circuit generates an error signal if the laser beam spots move away from the center of the pits. The error signal is used to ensure that the beam correctly tracks the line of pits. Usually there are three separate beams to monitor the tracking error. The reflected beams are converted into electric signals and fed into a pre-amp or operational amplifier, one for each beam. The tracking-error voltage is fed into a servo IC; in return the correction voltage is tied to the tracking coil in the laser pick-up head (Fig. 9-19). The focus and tracking drive coils with the pick-up motor are controlled by the servo-IC control component.

## SIGNAL CIRCUITS

The extremely weak signal from the pickup is amplified in an IC-pre-amp circuit (Fig. 9-20). In some players the preamplifier is used in conjunction with the servo IC. It is also used for detecting

227

Fig. 9-18. The flapper or disc assembly must be removed to see the laser head assembly.

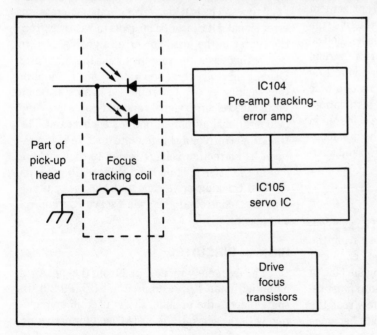

Fig. 9-19. To keep the laser beam pickup in line, a tracking error voltage is fed to a servo IC, focus drive transistors, and the tracking coil. When first turned on, the focus track assembly will move up and down.

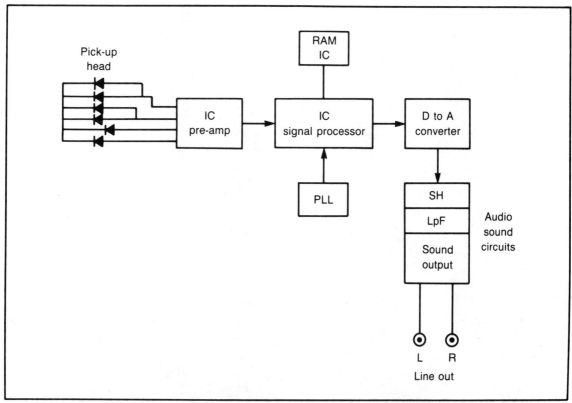

Fig. 9-20. The signal picked up by the laser diodes is fed to the rf amplifier and signal IC processor. The D to A converter changes the signals to audio which are fed to the sample hold and audio-output line jacks.

and correcting errors for focus and tracking. The rf signal may be referred to as an EFM signal in other players (eight-to-fourteen modulation).

The encoded disc is recorded during production with a predetermined sequence of digital audio information due to an interleaving process. The standard interleaving method is determined when the discs are manufactured. During playback the disc accordingly returns the signal to the original state.

When the disc is played back on the player, the digital audio information is restored to a normal sequence by reversing the interleaving process. The process of interleaving is done in the signal processor and RAM IC components. The PLL IC circuit tied to the signal processor basically consists of an 8.6436 MHz VCO (voltage-controlled oscillator).

In some models a digital-filtering circuit is found between the signal processor and D to A con-

verter. The digital-to-analog circuits convert the digital signal to analog information and finally to audio. A sample hold circuit separates the right channel data from the left channel and vice versa. Practically all disc players have a filtering network after the D to A circuits to remove the 44.1-kHz signal for a more natural musical sound to the audio circuits. In some models you may see a muting relay circuit between the audio and audio-output-IC circuits.

## SLIDE (SLED) MOTOR DRIVE CIRCUITS

The slide or feed motor circuit is used to move the pick-up assembly radially or towards the outer edge of the disc, keeping the objective lens constantly in line with the center of the optical axis (Fig. 9-21). The slide feed signal driving the slide motor is obtained by deriving only the dc component from the tracking activator (TAC) signal

229

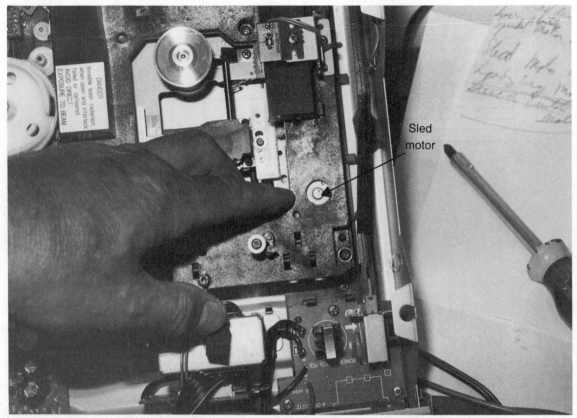

Fig. 9-21. The slide, SLED, or feed motor starts at the center of the disc and moves the head laterally across the disc. The slide motor is controlled by a servo IC and drive transistors.

through a low-pass filter network. Whenever the dc average of the TAC signal exceeds the predetermined level or when the operating position of the objective lens deviates from the center axis by a predetermined value, the slide motor signal sets the feed motor and the pick-up assembly back to its center axis position again (Fig. 9-22). Fast forward and fast rewind of the slide motor can be switched with a large drive voltage to the motor so the pick-up assembly can be moved at high radial disc speed.

## THE DISC OR SPINDLE MOTOR

The disc, turntable, or spindle motor is controlled by a CLV (constant linear velocity) system. The compact disc is recorded at a constant linear velocity so that different speeds are required at the start and end of the disc (Fig. 9-23). Unlike the phonograph, the pickup starts at the center and travels outward to the edge of the disc. The revolutions may vary from 500 RPM to 200 RPM.

The motor speed is controlled by a PLL circuit from the applied signal processor IC (Fig. 9-24). The different signals generated within the disc motor IC are compared with the signal entering for phase correction. The correction signals are applied to the regulated transistor circuits and on to the disc motor terminals. A defective signal processor may cause the disc or turntable motor to operate improperly.

## THE TRAY OR LOADING MOTOR

The tray or loading motor opens the disc tray. After loading the compact disc, the tray motor pulls the disc into loading position (Fig. 9-25). The open and close switches for the disc tray are controlled through the system control microprocessor. In

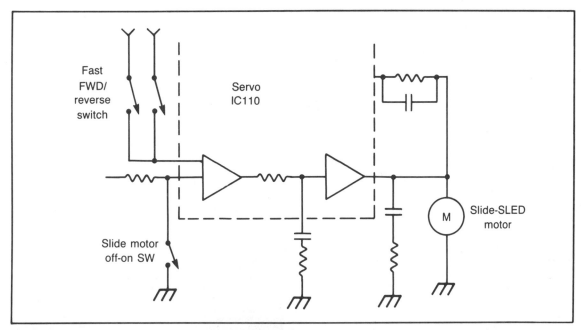

Fig. 9-22. In some models, one IC component may be included in the servo IC to drive the slide or feed motor. In other circuits, the feed signal goes to a pair of drive output transistors.

Fig. 9-23. The disc, turntable, or spindle motor is controlled by a constant linear velocity (CLV) system. The disc may start at 500 RPM and end at only 200 RPM.

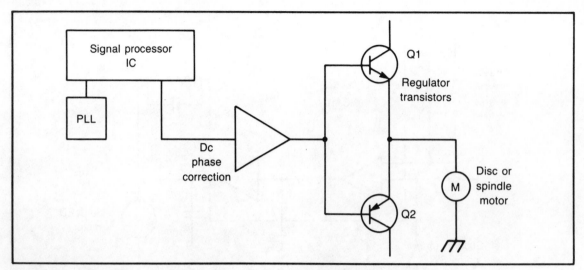

Fig. 9-24. The disc motor is controlled by a signal from the signal IC processor through a phase connection network and is driven by two regulator transistors. In some models, you may find one IC driving the disc motor.

Fig. 9-25. The tray motor loads and unloads the disc with the push of a button. When the tray is out, load the disc and then push the load button.

some models the loading motor is connected directly to pins of the microprocessor, while in others a transistor-regulated system furnishes power to the loading motor (Fig. 9-26). Suspect a defective microprocessor or regulator transistor when the loading motor will not operate.

## REMOVING AND REPLACING SENSITIVE PROCESSORS

After determining the large LSI (large-scale integrated) or CPUs and ICs are defective, use extreme care in removing the sensitive component. A vacuum tool or solder-wick material will remove the excess solder from the many terminals. A flat, mounted IC with terminals all around it may be removed by clipping each lead with a nipper tool. Be careful not to damage the PC wiring.

The pattern surface should be cleaned up with solder wick to remove any remaining leads or solder. Check each terminal lead of the new IC or processor and make sure the leads are straight and flat on surface-mounted components. With some flat ICs, solder flux must be applied for a good solder bond. Apply the flux with a brush to the surface PC wiring. The small ICs may be mounted and held into position with a pair of tweezers. Make sure the IC terminals are in the correct holes in the PC wiring.

Solder each row of IC terminals by slowly moving the soldering iron over the contacts and wiring while applying solder. If the iron is moved too quickly, loose or cold soldering may result. Do not leave the iron too long on each contact. Check each soldered lead with a magnifying glass or lamp. Do not use a tester or multimeter around the sensitive leads to check for a poor connection. Remember, the LSI or control processors may have from 30 to 80 separate terminal connections.

## GENERAL SERVICING PROCEDURES

The defective section of the compact disc player may be located and isolated with scope waveforms and critical voltage measurements. Try to isolate the trouble to the right section with schematic and block diagrams. Then take critical waveforms in the Signal, D to A, and Servo circuits to locate defective components. Compact-disc adjustment procedures may actually help to locate the defective component. Some manufacturers recommend the troubleshooting method of shorting out various service-loop components to ground to locate the defective section.

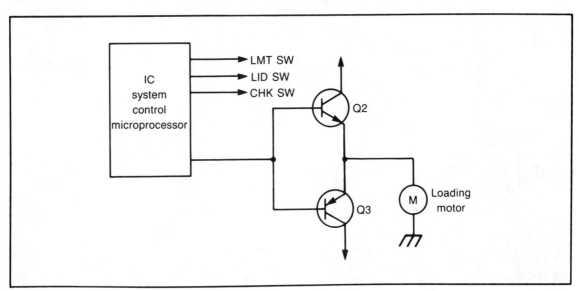

Fig. 9-26. The system control IC feeds a signal to the drive-loading transistors, Q2 and Q3, which makes the loading motor operate in either direction.

Critical voltage and resistance measurements on the IC components after isolating with waveforms may locate a leaky or open IC. Very low supply voltage at the IC terminal may indicate a leaky IC (Fig. 9-27). Accurate voltage tests on the suspected transistor may indicate if transistor is leaky or open. Transistor tests on critical transistors may indicate if the transistor is open or leaky. Continuity tests of motors, relays, and switches may help locate the defective component.

**Power-Supply Voltages.** Many different voltages are supplied by the low-voltage power supply. Since the compact disc player is manufactured for many different countries, you may see 220-240 volts at 50 Hz, 120-220-50 volts at 60 Hz, and 120-volt, 60-Hz power-transformer-primary connections (Fig. 9-28). Most power supplies are fused with a .25 to 1.0 amp replacement fuse.

Several positive and negative dc voltages are fed to the various components. In Fig. 9-29, there are seven different voltage sources supplying the various circuits. Two different bridge rectifier circuits with IC filter networks supply ± 12 volts and a + 5 and − 6 volt source to the servo and decoder circuits. The full-wave diode rectifiers with zener filter networks supply a − 18 volt source to the decoded section. In addition to a − 24 dc volt source, ac voltage is supplied to the control and display circuits.

Beside zener and IC regulation, you may find transistor regulators in many dc sources (Fig. 9-30). In the ± 5 volt sources, two separate regulator transistors with zener-diodes supply voltage to the system servo-control processor. The negative and positive 5-volt source ties into the tray motor drive, pre-amp, D to A converter, sample hold, and audio-output IC circuits. Any one of the circuits may cause a lower 5-volt power source with a leaky IC

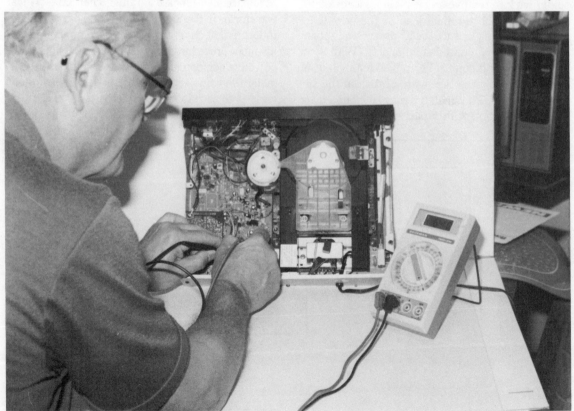

Fig. 9-27. Critical IC and transistor voltages may be taken with the digital multimeter. Voltage and resistance measurements can quickly determine if the IC is leaky.

Fig. 9-28. The small power transformer has several different ac windings at the secondary to enable it to use ac power lines in other countries with different voltages and cycle rates.

or processor in these circuits.

Critical voltage measurements on IC transistors or processors may locate a defective component or low-voltage power source (Fig. 9-31). Suspect a leaky IC or transistor when very low voltage is found at the supply terminal. Remember that within the compact disc many different components may be tied to the same voltage source. Remove the supply voltage source at the low-voltage power supply to isolate each component or trouble in the power source.

If the voltage returns after circuits are clipped from it, remove each component circuit until the leaky one is found. If the voltage source remains very low, suspect a voltage-regulator IC, zener diode, or transistor. Often leaky voltage-regulator components will become very warm and change color. Remove the suspected IC, transistor, or one terminal of the zener diode to check for leakage.

When the voltage source is low to a leaky IC or processor, remove the voltage-supply terminal and note if the voltage returns to above or near normal. Most IC terminals can be removed from the PC wiring with solder wick. Make sure the IC terminal is loose from the wiring. Now measure from the IC terminal to common ground for a leakage test. A very low resistance measurement under 500 ohms indicates a leaky component. Sometimes overloading within the IC or processor may not give a shorted or leaky measurement. Make sure the voltage source is normal to the suspected IC.

In addition to overloaded components, a shorted diode in the full-wave or bridge rectifier circuits may cause the fuse to open. Check the diodes with the diode test of the DMM. Remove one end of the suspected diode for accurate leakage tests. Remove the entire bridge network when one or more diodes are found shorted or open. Note that

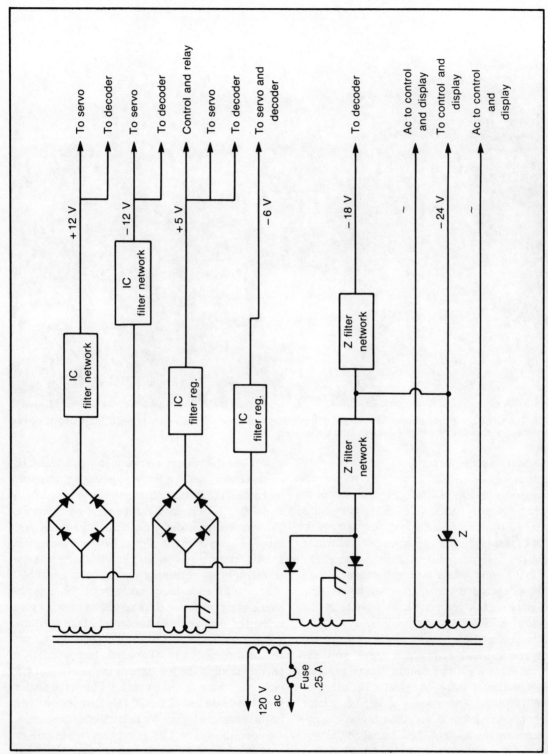

Fig. 9-29. Many different dc voltages are fed to the various circuits in the compact disc player. Many of the ICs and transistors have both positive and negative voltages tied to them for operation.

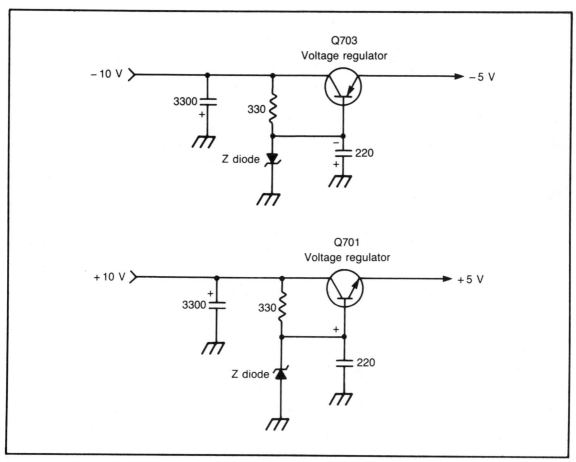

Fig. 9-30. You may find IC, transistor, and zener diode regulation circuits in the low-voltage power supply. Note the large filter input capacitors which provide excellent filtering.

very large filter capacitors are found in the low-voltage dc power circuits.

**Checking the Tray or Loading Motor.** The tray or loading motor may operate from a transistor or IC motor-drive circuit connected to the system servo-control processor (Fig. 9-32). When the tray will not open or close, check the negative and positive supply voltage at the loading drive transistors. A −7 volts should be found at the motor or emitter terminals of the drive transistors when it is open. When the tray is closed, a +7 volts should be measured. If not, check the voltage at the servo controller or control-system-IC terminal controlling the drive transistors or IC. A defective controller or control system IC may cause improper voltages at the base terminal of the motor-drive

transistors. Suspect a defective loading motor if the negative and positive voltages at the drive motor terminals are correct. The resistance of a tray motor should be around 22 ohms. Check for proper adjustments of the rotating disc so that the flapper closes fully over the compact disc (Fig. 9-33).

**Slide, Feed, or Sled Motor Tests.** The slide motor is controlled somewhat like the loading motor from a pair of slide-motor-drive transistors and a slide servo IC. The IC-slide-servo OP IC may be added in some units between the large servo processor and slide-drive motor transistors (Fig. 9-34). A positive and negative 10 volts is applied to the collector terminal of the slide or feed drive transistors.

With the disc rotating, check the voltage at the

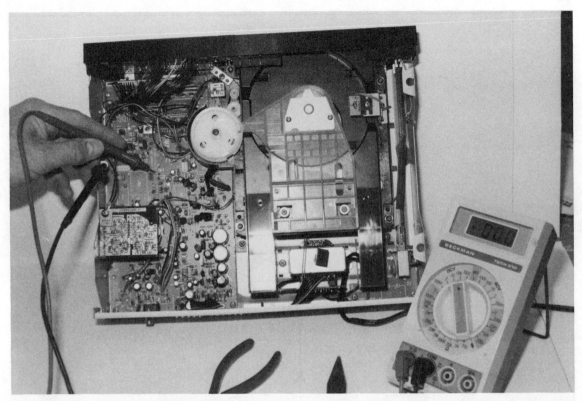

Fig. 9-31. Checking the output voltages of the low voltage power supply may determine if the correct voltage is being fed to the many circuits. A very low voltage measurement may indicate a shorted component or defective power source.

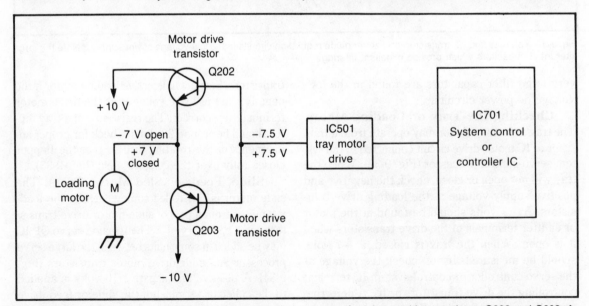

Fig. 9-32. The normal operating voltages of the tray loading motor are found upon drive transistors Q202 and Q203. A −7 volts is applied to the motor terminals when the tray is open and +7 volts with the tray closed.

238

Fig. 9-33. The rotating disc must let the flapper load down over the disc after loading. Check this adjustment if the flapper does not move or close downward.

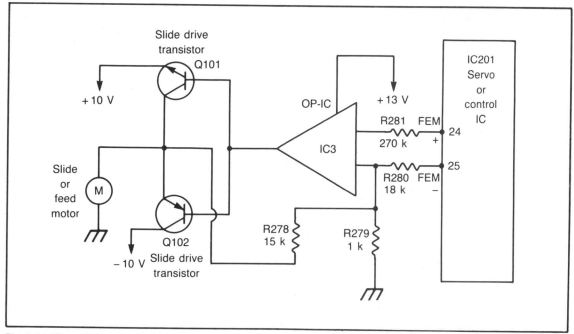

Fig. 9-34. The variable speed of the slide or feed motor is controlled by the servo and OP IC3 along with slide drive transistors Q101 and Q102. Check the ± 10-volt supply and voltage at the motor terminals when it does not operate correctly.

slide-motor terminals. Very low or no voltage may indicate improper feed signal or defective drive transistors. Check the positive and negative 10 volts at the transistor drive terminals. The normal emitter voltage should be around +3.5 volts. No or very low supply voltage may indicate a defective 10-volt power source. Suspect a defective motor if correct emitter voltage is found at drive transistors.

Go to the servo IC and check for correct voltage and waveforms on terminals related to the sled-motor circuits. Inspect the sled on/off and reset switch for no motor action. Check the slide-motor off-set adjustments and note if the motor responds. If the offset adjustments are not correct, the start of the disc may not read the program information properly. Replace the defective servo IC when waveform signals into the IC are normal but there is no feed-motor control.

**Troubleshooting the Disc, Turntable or Spindle Motor.** Rotation of the disc indicates the turntable motor is operating. Remember that the disc motor speed changes as it rotates. The servo-drive circuits may operate from two drive transis-

tors or from a drive IC component (Fig. 9-35). For no turntable rotation, check for a negative and positive 10 volts at the power drive transistor. Check the power-supply source if low or no collector voltage is found. If the turntable motor keeps rotating and will not stop, suspect a leaky or open drive transistor or defective drive IC. Check for +6 volts at the emitter terminal of the drive transistor if the motor will not start. If the correct voltage is present, suspect a defective spindle motor.

The turntable motor should stop immediately when the stop mode is set. Check for a −6 volts at the transistor emitters in stop mode. If incorrect or no voltage is present at the output transistors, check the voltage at the servo drive IC. Suspect a defective servo or control IC with no stop action. Remember that a defective signal-processing IC may cause failure in the disc motor-control circuits. First check the turntable motor and servo control ICs before tackling the signal-processing circuits.

**Checking the Focus Servo Section.** Does the pick-up lens move up and down when the disc platter is closed by pressing the open/close button?

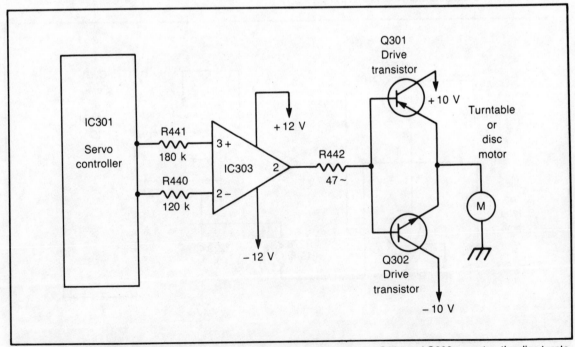

Fig. 9-35. A signal from servo controller IC301 fed to IC303 and drive transistors Q301 and Q302 operates the disc turntable motor. Scope the signal at IC301 and the voltage on IC303, Q301, and Q302 if the disc does not rotate properly.

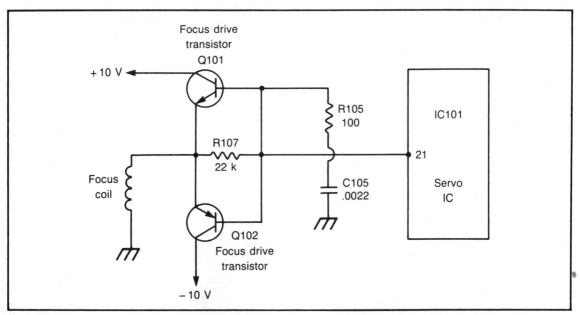

Fig. 9-36. The signal from servo IC101 to the focus drive transistor controls the focusing of the laser beam. Voltage measurements on Q101 and Q102 and a continuity check of the focus coil winding may locate the defective component.

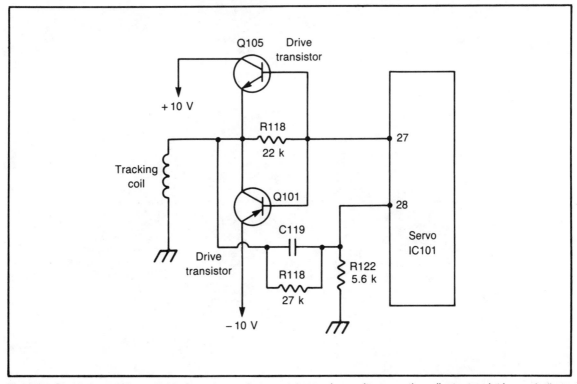

Fig. 9-37. Check the tracking-coil drive transistors, Q101 and Q105. Low voltages on the collector terminals may indicate a leaky drive transistor.

Fig. 9-38. Check for correct voltages and waveforms at servo IC101 when the slide or feed coil will not track properly. In some circuits, the drive output section may be inside the servo-control IC.

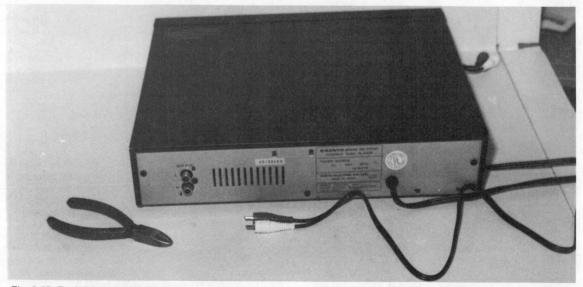

Fig. 9-39. Each line output jack audio signal may be checked with the external audio amp. Determine if only one channel is distorted and weak or if it is in both channels.

Check the power-supply voltages supplied to the collector terminals of Q101 and Q102 (Fig. 9-36). Note if the output waveform of focus zero-cross is found at pin 21 of servo IC101. Check servo output transistors if signal is present. Suspect a defective servo IC if there is no focus and there is a good signal applied to the focus coil drive circuits.

If the optical pickup does not move up and down when first turned on with a disc, suspect a defective focus coil assembly. Take a resistance measurement of the focus coil. The resistance should be under 10 ohms. Make a complete focus servo adjustment.

**Troubleshooting the Tracking-Servo Section.** The focus and tracking servo use the laser beam as a source of error signal. Check for an OK signal at servo IC101. In some players a servo drive IC or two transistors drive the tracking coil (Fig. 9-37). Measure the voltage on both collectors of Q105 and Q106. Check the output transistors if there is abnormal supply voltage. Scope terminals 27 and 28 of servo IC101 if the output drive circuits are normal.

Next make the tracking adjustments if the output drive circuits are normal. Note if the optical pickup moves to the inside edge of the disc, indicating the pick-up motor and servo IC is normal. If not, check the various tracking pin terminals on the servo IC101 for correct voltage and waveforms (Fig. 9-38). If signal is coming into the servo IC but is not applied to the tracking-coil drive circuits, replace IC101.

**Troubleshooting Audio Circuits.** If there is sound from the left but no sound from the right channel, suspect a defective sound IC312 in the right channel (Fig. 9-39). Check the muting circuit or relay if one is found in the right channel. No sound in both channels may be signal-traced from the D to A IC output terminals. Scope the input signal of the D to A IC and if present, suspect a defec-

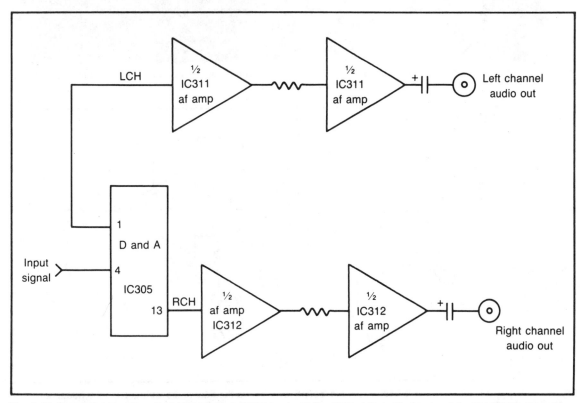

Fig. 9-40. Scope the input terminal of the D to A IC305 to check the EFM signal. Suspect a defective IC305 when there is no audio output signal in either channel but the input signal from the signal processor is correct.

243

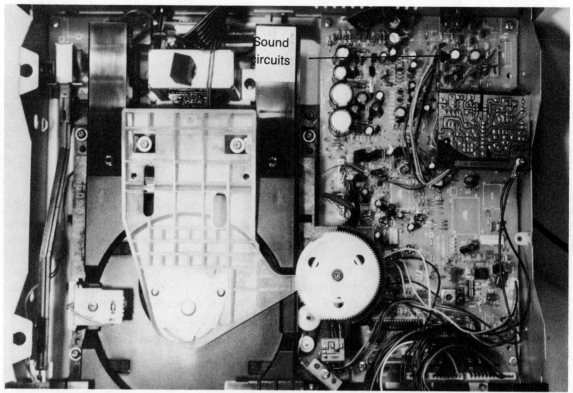

Fig. 9-41. Some models have headphone capability. Check the phone output IC when normal sound is found at both channel line output jacks. Locate the sound circuit on the PC board.

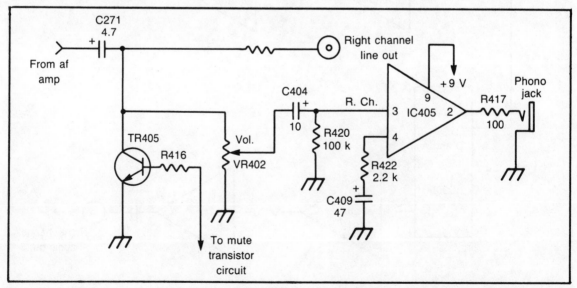

Fig. 9-42. Usually a volume control is used to set the sound level before the final audio output IC in the headphone circuits. Critical voltage measurements on IC405 may indicate a leaky output transistor that could cause distortion in one or both headphones.

tive IC (Fig. 9-40). Take accurate voltage and resistance measurements on IC305.

Headphone operation is found in some compact disc players. Check the phone output jack when one channel is noisy, erratic, or dead (Fig. 9-41). Usually the headphone audio is tapped after the output coupling capacitor and fed to an isolation transistor stage. A gain or volume control is found in the input circuit of the audio output IC.

Suspect a defective headphone output IC when sound is found in both channels at the line output terminals and no headphone audio. Take critical voltage and resistance measurements to determine if IC405 is leaky (Fig. 9-42). Note if both or only one channel is defective. The sound may be signal-traced with the external audio amp from the line output signal to the headphone jacks.

# Chapter 10

# Servicing Auto
# Compact Disc Players

WHEN SERVICING THE AUTO CD PLAYER, YOU will find that most parts fit tightly together and the whole player is quite small compared to the regular table-top compact disc player. Several connecting cables may be found attached to the CD player. Besides the battery power lead, a relay box control and ac power cable are found. Another cable may connect to the dc to dc converter. The input DIN and output DIN connector cables are attached to the rear panel.

When servicing from a regulated power supply, apply 14.4 Vdc. Most auto compact disc players pull around 2 amps of current during loading and eject of the disc. In playback mode, the current drain may vary from 800 mA to 1.5 amps of current. All American CD players operate with a negative ground system (Fig. 10-1).

## SPECIFIC MODELS AVAILABLE

Today there are several auto disc players being manufactured. In addition to regular features of bass, tone, and treble controls, the compact disc

player may have music search, music scan, repeat, pause, fast forward, reverse, and eject. I will discuss three different auto CD players with disc player specifications.

**Alpine/Luxman Model 5900.** This compact disc player has an optical pickup with a semiconductor laser at 780 nanometers. The spindle speed is standard at 200 RPM to 500 RPM (CLU). The digital to analog conversion is a 16-bit linear type with a two-channel audio-frequency response of 5 to 20 kHz ± 3 dB. The harmonic distortion is less than 0.008% (1 kHz) with a dynamic range of 90 dB (1 kHz) at a signal-to-noise ratio of 85 dB. The wow and flutter is below measurable limits. The quantization system is a 16-bit linear channel with a sampling frequency of 44.1 kHz. The player operates from a 14-volt battery with a playback current drain of 1.2 amps.

**Sony Model CDX-5.** This compact-disc digital audio system has a semiconductor laser assembly operating at 780 NM. The spindle speed varies from 200 RPM to 500 RPM (CLV). A Sony super strategy cross interleave read Solomon code is used

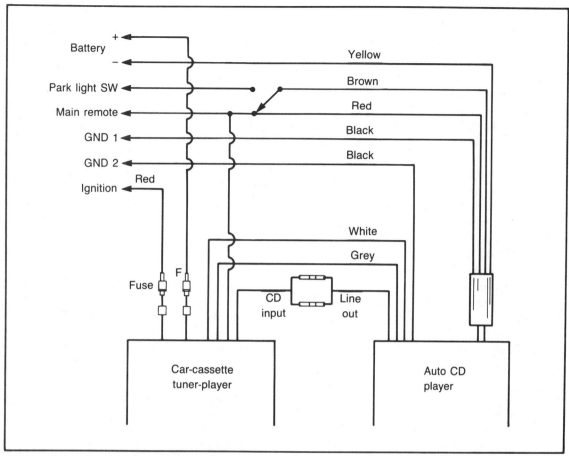

Fig. 10-1. Battery and CD input connections to a cassette receiver/tuner. The power switch of the cassette receiver controls the on/off switch of the compact disc player.

with error correction. The digital to analog 16-bit linear audio has two channels with a frequency response of 5 to 50 kHz ± 1.0 dB. The harmonic distortion is less than 0.005% (l kHz) with a dynamic range and signal-to-noise ratio of 90 dB. Channel separation is 85 dB with below measurable limit of wow and flutter. The quantization is a 16-bit linear channel with a sampling frequency of 44.1 kHz and modulation system of EFM. The player operates from the car battery with a playback drain of 840 mA and a 2-amp load driving disc loading or eject. The player operates from a negative ground system.

**Yamaha Model YCD-1000.** This compact disc player has a CD cartridge system with a laser wavelength of from 760 to 800 nanometers. The

frequency response is 20 to 20 kHz + 0/ – 3 dB with harmonic distortion less than 0.05% (1 kHz). The dynamic range is 92 dB with unmeasurable wow or flutter. A channel separation is 75 dB (1 kHz) with a 2-volt output at 330 ohms impedance. The operating voltage is 14.4 volts dc with from 10.8 to 16 volts allowable and a negative ground system with 14 watts power consumption. The player comes with a separate power unit measuring 5½ × 1⅜ × 2 inches.

## SAFETY PRECAUTIONS AND THE LASER PICK-UP ASSEMBLY

As with any compact disc player, extreme care must be exercised in handling or working around the laser optical pick-up and LSI processors. The laser diode in the optical pick-up block may suffer electrostatic breakdown because of the potential difference created by the charged electrostatic load, clothes, and the human body. Place a conductive sheet on the work bench so that the auto CD chassis touches the sheet. (This makes the player the same potential as the conductive sheet.)

The human body should be grounded with a wrist-strap to a grounded work table and conductive sheet. The strap works to drain away the static electricity buildup on the human body. Be careful not to let your clothes touch the laser assembly. A good conductive sheet may be of copper material which is grounded. All test equipment should be grounded to the copper sheet of material. The flexible laser board is easily damaged and should be handled with care.

**Eye Protection.** When servicing, do not approach the laser beam too closely with the eyes . The laser may be checked visually to make sure that it is working, but keep at least 30 centimeters from the laser or optical pick-up block. Do not stare constantly at the laser beam. Laser warning labels are found on the protective housing and interlock defeat label inside the top cover.

**Interlock Protection.** The car compact disc player reads the disc signals by laser detection. To avoid direct skin or eye contact, most auto CD players are equipped with an interlock to prevent the unnecessary laser output.

The laser outputs may be controlled by cutting off the voltage to the laser diode with an IC component (Fig. 10-2). When pin 30 is in H (high) level, the laser emits the beam; when it is in L (low) level, the laser does not emit the beam. Pin 30 is set in H level when the unit is loaded with the disc, and in low level with the disc tray out for loading. Be careful of the laser beam when overriding or shorting out the interlock switch.

## THE LASER DIODE

The laser-diode assembly is a delicate optical pick-up block and should be handled with care. The optical or lens assembly should be kept clean. Wipe off all dirt and dust from the lens assembly. The laser optical pick-up block should not be taken apart. If there is a breakdown with the diodes or APC circuits, the entire optical pick-up block should be replaced.

If the pick-up laser is suspected of having weak or poor reception, clean up the lens area. Next check the output voltage or current from the laser diodes. Do not attach meters or scopes directly to the laser assembly. Check the current label for correct operating current. The correct current for a Sony Model CDX-5 is shown in Fig. 10-3.

To check the laser emission, push the power play loading end switch terminals together to obtain play mode. Observe the objective lens and confirm that the laser diode is emitting light. At this

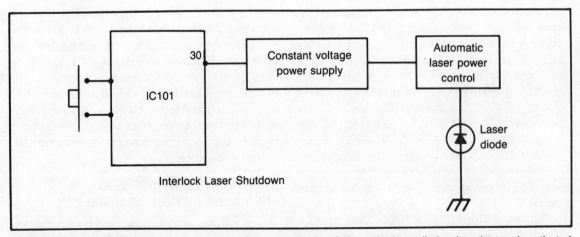

Fig. 10-2. In some models, the power-supply voltage is lowered by IC101 to the laser diode when the tray is activated for loading. Full voltage is applied to the laser control circuit after the disc is loaded and is ready to play.

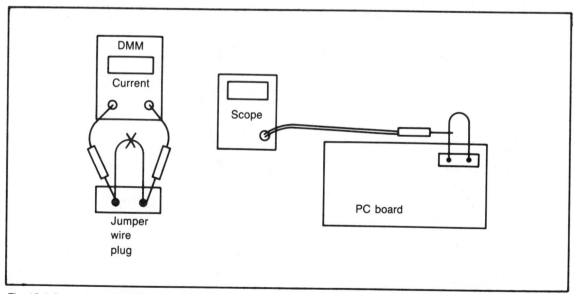

Fig. 10-3. The laser power label most auto compact disc players gives the operating current of the laser. Here the last three numbers in a Sony CDX-5 model signify 49.9 mA.

Sony
laser power
0.4 mW
KSS-110B
07740
0138- | 499 |
Label
Current value is
49.9 mA

time the laser diode goes on for a few seconds due to focus search. If not, the APC or FOP circuits are defective.

In the Sony Model CDX-5, a jumper wire is provided to check the laser current with a VOM or oscilloscope. Connect the current probe of the scope to the jumper wire or cut it and connect the VOM across the jumper wire (Fig. 10-4). Note if the milliampere measurement is within 60 mils. Remember that the current increases when temperature rises and decreases when it drops. If the current value has increased greatly, above 60 mils, the laser-diode assembly must be replaced. When the current is less than 49.9 mils, suspect a defective APC circuit. Follow the manufacturer's laser-diode current procedures.

## BLOCK DIAGRAMS

A quick look at the block diagram may determine what section is defective in the compact disc player (Fig. 10-5). Since the wiring schematic is quite large, use the block diagram to first locate the suspected section. Isolating the defective section on the block diagram may help to locate the section on the wiring schematic. After locating the possible defective sections, check the schematic

DMM
Current
Scope
PC board
Jumper
wire
plug

Fig. 10-4. In most compact disc players, the laser current is checked across a resistor from the laser circuit to the rf amp. A jumper wire may be used to check the current with the scope or DMM in the Sony Model CDX-5.

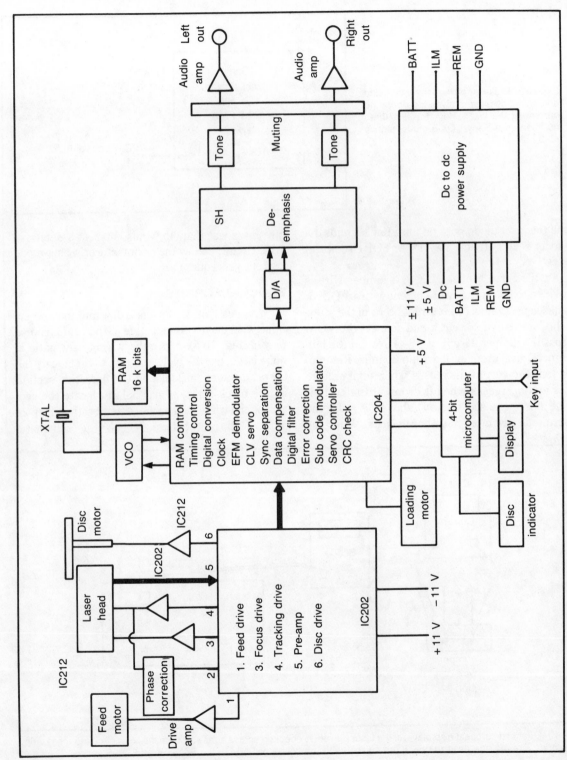

Fig. 10-5. Block diagram of a typical auto compact disc player.

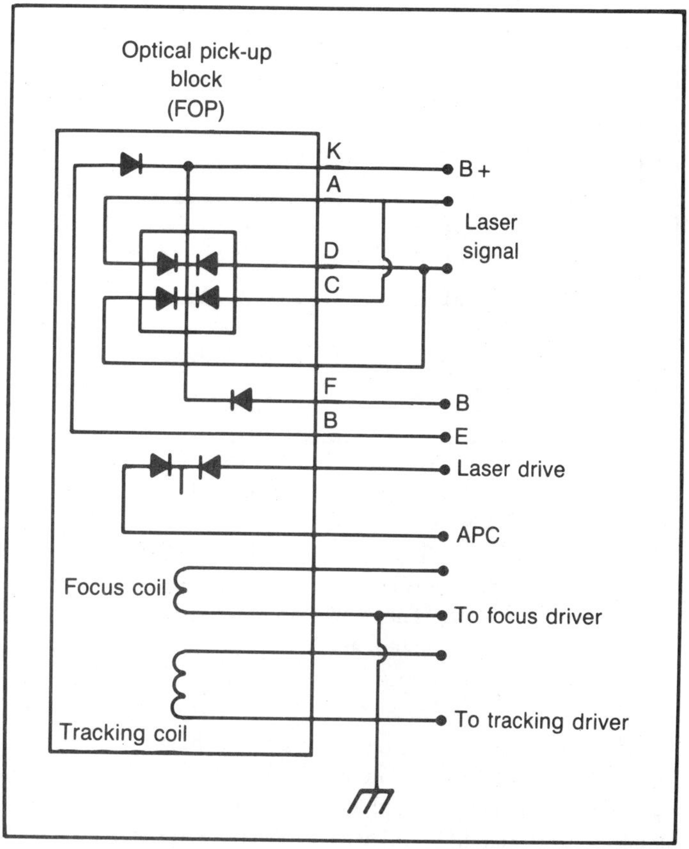

Fig. 10-6. The laser diodes are contained in the optical pickup block with APC diodes, tracking, and focus coils. When any one component becomes defective, replace the entire optical block assembly.

diagram. Now correct waveforms and voltage measurements will help locate the defective component.

## THE TEST DISC

The same test discs used for the table-top compact disc player are used for electrical and electronic adjustments in the auto disc players. All rf offset, focus offset, tracking offset, tracking gain, and focus gain adjustments are made with the YEDS-1 disc. Use the scope as the indicating device.

## REPLACING THE
## OPTICAL BLOCK ASSEMBLY

After determining that the laser output is pulling too much current or is defective, replace the entire optical-block assembly. Both top and bottom covers of the auto disc player must be removed to get at the laser assembly and mounting screws. Locate the optical-pickup block-mounting screws. Usually four or five screws hold the assembly in position. Sometimes the pick-up block assembly must be tilted to remove it from the player (Fig. 10-6).

Unplug the cable to the pick-up block assembly or remove the connecting wires. Mark down all color-coded wires attached to the laser optical assembly. Install the new pick-up block assembly in reverse order. Tip the assembly so it will slide into the original mounting spot. Secure the mounting screws. Replace connecting cable and wires. Laser-head pick-up alignment and adjustments should be made after installing a new pickup.

## CRITICAL CPU PROCESSORS

In many of the auto CD players, a master CPU

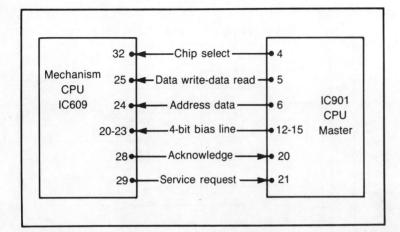

Mechanism CPU IC609

32 ●——Chip select———● 4
25 ●——Data write-data read——● 5
24 ●——Address data———● 6
20-23 ●——4-bit bias line———● 12-15
28 ●——Acknowledge———▶● 20
29 ●——Service request——▶● 21

IC901 CPU Master

Fig. 10-7. The most important IC processors in the auto disc player are the master and mechanism CPU chips. The master CPU (IC901) controls most of the mechanism CPU (IC609) functions.

microprocessor controls the system while another one controls the mechanism (Fig. 10-7). The master CPU (IC901) communicates with the mechanism CPU (IC609) to get the information necessary to control the system. These are the most critical IC components in the system and should be treated with kid gloves, so to speak.

The chip select (CS) is sent out from the master (IC901) to command the mechanism, IC609, from pins 4 to pins 32. The data (DW/DR) data read/data write is the signal which indicates if the master (IC901) should read or write the data of the mechanism (IC609). A/D, or address data, indicates if the signal on the bias line is an address signal or a data signal. The I/O bias is a 4-bit bias line between the master IC and the mechanism IC CPU. The acknowledgement signal indicates to the master that the mechanism CPU has received a CS signal and has caused out the command. The service request signal indicates to the master CPU that the data should be read out because a change has occurred.

## CRITICAL IC COMPONENTS

In addition to the optical pick-up head assembly, there are many IC processors which must be handled with care not only in testing, but also during removal and replacement of the many terminal leads attached to the chip. Some may have up to 80 different terminal connections. After the defective IC has been located with waveform, adjustment tests, and voltage measurements, be care-

ful not to damage the PC wiring while removing the processor.

There are many different IC chip devices found in the auto compact disc player. Some players have up to five different kinds of chip or ICs. The chips may consist of a thick film chip resistor, multilayer ceramic-chip capacitor, mini-mold chip transistor, mini-mold chip diode, and mini-mold chip IC.

Since the four kinds of chip devices have a similar shape and size, it is quite difficult to identify them at a glance. The resistor chip has a number for identification, while the ceramic capacitor has a line at the top with a letter of the alphabet and a number (Fig. 10-8). Transistors and diodes may be identified with a number and a letter. By referring to the manufacturers cross reference table, the transistor or diode may be identified. Each manufacturer may have their own types of transistors within the circuitry of the compact disc player.

**Handling the Chips.** These chip devices are not heat-proof or shock-proof. Use caution when handling them. Remember that these chips are made up of ceramic or plastic molded material. Install the chip flat on the printed circuit board. Do not apply unnecessary stress to the chip device. Do not push down on the chip terminals with the soldering iron because you may crack the chip. Solder each terminal individually. Use a low-wattage iron (30 watts) while soldering IC terminals. The battery-operated iron is ideal for IC replacement. Soldering should be done quickly. Chip devices cannot withstand rapid heating or cooling. Do not heat the chip itself; just heat the terminals of the chip device.

To remove the defective chip, use a forked iron tip. Heat the chip device with the forked tip and slide. Regular IC components may be removed with solder-wick material and soldering iron. Place the mesh wick over the IC terminals and suck up all the excess solder. After removing the IC chip, suck up the remaining solder with solderwick. Be careful not to damage the very small PC wiring.

## THE DC-TO-DC CONVERTER

The dc-to-dc converter has a battery input voltage of 14.3 volts dc with a regulated 14-volt dc output (Fig. 10-9). Q1 and Q2 along with IC101 provide a waveform at the large primary winding of T101. The positive and negative 14-volt source is rectified from a bridge circuit. The 30-volt supply has full rectification with D3 and D4. The −8.2- and +8.4-volt supply is rectified from a bridge circuit of D5, D6, D7, and D8.

These respective voltage sources are fed to transistor and zener-diode regulators. The 8-volt dc supply is regulated by Q523 and Q524 to a +5.2- and −5.2-volt source (Fig. 10-10). The Q527 and Q530 voltage regulator supply the +5-volt source. The +13.5 and +30 volt sources are not regulated and are taken directly from the rectifying diodes.

If the dc-to-dc converter is to be checked individually without a load, the converter must be loaded down with dummy load resistors. For example, the 30-volt source should have a resistance load of approximately 6.2 kilohms at ¼ watt. The 13.5-volt source should have a 2.7-kilohm, ¼-watt resistor and the 8-volt source a 1.6-kilohm, ¼-watt resistive load.

The dc to dc converter unit may be tested by taking voltage output measurements and waveform tests. Check the voltage output source at the bridge and full-wave rectifiers. If there is low or no voltage, suspect Q1, Q2, and IC1. Check the square-wave waveform at the collector terminals of Q1 and Q2. No waveform may indicate a defective transistor or IC. Measure the voltage at the emitter and base terminals of Q1 and Q2. A leaky transistor or IC may prevent the circuit from oscillating.

Remove either transistor from the circuit if in-circuit tests indicate leakage. Check for leakage after they are removed. Take critical voltage measurements on IC1, at pin numbers 1, 11, and 12 for correct voltage. Very low voltage at pins 1 and 11 may indicate a leaky IC1. Check D1 and D2 in the circuit with the diode test of the DMM.

Very low voltage and overheating of Q1 and Q2 may be caused by overloading in the voltage source or components tied to them. Leaky bridge and full-wave rectifiers in the secondary circuit of T101 may produce low or no voltage source. First check the rectifier diodes in the circuit with the diode test and remove for a good leakage test. A shorted bridge

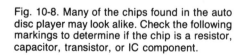

Fig. 10-8. Many of the chips found in the auto disc player may look alike. Check the following markings to determine if the chip is a resistor, capacitor, transistor, or IC component.

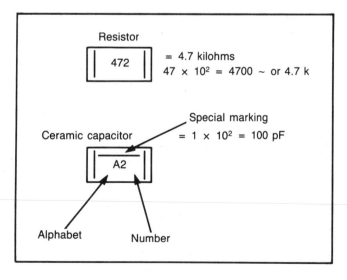

Resistor

472

= 4.7 kilohms
$47 \times 10^2 = 4700 \sim$ or 4.7 k

Ceramic capacitor

Special marking
$= 1 \times 10^2 = 100$ pF

A2

Alphabet      Number

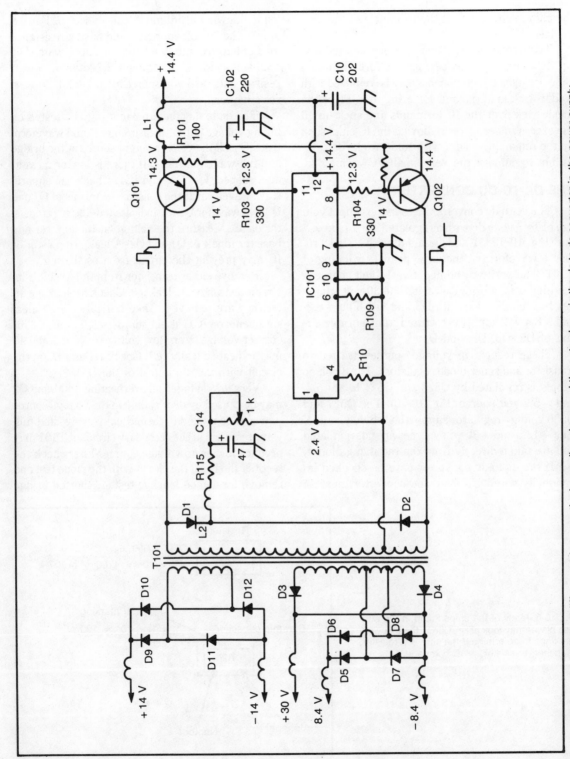

Fig 10-9. One of the biggest differences between the home disc player and the auto player is the dc-to-dc converter in the power supply.

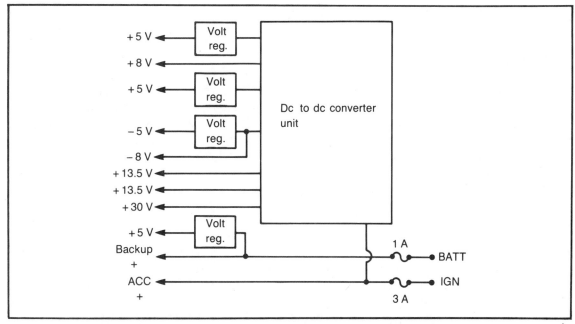

Fig. 10-10. Block diagram of the dc-to-dc power supply, indicating the many voltages developed here. Transistor and zener diodes are found in the positive and negative 5 and 8 voltage sources.

or full-wave rectifier in the secondary of T1 may shut down the dc-to-dc converter unit.

Improper voltage at the different output voltage sources may be caused by a component loading down the voltage source. Check each voltage-regulator transistor and zener diodes for leakage. Measure the voltage at the collector and emitter terminals to locate the defective source and component. Voltage-regulator transistors and zener diodes have a tendency to run warm and become leaky. Usually there is no measurable output volt-

age from an open regulator power transistor. The leaky zener diode may lower the output voltage source. If in doubt, remove one diode lead or the collector terminal of the regulator transistors for a leakage test.

## THE LOADING MOTOR

The tray motor pushes the loading tray out and takes the disc in to load over the optical pick-up assembly. The loading or tray motor may work directly from a pair of transistors or IC circuits. The

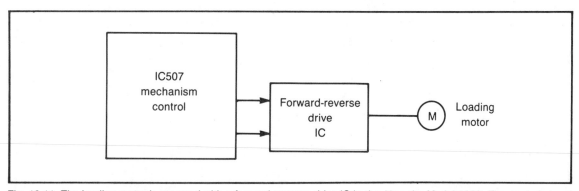

Fig. 10-11. The loading motor is powered with a forward-reverse drive IC in the Yamaha Model 5900. The control signal fed to the drive IC507 comes from Mechanism Control IC508.

signal controlling the loading motor is controlled by the mechanism control IC in some models (Fig. 10-11). Forward and reverse rotation is controlled by the IC driver.

Check the voltage applied to the loading-motor terminals. These voltages may be quite low because only 3.6 volts is applied to the driver IC in many models. Remove the motor lead and check for continuity. A low resistance usually indicates that the motor is good. Check the loading-motor voltage that supplies the signal to the driver IC at the mechanism IC. No or very low voltage may indicate a defective mechanism IC or leaky driver IC. Do not overlook a jammed or binding tray assembly. A bent or poor contact on an end-detector switch may prevent the tray from working.

Sometimes when the disc is inserted upside down in the player and the open/close switch is pressed, the disc tray automatically comes out within a few seconds and will not play in some models. A very dirty disc with dust, fingerprints, food particles, etc., may cause this problem. Be sure to check the disc for defects or try another disc before tearing into the disc player.

## SLED MOTOR

The SLED motor may be controlled with a signal from the servo-focus-tracking-SLED IC and fed to SLED amp and driver output transistors (Fig. 10-12). The positive and negative motor leads may be controlled by SLED driver stages. Check the voltage across the motor terminals to determine if the driver stages are working. If not, test the output transistors for leakage or open conditions. Measure the motor resistance with one lead removed from the circuit. Replace the motor if the winding is open. Check the voltage and signal at the servo-IC terminals feeding the SLED motor drive circuits. Make sure the SLED on/off switch terminals are normal.

The SLED motor may be checked by applying an external 3-volt dc source to the windings. Re-

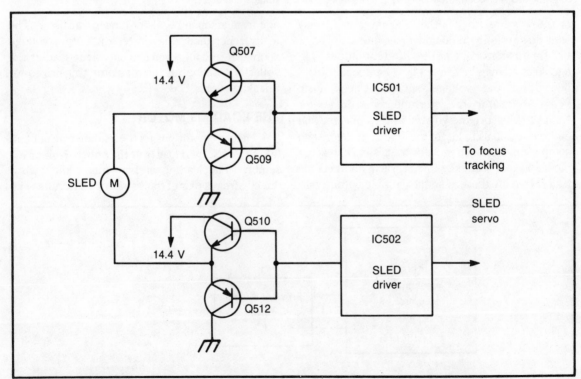

Fig. 10-12. The SLED or feed motor is controlled by a SLED driver transistor. In some models, the control signal from the Focus/Tracking/SLED Servo IC feeds the signal via the SLED amp IC and SLED driver transistor.

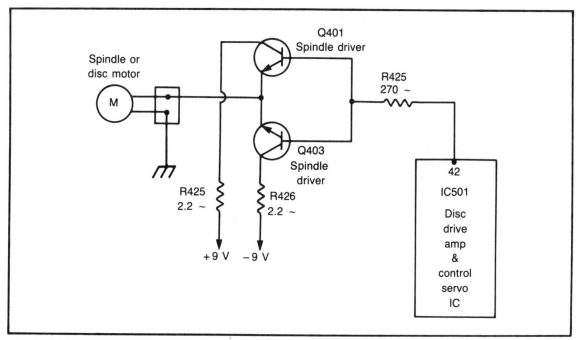

Fig. 10-13. The spindle, disc, or turntable motor may be controlled by the Control/Servo IC to a pair of output drive transistors. Check for proper voltage at the transistors and disc motor when the motor will not rotate.

move one terminal and temporarily clip the positive lead to the motor. The motor should move the FOP assembly. If the SLED assembly is at one end, reverse the 3-volt polarity to the motor. The current-driving movement may vary from 120 to 150 milliamps. A 1½-volt dc source should operate the motor very smoothly between the outer and inside circumference of the geared movement.

## THE DISC MOTOR

The turntable or disc motor is a very sensitive device which is controlled from the CLV servo amp and CLV (constant linear velocity) control IC. The disc motor speed changes as it rotates. When the laser disc assembly starts at the center of the disc, the motor rotates at 500 to 200 RPM towards the outside edge of the disc.

The disc motor signal may be controlled from a driver IC or several driver transistors. The motor signal from the output driver stage may come from the IC amp or directly from the CLV servo-amp processor (Fig. 10-13). Measure the dc voltage applied to the motor terminals. A continuity test

of the motor should be under 20 ohms.

You may find a solid-state type disc motor in some models without a low continuity measurement. Check the separate battery voltage and clock timing frequency (44.1 MHz) applied to one of the motor terminals (Fig. 10-14). Improper disc speed may result from a defective motor, timing signal, motor driver IC or transistors and CLV processor. Suspect a defective motor if there is correct applied voltage and signal.

The disc, spindle, or turntable motor is located close to the laser pick-up assembly. These motors are directly driven and have a spindle or platform on which the disc rests after being loaded. The platform sits on top of the motor shaft. The turntable motor may be mounted to the main plastic chassis with three small phillips screws.

## TEST-DISC ADJUSTMENTS

Most adjustments are made with a YEDS-1 test disc, oscilloscope, DMM, and frequency counter. The digital multimeter or VOM and oscilloscope are used to make the rf offset adjustments. The focus, tracking gain, and tracking offset adjustments are made with the test disc and scope as indicator. The PLL free-run frequency adjustment is made with a frequency counter. Although many of the adjustments for several manufactured auto CD players are the same, it's best to follow each manufacturer's setup and adjustment procedures.

## SIGNAL CIRCUITS

The signal path starts at the output terminals of the optical pick-up block (A, C, D, and B). The laser-diode signal is fed to terminals 5 and 6 of the rf amp/signal processor (IC652). The EFM output signal of terminal 20 feeds directly to pin 5 of the digital signal processor/CLV servo IC 502 (Fig. 10-15). The D/A signal of terminal 78 feeds to the D/A converter IC terminal 10 (IC301). The left audio signal from pin 18 feeds to the integrator and sample hold IC101. From pin 7 the signal goes to pin 14 of switch IC302 to the de-emphasis/tone amp, IC102. The left-channel volume control feeds the signal to the line amp, IC401, and then a switch relay and finally to the left output line jack. Of course, the right channel is separated from the D/A converter at pin 17 and follows the same signal path as the left channel to the right line output jack.

## CRITICAL WAVEFORMS

The rf-amp/signal processor may be checked with an EFM waveform and voltage measurements on the rf IC. Check the focus/track/SLED motor IC waveforms and take critical voltage measurements. A defective digital signal processor and CLV servo processor may be isolated with waveforms and voltage measurements. The audio output may be checked at the separation of the left and right channels at the D/A converter processor. The rest of the audio channels may be signal-traced in the line output terminals. When the audio disappears, take critical voltage measurements on the audio IC and transistors. Do not overlook the relay switch transistors to the line output jacks (Fig. 10-16). The audio signal may be signal-traced from the D/A converter IC to the line output terminals.

## CONCLUSION

The auto compact disc player may be serviced in the same manner as the regular table-top disc player. Of course, the components are packed tightly together and in some cases critical parts may be mounted underneath the PC boards. Several PC boards are found in the compact disc player. Always follow the manufacturer's test points (TP) in

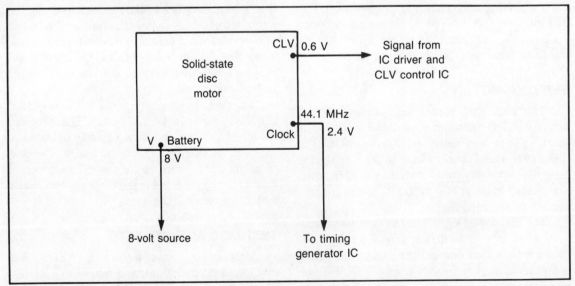

Fig. 10-14. In some auto disc players a solid-state disc motor may have a fixed voltage fed to one of the terminals and a control signal from the IC driver and CLV control IC.

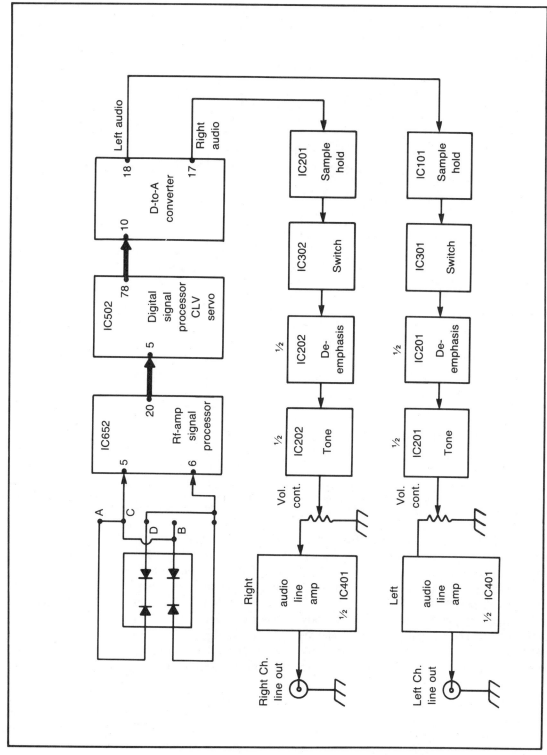

Fig. 10-15. The signal path starts at the laser optical pick-up block from the playing disc to the various IC components. The D to A converter converts the EFM signal to the audio channels.

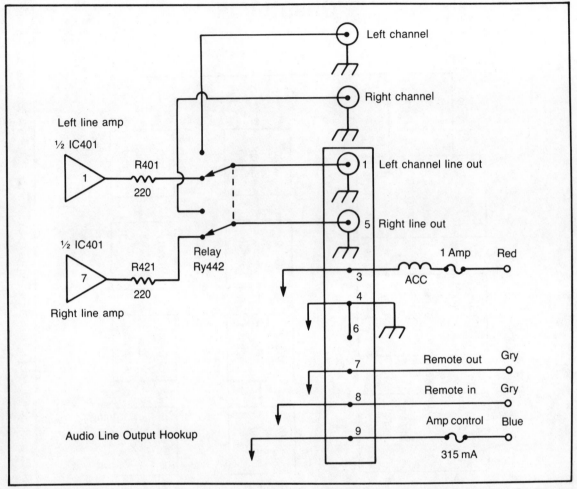

Fig. 10-16. The audio output line signal may be switched by a relay in some models at the last audio line amp ICs. Besides the line output jack, note the many other cable connections at the rear of the auto disc player.

taking critical voltage and waveforms. Sometimes the defective section may be isolated by making the critical alignment adjustments.

The big difference between the auto and regular compact disc player is the dc-to-dc converter. Critical voltage output and input tests may quickly locate the defective component. Transistor and diode in-circuit tests may locate an open or leaky component. Make sure the bench power supply is big enough (14 volts at 2 amps) to handle operation of the disc player.

Many of the newer auto radio-cassette players have line input terminals for a compact disc player. The high-powered amplifier of the auto stereo-cassette player may have auxiliary jacks which can be used for the disc player. In other amplifiers, the stereo audio channels may be converted to compact disc player operation.

260

# Chapter 11

# Telephone Answering Machine Repairs

MANY HOMES AND OFFICES HAVE TELEPHONE answering machines and sooner or later they require service. They are sometimes called jotters, telephone-answered devices, or just answering machines. Some answering machines have dual cassettes, multifunction remote systems, and voice-operated recordings (Fig. 11-1). Many of the answering devices may be connected to several different telephone hookups. I will discuss the features of two of these machines in detail.

## SPECIFIC MODELS AVAILABLE

There are a number of companies currently putting out electronic telephone answering machines. The following two are typical of those offering remote control or dual-cassette operation.

**Panasonic Model KX-T1421.** By using a tone telephone at a remote location, you may rewind the ICM (incoming message) tape and listen to recorded messages. The secret remote-calling code is easily changed with the tone remote control system. When the phone rings, the machine an-

swers and your pre-recorded message plays back. The recording time of the outgoing message (OGM) is variable. It can be set to any length up to 30 seconds.

After your pre-recorded message is played, the caller's incoming message (ICM) is recorded. While the incoming message is being recorded, you can monitor the call. This makes it possible to screen incoming calls and to decide whether you want to pick up the handset. A message can be recorded on the incoming message tape which can be heard by someone using the tone telephone. The tape can be quickly erased in forward or reverse direction by using either the erase button or the cue or review button.

**Radio Shack TAD-210 Answering Machine.** The nominal message recording time is 15 and 50 seconds with an outgoing and incoming tape speed of 4.75 cm/sec. Wow and flutter are less than 0.5 WRMS. The signal-to-noise ratio (S/N at 1 kHz) is around 10 dB with a frequency response of 500 kHz at a −5 dB. The distortion in rec/play at 1 kHz

Fig. 11-1. Many telephone-answering machines have single- or dual-cassette operation. The function switch may be a rotating or push-button type.

is a nominal 5%. The beep tone frequency (outgoing-incoming) is about 800 Hz.

The TAD-210 is a basic dual-cassette telephone answering machine with fast-forward, ring delay, adjustable incoming message length, and LED indicators for standby and received calls/record (announcement). The outgoing announcement is stored in an endless loop cassette and is recorded with a built-in electric microphone.

A noise generator activated by the supply reel table keeps the TAD-210 on when it turns. When the incoming cassette runs out of tape and stalls, the electrical noise stops, which causes the TAD to shut down after emitting a short beep tone. If a call comes in after the incoming cassette is full, the tone signifying the beginning of the incoming portion of the cycle will sound, as usual, after the announcement ends, followed in four or five seconds by a shorter tone burst signifying that the cas-

sette if full. Callers will need to recognize that the second tone, which closely follows the first tone, indicates that something is wrong.

## TYPICAL CIRCUIT OPERATION

Many of the older telephone-answering machines are transistor operated. The latest units contain both transistors and IC components. Some of the units have quad IC amplifiers, which means that there are four separate amplifiers in one IC (Fig. 11-2). Often these IC amplifiers have a 60 to 80 dB gain.

The output of the amplifier section is shown at the tip of the arrow in the diagram, and the two inputs are at the base (Fig. 11-3). The upper input is negative, or opposite to that of the output. This makes it possible to establish negative feedback around an amplifier by connecting a resistor between the output and the negative input. The lower

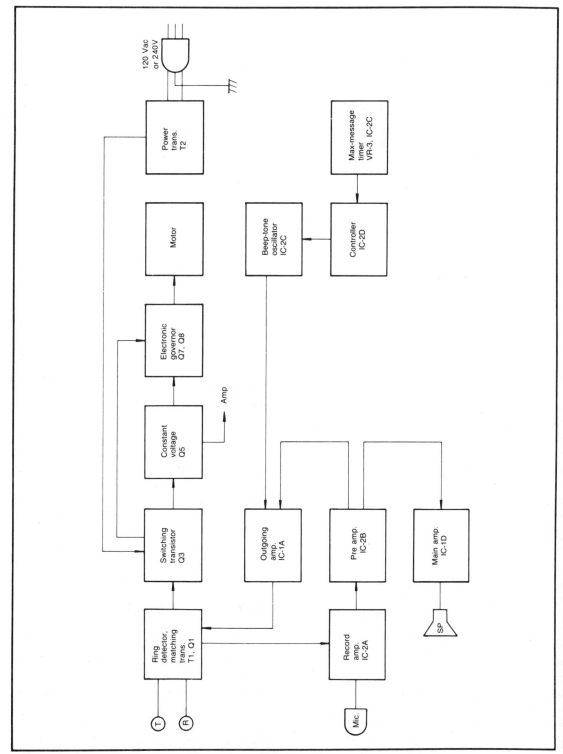

Fig. 11-2. Block diagram showing the various stages of a telephone-answering device (TAD).

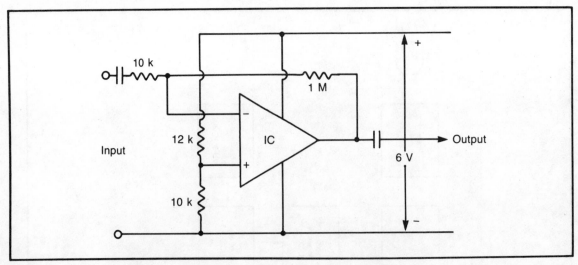

Fig. 11-3. You may find one large IC component doing the work of many stages in the TAD. The upper input is negative which is opposite in phase with respect to the output terminal.

input is positive. If the output were connected to this input through some impedance, the amplifier would go into oscillation.

The internal circuitry consists of a differential amplifier, and the voltage difference between the two inputs determines the output. The gain is determined by the ratio of the feedback resistor (1 MΩ) to the input resistor (10 k) as long as it is less than the open-loop forward gain of the IC section. In this instance, the gain is 100 × or 40 dB. The total input impedance is only a little greater than 10 k, because the impedance to ground at the negative input terminal is very small when connected in this manner. Essentially no current flows in the 1 MΩ feedback resistor.

The negative input terminal is at the same quiescent dc voltage as the output terminal. Because of very high forward gain, the negative and positive terminals must always be within a few millivolts of each other. For the output terminal to read approximately ½ B+, the positive input terminal must be biased at one-half B+. Because the output terminal cannot swing all the way up to B+ at maximum output excursion, the optimum bias is actually a little less than one-half B+.

**Turn-off on Shutdown.** One way of shutting down or disabling the quad IC is to inject positive voltage into the negative terminal. This swings the output hard against ground and keeps it there as long as the input signal is less than the positive turn-off voltage. This technique is used in many answering devices to turn amplifier stages on and off.

In Fig. 11-4, the IC amp is connected as bistable circuit. At B+ turn on, the output is at ground because of voltage applied to the input terminal through the 4.7 MΩ resistor. A plus pulse, whose peak amplitude is higher than one-sixth of the B+ voltage as measured at the + input, will swing the output pin to B+. This will result in a dc voltage at the positive (+) input terminal of ⅓ B+, because of the divide-down ratio of 47 k and 100 k. Since ⅓ is larger than ⅙, the output pin will stay at B+ until B+ is removed, the positive (+) input terminal shorted to ground, or a higher positive voltage applied to the input than appears on the positive (+) input.

## EQUIVALENT CIRCUIT OF PHONE LINE

A typical telephone line has an open-circuit voltage of 48 volts dc, an internal line impedance 400 to 2000 ohms, and an off-hook dc current handset load of approximately 30 mA. The dc source is assumed to have no internal resistance because it is regulated (Fig. 11-5).

The impedance is the sum of the internal signal generator impedance and an added external re-

264

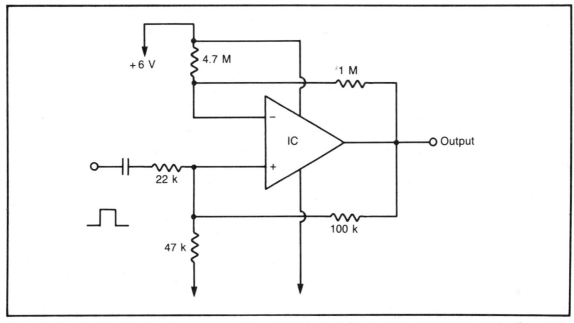

Fig. 11-4. Here one of the IC voltage amps is connected as a bistable circuit. The input signal is tied to the positive IC terminal.

sistance. The output attenuater of the signal generator should be capable of changing the previously specified 30 mA dc. The off-hook resistance for dc is about 150 ohms.

## FAIL-SAFE NOISE GENERATOR

To keep the telephone-answering device operating in some models, a noise is generated as long as the supply reel rotates (Fig. 11-6). The supply spindle is molded with conducting material embedded in the plastic. This forms a semiconducting, electrically noisy path between its shaft, which is insulated and connected to a source of positive ( + ) voltage, and the ground connection through the rubbing spring arm. So long as the supply reel turns, it generates electrical noise which keeps the telephone-answering machine operating. When the incoming cassette is full, the supply reel stops rotating, and the internal telephone-answering circuitry

Fig. 11-5. The telephone line is equivalent to the internal line impedance, ac signal, and dc applied voltage.

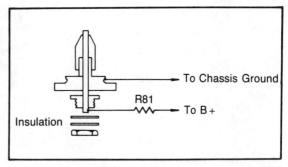

Fig. 11-6. In some models, a noise generator is used to keep the telephone-answering machine operating. Here the noise is generated by a B + voltage tied to a plastic bushing. Noise is generated as the supply wheel rotates.

265

interprets the resulting absence of noise as a shut-down signal.

## TAPE HEAD CLEANUP

To keep oxide from building up on the tape head, the tape head and sensing posts should be cleaned up each time the unit is brought in for repair. The messages may become weak, noisy, lose high-frequency response, and become slow or jam because of a dirty tape head. A weak or hiss symptom may be cured by a good tape-head cleanup.

The tape head may be cleaned with alcohol and a cloth, head cleaning sprays, and solvents. The head may be sprayed with a head cleaner solution and wiped off with cloth or cleaning stick. Alcohol applied to cleaning sticks or swabs does a good and inexpensive job. A regular cassette head cleaning kit may be purchased for only a few dollars. The head-cleaning cassette may be inserted for a few seconds with felt pads and cleaning fluid applied to clean those tape heads.

## COMPONENT CLEANUP

In addition to the tape-head assembly, clean up the sensing posts and turntables of the cassette. Often oxide dust settles down into the turntable area and eventually falls into the belt and pressure-roller assemblies (Fig. 11-7). When the button panel is removed for surface, don't forget to clean off all pulleys, belts, and moving surfaces. Clean the pinch rollers of brown oxide dust. Remove the pinch-roller assembly and clean up if the oxide cannot be removed from the top of the cassette chamber.

Clean the flywheel assembly and drive belt of grease or oxide dust. Check the idler and end-pulleys for slick spots. Clean off the motor pulley

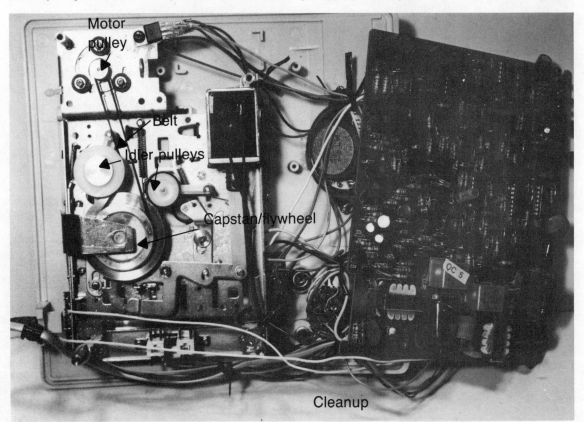

Fig. 11-7. Like the cassette player, a good cleanup of the tape heads and moving components will keep the telephone answering machine operating. Clean off belts, flywheel, and idler pulleys with alcohol and cleaning stick.

266

and both forward and rewind reels. Visually inspect the different rubber parts for cracks or worn areas while cleaning up the various moving components. Usually lubricant is not necessary, although sliding metal and plastic surfaces should have a light oil or grease applied if they are dry. Make sure everything is clean and in proper working order before re-assembling the unit.

## THE CASSETTE TAPE

A sensing foil is attached to the endless cassette tape. If the sensing foil does not contact the sensing pole, the endless tape cannot stop automatically. Check the foil and note if it is worn, cracked, or torn. Replace it if it is worn and does not stop. For correct operation and sound quality, the endless cassette tape should be replaced every six months. It's best to secure the new cassette from the same manufacturer of the answering machine.

Never place a cassette tape near a magnetic source, such as a magnet or TV set. Keep the cassette away from strong stereo speakers. Mount the answering machine away from the floor because an electric sweeper may magnetize the tape heads and tape. Do not bring magnetic or metal objects such as screwdrivers near the head assemblies because they can magnetize the heads. Take up the slack in the tape by tightening and rotating the tape reel with a pencil pushed into the hub area of the cassette.

## DEMAGNETIZING THE TAPE HEAD

After cleaning the tape heads for oxide-deposit buildup, demagnetize the tape head. It's best to obtain a regular cassette player demagnetizing tool so you can get down close to the tape heads. The demagnetizer removes residual magnetism from the heads, improves the signal-to-noise ratio, reduces hiss, and restores high-frequency response.

A demagnetizer and cleaner cassette may be used to clean the tape and demagnetize the tape head at the same time. Insert the cassette and run the tape for a full minute after ten or twelve hours of operation. The cleaner-demagnetizer cassette keeps the tape path and head clean, prevents loss

of the "highs," and reduces hissing noises. You can purchase a cordless battery-operated cassette that loads like a regular cassette. An LED indicates when the head is demagnetized.

## MECHANICAL
## DUAL-CASSETTE OPERATION

You may find that a single motor operates both cassettes (one at a time) in some dual-cassette answering devices. This is done by building into each capstan flywheel a clutch that grabs when the flywheel spins clockwise and slips when the flywheel spins counterclockwise. The pulley driving the linkage to the take-up reel has another clutch assembly. The rubber drive belt is strung in such a manner that the spin directions of the two flywheels are opposite each other (Fig. 11-8). The take-up reel pulley spins in the same direction as the incoming message flywheel. When the motor spins in one direction, the outgoing announcement cassette tape is made to move. When it spins in the other direction, the announcement tape stops and the incoming-message cassette tape moves. Thus, one single motor does the work of two.

**Clutch Operation.** The clutch assembly may consist of a flywheel, cup, and rubber pucks. The capstan is firmly staked to the cup, while the flywheel spins freely on the capstan (Fig. 11-9). The

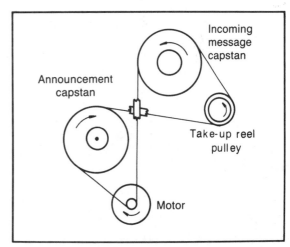

Fig. 11-8. Here a rubber drive belt is running around two different flywheel-capstan assemblies. A single motor performs both incoming and outgoing message operations.

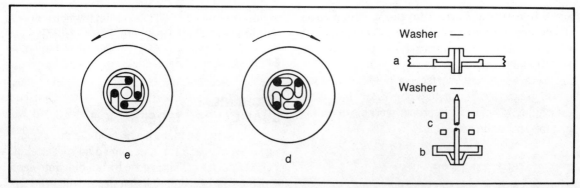

Fig. 11-9. The clutch operation shown here is found on the bottom of the flywheel assembly. The rubber pucks move outward when the flywheel rotates clockwise.

rubber pucks move loosely in grooves tooled into the underside of the flywheel. When the flywheel turns clockwise, the pucks move outward because of centrifugal force and friction from the surface of the cup, where they wedge between the inside surface of the cup wall and the grooves in the fly-wheel, thus locking the flywheel and cup to each other. When the flywheel turns counter-clockwise, the pucks are urged inward, disengaging the fly-wheel from the cup. If the clutch mechanism ap-pears sluggish or does not function, change the rubber pucks. A cleanup of the clutch assembly may solve intermittent or erratic operation.

**Outgoing Tape Mechanism.** The ordinary answering machine has two tape heads, one for erase and the other for play/record. In the two-cassette decks, one is used for incoming and the other for outgoing messages. The pinch roller is pressed against the capstan during outgoing tape operation, while the motor rotates and turns the capstan/flywheel assembly (Fig. 11-10). The pinch roller presses the tape against the capstan to trans-port the tape as the capstan rotates. The pinch roller is pressed against the capstan during outgo-ing tape operation, while the motor rotates and turns the capstan/flywheel assembly (Fig. 11-10). The pinch roller pressure may be anywhere from 320 to 360 grams. The outgoing-tape mechanism sends out the recorded message when the telephone rings.

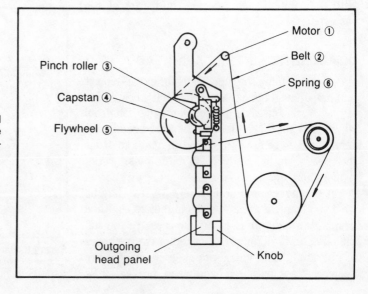

Fig. 11-10. The pinch roller is pushed against the capstan during outgoing tape operation with the motor rotating the cap-stan/flywheel assembly.

**Incoming Tape Playback Mechanism.**
The pinch roller is held against the capstan by a tension spring. The forward reel or turntable, idler, and drive shaft are pressed against each other by the tension spring (13). When the function lever is set to playback, the motor rotates, and the rotation turns the flywheel and clutch assembly by means of the motor drive belt (Fig. 11-11). The flywheel transmits the rotation to the capstan and clutch assembly, rotating the drive shaft. The capstan rotates the pinch roller, drive shaft, and provides rotation to the forward or take-up reel with the idler pulley (10).

**Incoming Tape Rewind Mechanism.**
With the function lever set to rewind mode, the cam moves forward and moves the lever so that the idler gear meshes with idler gear 15. The lever arm pulls the pinch roller away from the capstan so the tape is not pressed against the tape heads (Fig. 11-12). The motor rotates the flywheel and clutch assembly at a fast rewind speed. The tape is quickly wound around the rewind reel or turntable. The rewind wheel torque usually ranges from 100 to 150 gcm.

**Mechanical Trouble.** A lot of speed prob-lems are caused by oil or oxide on the belt, capstan, and motor pulley. Clean off all moving parts with alcohol and cleaning stick. A loose or stretched belt may produce slow speeds—replace it. Note if small pieces of rubber belt are building up on the motor pulley. Sometimes extra pressure must be used to clean up the motor pulley. Slow speed and wow may be caused by excess tape wrapped around the pressure roller. Always check the pressure roller when tape pulls out of the cassette.

A dry capstan/flywheel bearing may cause wow or slow speeds. The flywheel assembly should be removed and cleaned up with a drop of light oil applied to the capstan bearing. Dry cams, levers, and idler wheels may prevent proper function. Check the lever arm for bent areas. Lubricate the dry surfaces with a drop of light grease. Do not overlubricate any parts as the oil may drip on the motor belt, producing no operation or slow speeds. After applying lubricant, wipe up excess oil with a cloth or cleaning stick.

## RING RESPONSE AND TURN-ON

A typical ring response and turn-on starts with a telephone ring signal which triggers a self-latching

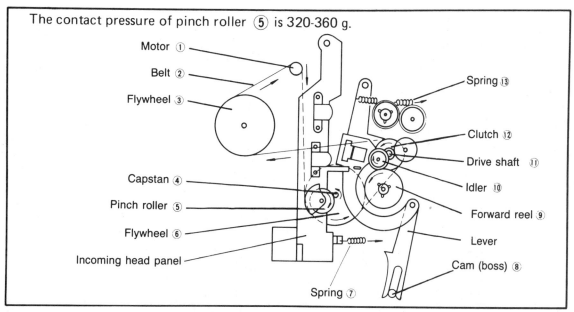

Fig. 11-11. The motor rotates when the function lever is set to playback. The rotation turns the flywheel and clutch assembly through the motor drive belt in the incoming signal mode.

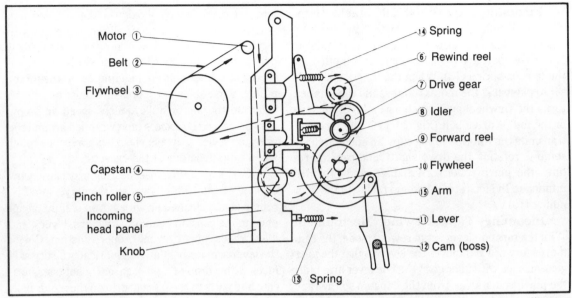

Fig 11-12. In the incoming tape rewind mode, the cam and lever pull the pinch roller away from the capstan so the tape does not press against the tape head.

circuit and turns on B+ to the rest of the answering circuits. A relay then seizes the telephone line. At the end of the answer cycle, the self-latching circuit is broken and shuts down the machine. In Fig. 11-13, the block diagram illustrates how the telephone ring and latch circuits perform in a Radio-Shack Model TAD-210.

Typically, a telephone ring signal is on for two seconds and off for four seconds. During its two-second on-time, it consists of an approximately 80-volt rms burst of 20 Hz signal, or forty successive sine waves. D1, in combination with C1, is a half-wave rectifier of the ring signal so that the neon bulb will flash once during each sine wave of the incoming ring signal. This occurs when the ring signal is as low as 40 volts rms (Fig. 11-14). Zener diode D2 is to prevent the neon bulb from flashing at lower signal voltages caused by line noises or signal transients.

The neon bulb pulses draw current through the primary of T1 and are short and sharp enough to also appear at its secondary. Q1 and D3 act as clippers. Only the top half of a ring pulse is found at the collector terminal of Q1. The polarities of D1 and T1 are such that the dominant energy pulse in the plus direction fully turns on Q1.

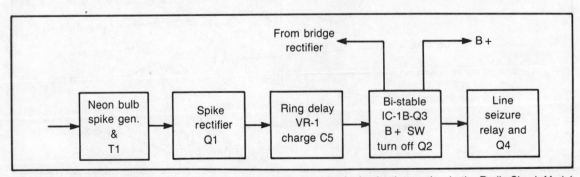

Fig. 11-13. This block diagram shows how the telephone ring and latch circuits tie together in the Radio-Shack Model TAD-210.

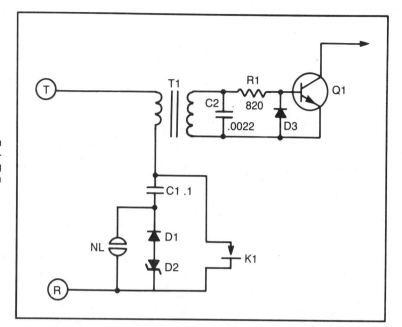

Fig. 11-14. D1 and C1, along with the telephone ring circuits, constitute a half-wave rectifier for the ring signal so the neon bulb will flash only once driving each ring cycle.

As the current pulses through Q1, a voltage change occurs at C3. Each pulse dumps a certain amount of charge into C3 and raises its voltage a little bit. The value of C3 is chosen so that at the end of 40 successive pulses it is charged up to the B+ source and Q1 is in saturation. When the train of pulses stops, C3 discharges to ground in a fraction of a second through R3.

While C3 is close to the B+ voltage, current flows into C5 through R2, VR1, and D4 (Fig. 11-15). When C5 reaches approximately 1.3 volts dc, IC-1B is turned off, starting the machine's turn-on cycle. How many rings are required before C5 reaches its critical voltage depends upon the setting of VR-1. D4 prevents the charge from flowing backwards from C5 into C3 between rings.

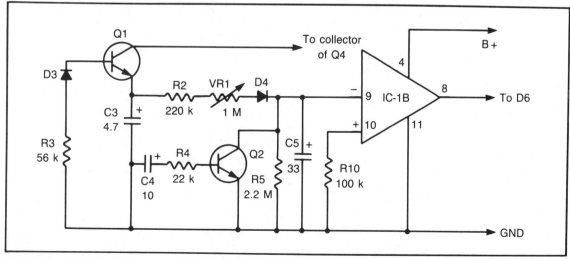

Fig. 11-15. When C5 reaches approximately 1.3 volts dc, IC-1B is turned off, starting the answering machine turn-on cycle. Adjustment of VR-1 determines how many rings are required to charge C5.

The B+ switch (Q3) with IC-1B forms a bistable circuit (Fig. 11-16). When power is applied from the ac power supply to IC-1, IC-1B turns on with its output pin at B+ because of the voltage (about 1.3 volts) at its plus pin (10), cutting off Q3 and making it nonconductive. If positive voltage in excess of 1.3 volts is applied to the minus pin, 9, the output pin, 8, will swing down to ground and put Q3 into saturation. The collector of Q3 now becomes the B+ source for the rest of the answering-device circuitry. This causes more plus voltage to be applied to the minus input through R6, ensuring that the IC-1B and Q3 combination stays latched. When C3 conducts, current enters the base of Q4 and closes relay K1, which latches the telephone line and stops the telephone ring.

The self-latching combination of IC-1B and Q3 can be turned off if the plus voltage is momentarily removed from the minus input pin to IC-1B. This is done by applying a plus voltage to the base of Q2 so that its collector is grounded, discharging

C5. This happens at the end of "announce only" and "record" functions when the foil bridges contacts J1/J2, and also during "answer" when IC-2C flips for the second time at the end of the preset elapsed incoming-message time (Fig. 11-17).

## AUDIO CIRCUITS

The audio from the telephone line is amplified and recorded upon the incoming cassette. This recording may be heard in the play position of the selector switch. The built-in microphone is used for making and changing outgoing messages. Usually, the recording amplifier is disabled during audio playout and the audio pre-amplifier is disabled during the incoming messages.

The audio circuits may consist of an IC voltage amplifier driving two transistors in push-pull operation (Fig. 11-18). You may find only IC circuits in the latest telephone-answering audio circuits. IC-1D is turned off during record and rewind

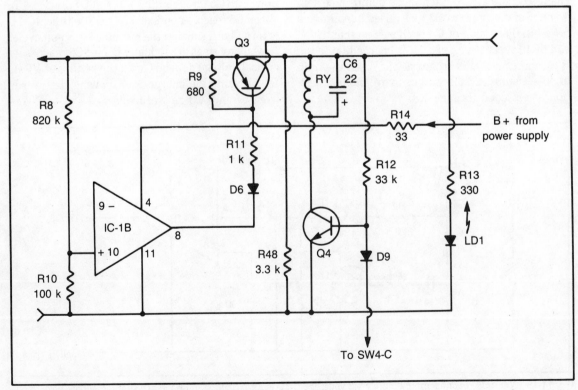

Fig. 11-16. The B+ switch (Q3) with IC-1B forms a bistable circuit.

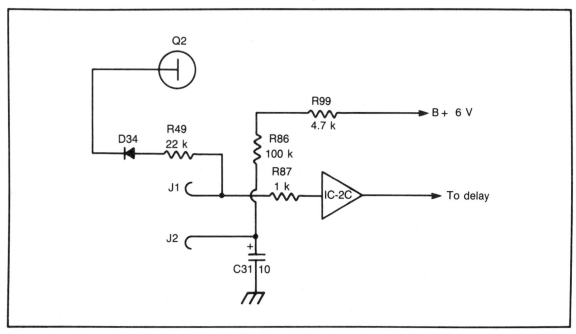

Fig. 11-17. When the foil of the tape bridge contacts J1/J2, IC-2C flips for the second time at the end of the preset elapsed incoming message time while applying a positive voltage to the base of Q2.

by voltages D32 and D40, which are connected to pin 3 and 6 of SW4-D.

**Radio Shack TAD-120 Audio Operation.** When the TAD B+ turns on in response to an incoming ring, voltage is injected into the minus pin of IC-2A through D27 from the collector of Q18, so that it is turned off (Fig. 11-19). As a result, there is no turn-off voltage sent to IC-2B

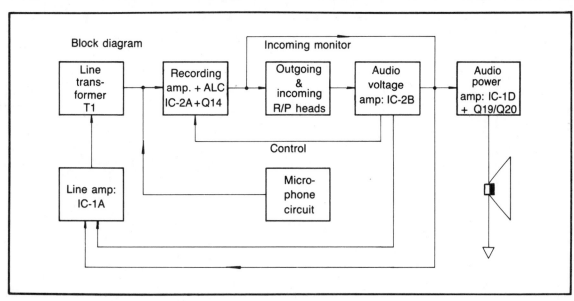

Fig. 11-18. Block diagram of the audio circuits in a typical telephone-answering machine.

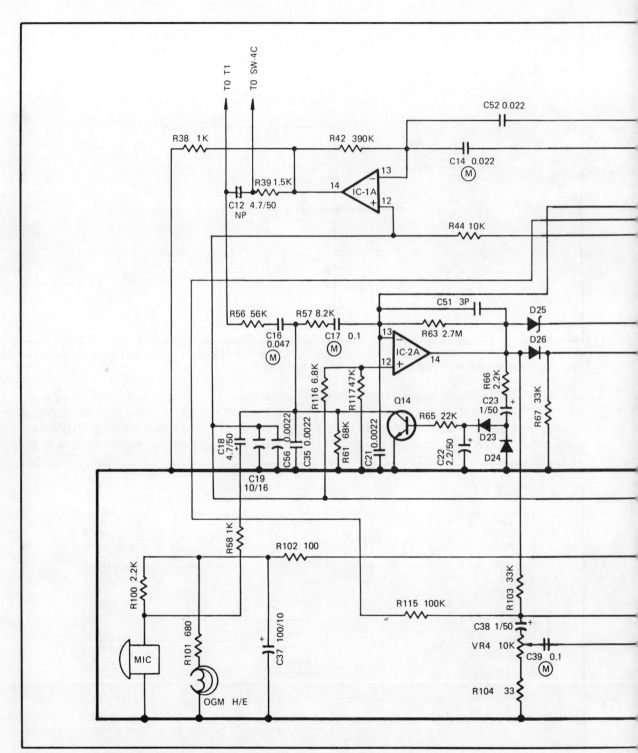

Fig. 11-19. A complete audio schematic of Radio Shack's Model TAD-210.

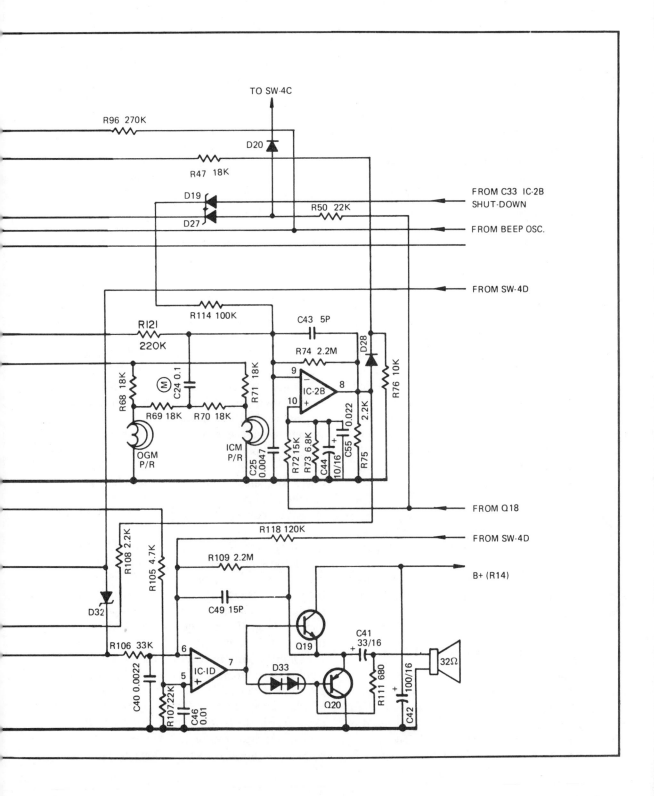

275

through D25 and IC-2B is on. Its output pin floats at about 2 volts as a result of voltage on its positive input, as divided-down by R72 and R73, also from the collector of Q18. The motor begins to turn in a direction that moves the outgoing-announcement cassette tape. The announcement message is amplified by IC-2B, fed to the line amplifier IC-1A through D28, R47, and C14, and then passed on to the telephone line through R39, C12, and T1.

When the announcement ends, J1/J2 are bridged, a beep tone sounds, and the motor reverses so that the announcement tape stops, and the message tape begins to move. At this point, IC-2B is turned off by voltage through R114 and D19 during the beep tone. If this were not done, voice information on the incoming tape could inadvertently be transmitted over the telephone line during this short interval since the incoming tape is now moving. When the beep tone ends, Q18 flips, removing the turn-off voltage to the input of IC-2A. As the IC-2A output pin rises to about 3 volts, turn-off voltage enters the negative input of IC-2B through D25, shutting it down. At the same time, the positive voltage is removed from pin 10 so that its output pin drops to ground voltage, activating the diode gate D28 for more immunity to overall system oscillation. This puts the TAD-210 in the incoming message mode with the recording amplifier on and the pre-amplifier off.

D19, D27, and D32 are zener diodes. When operated in the forward direction, they act like ordinary silicon diodes and pass current with only a small voltage drop. Because they are constructed of multiple junctions, they exhibit a much higher back resistance in the presence of elevated temperatures. This is why they are used in the audio shutdown path.

## AUDIO CIRCUIT PROBLEMS

No sound from the speaker may be caused by a defective audio-output transistor or IC component. The open speaker may result in no sound. Erratic or intermittent recording may be caused by a defective speaker, output transistors, poor recording head connections, or a defective cassette. In-

sert a regular recorded cassette to see if the amplifier circuits are normal. Do not overlook dirty switch contacts if there is erratic or intermittent operation. Spray each contact section with cleaning spray.

**Defective Tape Heads.** You may find a separate erase and recording tape head in different telephone-answering machines. A dirty tape head may cause weak and distorted messages. Always keep the tape heads clean. A loose mounting screw may prevent the tape head from resting upon the tape and prevent proper record or playback. A worn tape head may cause a loss in high-frequency response. Before removing or installing a new tape head, jot down the tape-head wire connections. It is important to observe correct polarity when replacing either the R/P or erase heads. If the connections to either head are reversed, the residual erase magnetism and dc recording bias will oppose each other, resulting in a very weak recording. Check the continuity of the tape head winding with the low-ohm range of the VOM or DMM.

**Does Not Record New Outgoing Message.** Trace the signal path from the microphone through to the IC components. Take critical voltage and resistance measurements on the IC. Check for open coupling capacitors between components. Do not overlook a possible defective microphone. Check for damage caused by foreign objects poked into the microphone opening. Intermittent recorded messages may result from poorly soldered connections at the microphone terminals.

**Does Not Record Incoming Messages.** Check the same signal path as above and try to locate where the signal disappears. It's possible that the audio is being recorded properly and that the playback is defective. Inspect the tape head for packed oxide. Try another pre-recorded cassette to see how it sounds.

**Oscillations in Recordings.** Look for open feedback symptoms from the output IC terminal to the input terminal. Check for dirty record/play switch contacts (Fig. 11-20). Shunt the main filter capacitors in the power supply. Bridge electrolytic decoupling capacitors in the power-supply feed circuits. Sometimes audio oscillation may be stopped

Fig. 11-20. Oscillation may occur in telephone-answering machines because of dirty function and push-button switches.

by adding a 47 pF capacitor from the output pre-amp IC terminal to the input terminal. This trial and error method may solve the audio oscillation problem.

Check for shorted or leaky blocking diodes in the signal path circuits. Poor ground connections at the R/P tape head or shields lead-in may cause oscillations. Do not overlook a possible defective IC input or output. Voltage and resistance measurements on the suspected output IC component may still not indicate it is defective so be sure to replace it.

## POWER-SUPPLY PROBLEMS

Most power-supply circuits consist of a power transformer, bridge rectifier and large filter capacitors (Fig. 11-21). A B+ switch may be used to switch power to the various circuits. Very little cur-

rent is drawn in the power-supply circuits when the B+ switch is in the off position in this model. The power transformer and bridge rectifier have voltage applied until the function switch is rotated.

Improper or no voltage at the output of the power supply may be caused by overloading components or trouble within the power-supply components. A shorted diode or bridge rectifier may open the primary winding of the power transformer. Check for an open winding at the ac plug with the low-ohm scale of the VOM or DMM. If the winding is open, check for a shorted rectifier diode. It's possible to find a burned diode with no damage to the transformer.

The defective power transformer should be replaced with the original. If the manufacturer is out of the business or the transformer cannot be located, determine the output voltage and select a universal power transformer. The bridge rectifier

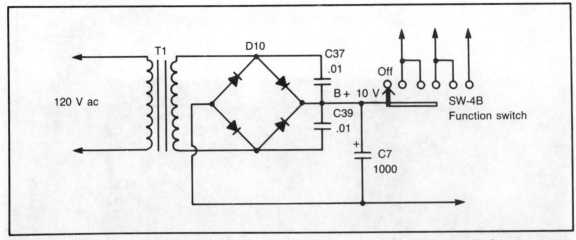

Fig. 11-21. Most telephone-answering machines have a simple full-wave or bridge rectifier circuit with only a few components.

component may be subbed with four different 2.5-amp silicon diodes if the original cannot be located.

Excessive hum or distorted messages in the speaker may be caused by a dried-up filter capacitor. Remember, these are large capacitors and should be shunted with 1000 μF units to test for a defective filter capacitor. Clip the capacitor across the suspected one with the power off. Shunt each filter and decoupling capacitor in the low-voltage regulator or power supply.

Overloaded circuits tied to the low-voltage power supply may produce low voltage or weak and distorted messages. Monitor the low-voltage cir-

cuits across the large filter capacitor with the DMM. Now rotate the function switch and note if the voltage returns to normal or is low only in one position. Check those circuits with low voltages that are tied to the function switch. Leaky output transistors and IC power components may lower the supply voltage. Check the motor regulator transistor circuits for a leaky transistor.

## MOTOR CONTROL CIRCUITS

You may find a voltage regulator/motor-speed control circuit in several telephone-answering devices. Figure 11-22 is a block diagram showing how the motor control and regulator circuits are

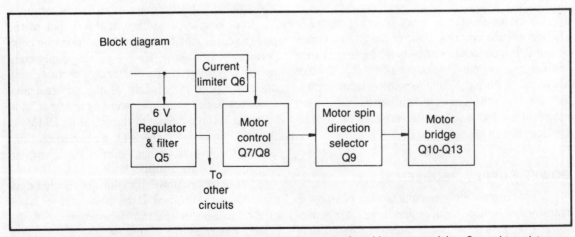

Fig. 11-22. A B+ transistor regulator and motor control circuits may be found in some models. Several transistors are located in the current, motor control, motor direction and bridge circuits.

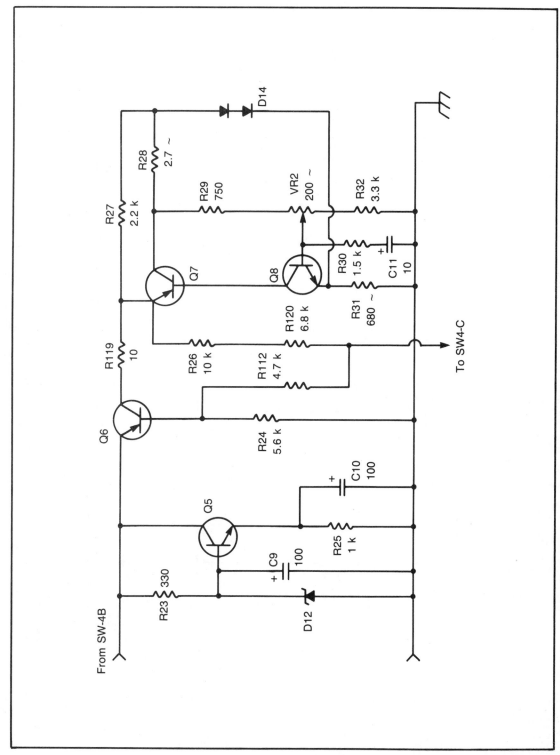

Fig. 11-23. Q5 operates as an emitter-follower voltage regulator. The effective filter capacitor value from Q5 to ground equals 50,000 µF.

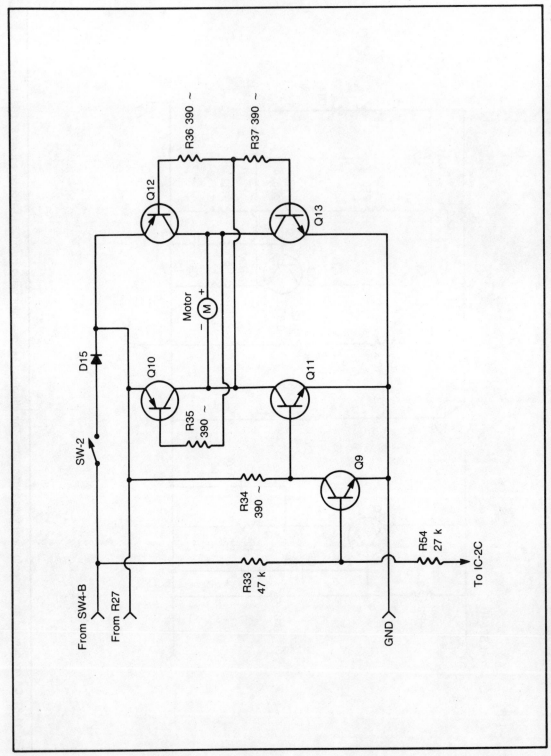

Fig. 11-24. Bridge rectifiers Q10 through Q13 determine the voltage, polarity, and motor direction. If there is improper or no rotation, check transistors Q10 to Q13.

280

**Table 11-1. Troubleshooting Chart.**

| Symptom | Check and Repair |
|---|---|
| Tape does not move | Does motor run? Check for belt off or loose belt. Check for a dead power supply, defective motor regulator and control circuits, or a defective motor. |
| No rewind or play | Check belt and idler pulleys. Check motor regulator. Check frozen rewind and play turntable. |
| Outgoing message does not play | Determine if motor runs clockwise. Check for leaky or open motor control transistors, a defective motor or leaky ICs. |
| Motor does not move in playback or rewind mode | Defective or dirty function switch. Shorted bridge motor transistors. Leaky motor-regulator transistor. |
| Wow and flutter | Tape wound around pressure roller. Dry capstan/flywheel. Defective motor. Check motor-control circuits. |
| Excessive motor noise in audio | Defective motor. Reroute motor leads from tape-head cables. |
| Motor does not stop in answer mode | Defective transistors and ICs in input circuits. |
| No erase of outgoing tape | Defective erase head. Check with a known cassette recording. |
| No erase of message tape | Defective erase head. Poor or dirty switches. |
| Tape spills out | Check worn pressure roller. Check take-up reel for erratic rotation. Check for contaminated capstan. Try a new cassette. |
| No message playback | Check speakers. Check ICs. Check audio-output circuits. |
| Does not record both announcement and message | Check microphone. Check input IC or transistors. Inspect dirty function switch. Defective play/record head. |
| Does not record message only | Check input capacitors and resistors. Defective message play/record head. Dirt-packed tape head. |
| Weak or distorted announcements | Dirty or coated P/R head. Defective microphone. Defective tape. |
| Weak or distorted message | Dirty message P/R head. Defective message P/R head. Defective cassette tape. |
| Weak or distorted audio signal | Inspect speaker. Check audio-output transistors and ICs. Measure low voltage at audio section. |
| Amplifier oscillates in playback mode | Clean up function recording switch. Check for leaky blocking diodes. |
| No response to ring, but unit starts | Neon lamp does not fire open coupling capacitors and diodes. Defective telephone cord. Check input line transformer. Check setting of ring variable resistance. |
| Unit loads line to stop ringing but does not play or record tape | Check function switch. Defective endless tape. Replace cassette. Check low voltage. Check motor. Check motor-control components. |

tied together. Q5 is an emitter-followed voltage regulator that derives its reference voltage from zener D12. The emitter voltage is always approximately 0.6 volts less than the voltage developed across the zener diode. C9 is the main filter capacitor for this circuit. The effective filter capacitor value from Q5 emitter to ground is the transistor beta times C9 and is equal to 50,000 $\mu$F. C10 is used to suppress parasitic oscillation between the various elements of the circuit (Fig. 11-23).

Transistors Q7 and Q8 form a voltage-regulator motor-speed control circuit with VR-2 adjusting the output voltage. At junction R27 and R28, the voltage rises as more torque is demanded by the motor. Therefore, more current is drawn from the supply. The voltage at the junction of R31 and the emitter of Q8 is always the motor transistor bridge voltage minus the two silicon-junction diode (D14) forward voltage drops or 1.3 volts. If the motor varies up and down, this voltage will vary right along with it. The voltage at the arm of VF-2 is approximately one-half of the motor voltage and will vary up and down at half the rate of the motor voltage.

When the motor draws more current as it is loaded more heavily, the left side of R28 will rise because of the voltage drop through this current-sampling resistor. This results in a rise in the voltage at the arm of VR-2, which causes a still greater use of voltage at the collector of Q7. The corresponding increase in the voltage at the emitter of Q8 is a stabilizing influence and prevents runaway operation.

Which capstan spins and drives its cassette tape forward depends on the spin direction of the motor. The transistor bridge (Q10 through Q13) determines the voltage polarity applied to the motor terminals and the direction of rotation (Fig. 11-24). When the base of Q9 is grounded, no current is fed to it through R33, R54, or R55. Its collector is an open circuit and heavy current enters the base of Q11 through R34. This grounds the collector of Q11 and establishes ground voltage on the left side of the motor. The grounding of the collector of Q11 simultaneously turns off Q13, since no bias current can now enter its base, and turns on Q12 with heavy bias current through R36. Now the right side of the motor is positive. When bias current enters the base of Q9, its collector drops to ground, and therefore no current enters the base of Q11. The collector rises to the motor supply voltage, turns off Q12 and turns on Q13, whose collector drops to ground, in turn causing full conduction of Q10. The polarity on the motor is now reversed with the left side positive and the right side negative.

## CONCLUSION

The telephone-answering device may be serviced in the same manner as any other piece of consumer electronics. Checking the diodes and transistors in-circuit with the diode test of a DMM may uncover a leaky or open component. Critical IC components may be located with accurate voltage and resistance measurements after signal in and out tests are made. Knowing how transistor and IC switching circuits work may help isolate a defective section. Although some telephone answering machines may appear quite complicated while others seem simple, they all basically operate in the same way to record and play back the required incoming and outgoing messages.

Table 11-1 shows some additional problems along with their possible causes and troubleshooting suggestions.

# Chapter 12

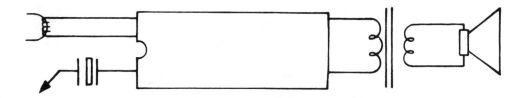

# Stereo Speaker Repairs

THE STEREO SPEAKER IS THE MOST IMPORtant piece of equipment found in a stereo system. Speakers convert electronic audio into a mechanical movement of the speaker cone. The movement of air caused by the speaker is what we hear. The greater the movement, producing sharp clarity of sound and a wide range of frequencies, the better the speaker will be.

## SPEAKER TYPES

Speakers come in many sizes and shapes (Fig. 12-1). Most average speaker enclosures have a large woofer, mid-range, and tweeter speakers. The lower priced shelf-type units may have one or two speakers. In very large speaker systems, you may find four tweeters, up to eight mid-range and one large woofer. The speakers used for the high frequency (tweeter) range may be a small metal, hardconed or horn-type speaker. Mid-range speakers may vary from 3 to 6 inches with 8 to 12 inches for woofers.

The best frequency response is from 20 to 20,000 Hz; most speakers vary from 37 to 20,000 Hz. Very few men can hear above 15,000 or below 50 Hz, while women may hear above 22 kHz. The most important thing, however, is how a set of speakers sounds to your own ears.

In addition to the frequency response, how a speaker sounds is influenced greatly by the speaker enclosure. Several of these are discussed below. Table 12-1 lists a number of different enclosures by type along with their maximum wattage ratings.

**Acoustic Suspension.** The speakers in an acoustic suspension enclosure are completely sealed without any extra openings. The AS enclosure offers easy listening to all types of music, whether soft rock, country, or popular music. The three-way acoustic suspension speaker system may have two or three speakers. Since it takes more power to move the air with AS speakers, they usually have a higher maximum power handling capacity. The tweeter may be a one- or two-inch cone, dome, or ribbon-type speaker. The midrange speaker may consist of a two- to five-inch cone or dome-tyr

Fig. 12-1. The speaker cabinets include both shelf and floor-type enclosures with many different sizes of speakers.

speaker. A woofer speaker in the AS enclosure may be six, eight, or ten inches in size. The average AS (acoustical suspension) frequency response may vary from 22 to 40 kHz, although many acoustical-suspension-speaker frequency responses may go above 50 kHz.

**Bass Reflex.** The bass reflex speaker produces stronger and deeper bass frequencies

Table 12-1. Various Speakers and Their Maximum Wattage Ratings.

| Name | Model | Acoustical Suspension | Bass Reflex | Passive Radiator | Max Wattage |
|------|-------|----------------------|-------------|------------------|-------------|
| Advent | 6003 | X | | | 300 |
| ADS | L1090 | X | | | 175 |
| Bose | 501 | X | | | 125 |
| Celeston | DL6 | | X | | 150 |
| Design Acoustics | PS10 | X | | | 250 |
| EPI | T/E360 | | | X | 250 |
| Fisher | ST-828 | | X | | 100 |
| Infinity | ES-82 | | | X | 130 |
| Marantz | SP1000 | | X | | 110 |
| Pioneer | DSS-7 | | X | | 210 |
| Radio Shack | 40-4032 | | X | | 160 |
| Sony | APM-707 | | | X | 160 |

Fig. 12-2. A three-way bass reflex speaker cabinet with a tweeter, mid-range, and woofer speakers. A tuned port hole is shown at the top of the cabinet with the plug-in grille removed.

(Fig. 12-2). They are designed with a tuned porthole to allow the enclosure to resonate and produce low-frequency notes. Some bass-reflex enclosures may have up to three different sizes of portholes. Bass reflex speakers may be driven harder and are designed for those who like high-powered music.

The small bass-reflex enclosure may have two speakers with a bass-reflex porthole, and a one- or two-inch cone speaker supported with synthetic resin for eliminating distortion caused by edge-resonance. You may find a one- to two-inch cone or dome speaker as tweeter, with a two- to six-inch mid-range and an eight, ten, or twelve-inch speaker as woofer. For power-handling capacity, heat-resistant voice coils and adjustable thermal-relay protection circuits are found for safety under high-power driving. A carefully tuned bass-reflex enclosure for producing tight and solid bass reproduction is found along with an anti-resonating baffle-board in some units.

The bass-reflex enclosure provides good reproduction for classical, jazz, easy listening, rock, and country music. The average frequency response varies from 35 to 20 kHz. These speakers can respond to the bass, harp, tuba, and bass trombone musical instruments which may have frequencies below 30 Hz. The bass-reflex speaker is capable of covering the entire musical range.

The power handling capacity of the linear phase, bass reflex speaker system must always be greater than those of the amplifier. Likewise, if a lower power-handling amplifier does not have enough power, the linear phase speaker system may cause distortion. Damage or extra heat applied to the voice coils may cause speaker damage with excessive driving or power applied to the speakers.

**Passive Radiator.** The passive-radiator speaker enclosure produces greater bass than any other type of speaker. The passive radiator enclosure has two separate woofer-type speakers, but one is a simple cone without any voice coil or signal applied to it. Actually, the passive-port cone acts

Fig. 12-3. The ceramic magnet may come loose when the enclosure is dropped, producing a frozen cone and mushy-sounding music.

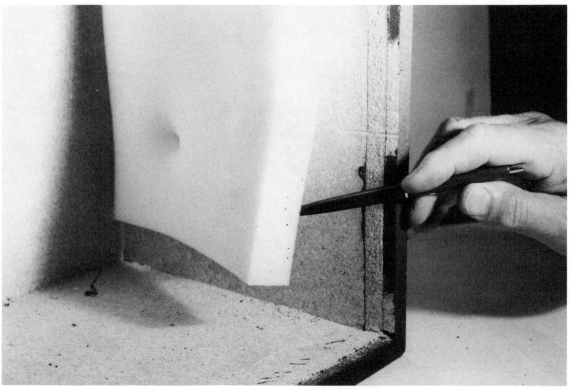

Fig. 12-4. Sometimes a vibrating noise in the speaker cabinet is caused by loose insulation or a panel section instead of the speaker.

as a variable port, increasing the bass frequency response. A two-speaker PR enclosure may have a one-inch dome and eight-inch speaker along with another eight-inch dud cone. The three-speaker system may have a one-inch dome for tweeter, a two-inch dome as mid-range, and a ten or twelve-inch speaker as woofer with another ten or twelve-inch dud cone. The passive radiator may be larger than the bass speaker. In some units, the woofer cone may be a special design with corrugations for wide-range response.

## SPEAKER PROBLEMS

A defective speaker may have an open or damaged voice coil. Mushy or tinny music may result from a dropped cone, the voice coil riding upon the center pole piece. A frozen cone may result from too much applied power or dc voltage from the amplifier circuits. When the speaker column is dropped, the speaker magnet can break away, causing a frozen cone (Fig. 12-3). A blown voice coil is the result of too much power applied from the amplifier. The erratic or intermittent speaker may have a poor connection at the voice coil or speaker terminals.

Vibration noises may be caused by holes torn or poked into the cone area. Loose packing or damping material may cause vibration noises (Fig. 12-4). Loose sections around the rim area of the cone may come loose and vibrate. A broken or unglued spider (next to the voice coil) may vibrate and produce blatting sounds. Small holes poked in the cone may be repaired with speaker cement without any decrease in speaker performance (Fig. 12-5), but a speaker with large holes or a cracked cone must be replaced.

**Checking the Voice Coil.** Continuity tests on the voice coil may indicate a shorted or open speaker. Measure the voice-coil resistance with the VOM or DMM (Fig. 12-6). The speaker impedance

287

Fig. 12-5. Holes poked into the speaker or broken cone areas may produce vibrations. Small holes may be repaired with speaker cement.

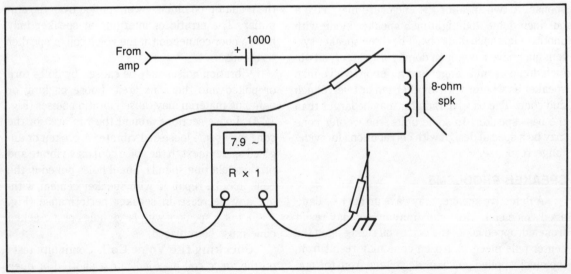

Fig. 12-6. The voice coil of a speaker may be open or shorted and can accurately be checked with the low-ohm scale of the DMM.

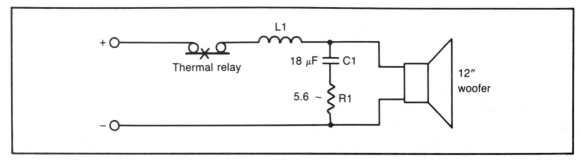

Fig. 12-7. Some speakers are protected from dc or excessive volume by a thermal cutout at the rear of the cabinet. These overload circuit breakers are similar to those found in the TV chassis.

may not measure the same with the VOM, while the low voice coil resistance may be quite close to the impedance on the digital multimeter. An 8-ohm speaker impedance may measure 7.9 ohms with the DMM.

Today the speaker enclosures may have an impedance of from 4 to 16 ohms. Most speakers are rated at 4 or 8 ohms. Some speaker units have a built-in speaker cone protection circuit which protects the speakers from damage by excessive input power (Fig. 12-7). A thermal relay protects the

speakers from excessive power or abnormal signal. Usually the woofer is the one that is damaged from too much power because it is connected directly across the amplifier output terminals. The tweeter or mid-range speakers may have a linear cross-over network with a capacitor between the speaker and terminals.

Sometimes there is a level control within the tweeter or midrange speaker circuits (Fig. 12-8). The resistance may be rotated to set the level of power applied to the speakers. The level or speaker

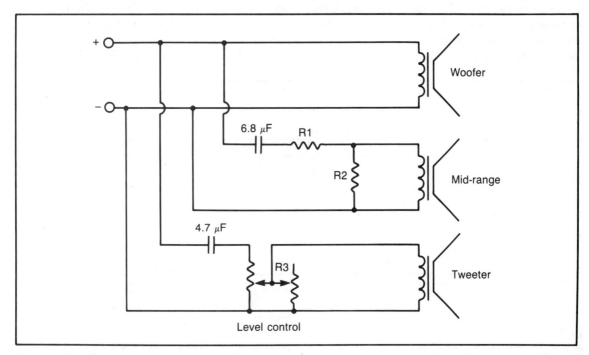

Fig. 12-8. Sometimes a level control is provided for the tweeter or mid-range speaker so the speakers cannot be damaged by excessive volume.

thermal cutouts may be located at the front or rear of the speaker enclosure. When mounted in the front area, they are often protected under the grille cloth cones. Sometimes they get bumped or broken when mounted at the rear of the speaker.

**Checking Speaker Cables.** An intermittent or a dead speaker may be caused by a broken speaker wire. Often the cable breaks right where it enters the cabinet, at the amplifier, or where the cable is spliced. A shorted cable at the spliced ends may knock out the speaker fuse or damage the audio output transistor or IC component.

First inspect the spliced connection. It's best never to splice the speaker cable. Always run a new pair of speaker wires from amp to speakers. Remove the tape from the connecting cables and inspect the wiring. Pull off the wires going to the speaker and take a continuity measurement with the VOM or DMM. The speaker resistance should be about 4 to 8 ohms. Suspect a broken cable or an open speaker if there is no measurement. If the measurement is normal, check each cable wire from the amplifier connection to the removed ends.

Stagger the spliced speaker cable wires if the cable must be extended (Fig. 12-9). Now the wires cannot touch each other if the tape comes off. Solder each speaker connection and tape each connec-

tion separately. Wrap both connections with plastic tape.

Suspect an open speaker when no measurement is obtainable at the speakers. Stick a safety pin or needle through both cable wires right where the cable enters the enclosure of a sealed unit. Take another continuity test to determine if the cable is broken. If the measurement is a dead short, suspect the woofer speaker is open. Of course, in speaker enclosures with a pull-off grille cloth assembly, the speaker and cable connections can be checked by removing the woofer.

Sometimes only one speaker may be defective in the speaker cabinet. Put your ear close to each speaker while the music is playing. Try to determine which speaker is dead. If all speakers are dead, check for a broken speaker cable. The woofer is easy to spot because it provides the most volume. Remove the mid-range and tweeter speakers separately to determine which one is open with ohmmeter tests.

**The Sealed Speaker.** A defective speaker within a sealed cabinet is more difficult to locate until the front or back cover is removed. First note if the front cover can be pried off to get at the speakers. Usually the front panel is fastened with staples and can be removed if the grille cloth is

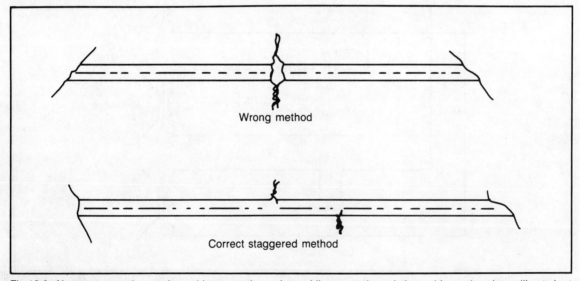

Fig 12-9. Always stagger the speaker cable connections when adding on to the existing cable so the wires will not short out, blowing the fuse or damaging the power-output transistor or IC.

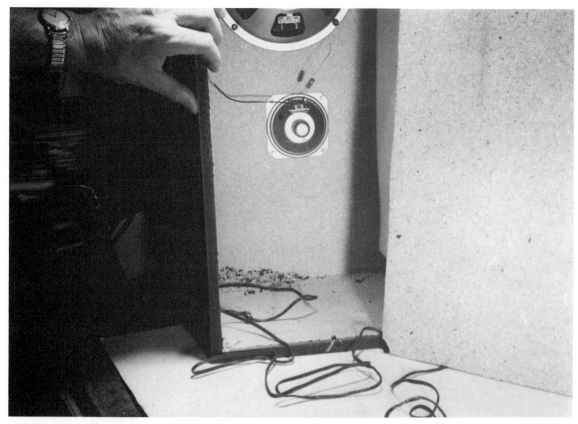

Fig. 12-10. Here the back cover was cut out of the wood cabinet with a saber saw to check a defective speaker.

overlapped at the sides. Remove the back cover if the front part of the cabinet is recessed (Fig. 12-10). Rather than repair them, some manufacturers want the speaker units returned if they become defective during the warranty period.

Saw out the back cover when it is glued to the side pieces. Leave a ¼- to 1-inch lip around the outside of the cabinet. The saber saw is ideal for cutting out the back cover. Be careful when sawing at the bottom area around the speaker cables. Remove the back piece and dump out the sawdust (Fig. 12-11).

Now check each speaker with the ohmmeter. Locate and replace the defective speaker. Solder all connections and check out the wiring. Connect the speaker to the amplifier and test it before sealing the cabinet. Cut a piece of Masonite board to fill the entire rear panel of the enclosure. Glue and place wood screws every four inches in the

Masonite back panel.

**Speaker Damage.** Excessive power applied to the speakers may blow out the voice coils and possibly damage the output transistors or IC components. Turning the volume wide open before the relay furnishes voltage to the output circuits damages speakers. Overloading the amplifier with too many add-on speakers may also damage the amplifier. Connecting a powerful amp to a set of low-powered speakers may cause speaker damage. Placing tin foil around the speaker fuses, instead of replacing with new fuses, may damage both speakers and amplifier (Fig. 12-12).

High-powered amplifiers should never be connected to low-wattage speakers. It is difficult to keep the volume down and will eventually destroy the speakers. When servicing high-wattage amplifiers with small test speakers, keep the volume at the lowest audible level. Always keep a load across

291

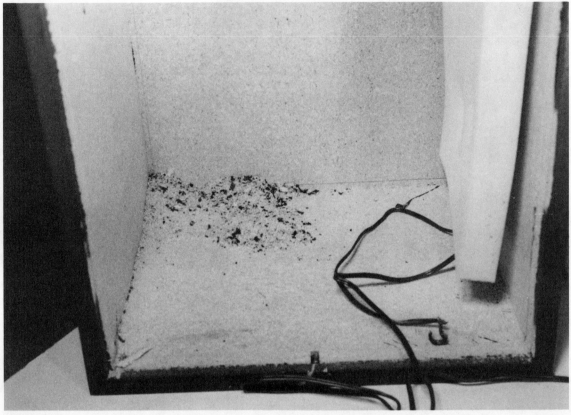

Fig. 12-11. blow out or dump all sawdust left in the cabinet when removing the back cover. Check the good speaker for sawdust around the cone or magnet area.

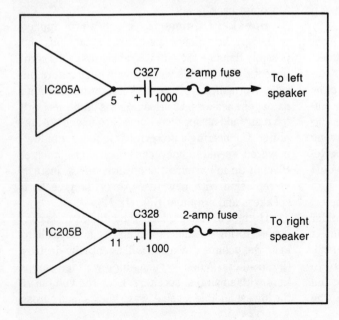

Fig. 12-12. Replace the blown speaker fuse with the correct amperage listed on the amp or fuse case. Do not wrap tin foil around the fuse or speaker or amp damage may result.

the speaker terminals and turn the volume way down when servicing the amplifier. Before plugging in the power cord, connect the speakers to each stereo channel.

Often speaker enclosures are rated with minimum and maximum operating power. Never exceed the maximum rating. Select a speaker system above the amplifier wattage output. For instance, if the speaker maximum power handling capacity is 90 watts, never connect a single stereo channel amplifier of over 75 watts. The total stereo speakers' wattage of 180 watts may be connected safely to a 150-watt amplifier.

Speaker damage may be caused by a leaky output transistor or IC in directly coupled (dc) circuits (Fig. 12-13). If the speaker fuse opens under normal operating conditions, check for low dc voltage at the fuse terminal. Keep the volume control at zero. Measure for dc voltage at both speaker fuses if the speaker voice coil is damaged. No dc voltage should be found at either speaker ( + ) terminal. If you replace the speaker and connect it back to the

speaker terminals of the amplifier, the new speaker may be damaged by dc voltage present.

In some amplifiers, speaker fuses are used to protect the speakers. In others there is no speaker protection (Fig. 12-14). Protect those expensive speaker columns by placing a fuse block at the rear of the amplifier or inserting a fuse in each positive speaker lead. Pick up a speaker fuse holder available at most stereo or radio TV supply stores and solder it into the speaker leads. Some of these fuse holders will plug right into the amp speaker terminals with the fused speaker leads inserted into the fuse holder (Fig. 12-15).

**Replacement Speakers.** Always try to replace the damaged speaker with the exact manufacturer's replacement in high-powered speaker enclosures. They are the correct size, required wattage, and impedance. In addition, these speakers are balanced for each stereo channel. Most manufacturers prefer the speakers be returned for replacements when in the warranty period.

Inexpensive or lower wattage speakers may be

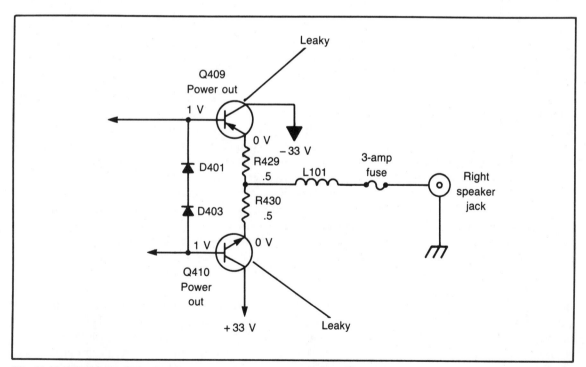

Fig. 12-13. A leaky power-output transistor or IC may place dc voltage on the speaker voice coil if a big fuse is installed and ruin the speaker.

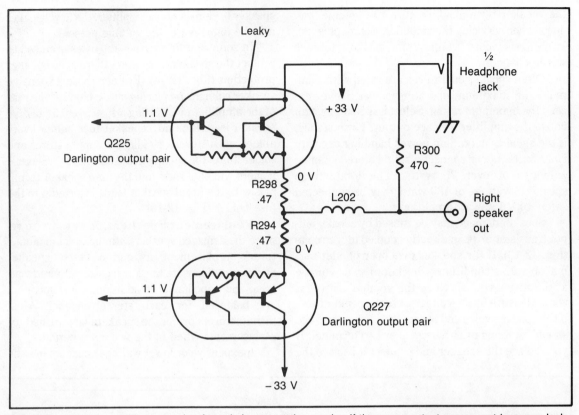

Fig. 12-14. In some amplifiers, speaker fuses help protect the speaker if the power output component becomes leaky in a directly coupled circuit. Here there is no fuse between the Darlington output transistors and the speaker.

replaced with universal replacements. Select the same size speaker and impedance. Try to replace with the same weight of the rear magnet. Small universal replacement speakers can be found at most radio and TV supply stores.

**Speaker Matching and Phasing.** For maximum stereo performance, all speakers should be connected so they are in phase with one another. The cones should go in and out all at the same time. To do this, the positive terminals of all the speakers are connected together, and the negative terminals are connected together inside the cabinet (Fig. 12-16). Be sure to connect the positive and negative terminals of the amplifier in the same way. In other words, all the speakers should be connected in parallel with each other and with the amplifier through common terminals.

When exact replacement enclosure speakers are replaced, the positive terminal of the speaker

is marked. Make sure the speaker is in phase when using a universal replacement. Take a 1½-volt flashlight battery and solder a couple of alligator leads to it (Fig. 12-17). Momentarily touch the battery clip across the speaker voice coil. Put the positive terminal of the battery on the speaker. Note if the cone pulls in or goes out. Check all speakers within the column in the same manner. Connect the speakers so they go in and out in unison.

**Connecting Extra Speakers.** Connecting too many speakers to a given amplifier may damage the output circuits or cause the speaker fuses to blow. If the additional speakers are connected in parallel to the existing speakers, the impedance load may be less than 1 ohm instead of 8 ohms. This places the equivalent of a short across the speaker terminals and will blow out the IC or output transistors. You may not find speaker protection fuses in some amplifiers.

Fig. 12-15. Wire the speaker fuse holder into the speaker terminal wires. Place the correct fuse in the external speaker fuse holder and insert the speaker wires into the end of the holder.

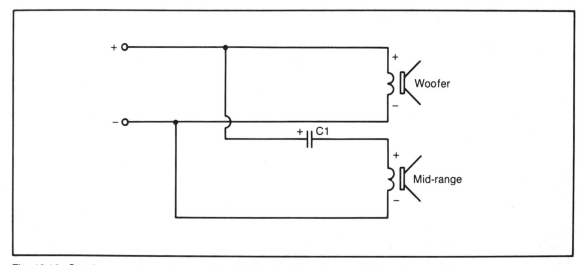

Fig. 12-16. Speakers may be polarized with a flashlight battery. Connect all positive speaker terminals to the positive (red) terminal of the amplifier.

Fig. 12-17. Clip one end of the battery to the voice coil terminal and just momentarily touch the other terminal from the battery. Note if the speaker cone is pulled in or out.

Besides overloading the output components, the audio signal may be distorted by adding too many speakers. When amplifiers are overloaded, they sometimes generate abnormal signals which may in turn destroy the speakers. With overloaded speakers, the power transistors or ICs will often run red hot and will eventually be destroyed.

Connecting two pairs of 8-ohm speakers in parallel results in 4 ohms (Fig. 12-18). Today most large amplifiers will produce enough power to drive speakers under a 4-ohm load. Check the manufacturers spec sheets for correct power and lower ohm impedance requirements. The typical low-powered amp will not drive two pairs of 8-ohm speakers with a 4-ohm load.

Some large amplifiers may have an internal switch which connects two different sets of speakers in a series-parallel arrangement. When speakers are connected in series, the total im-

pedance is simply the sum of each individual speaker impedance. In other words, if two 4-ohm speakers are connected in series, the total impedance is 8 ohms, which works nicely for an 8-ohm amp load (Fig. 12-19). Connecting two 8-ohm speakers in series would produce 16 ohms.

Choose speakers of the same make and impedance when adding extra speakers. Make sure the total impedance of either a series or parallel hookup is never under 4 ohms. Select the amplifier with enough power to supply the total speaker minimum-wattage requirements. You may have to step up to another higher wattage amplifier.

**Choosing Speaker Wire Size.** Most low-cost speaker cabinets have a 22 gauge size connecting cable. This cable will do if the speaker is not more than 20 feet from the amplifier. The longer the cable, the higher the resistance, or the lower the power that is applied to the speaker. The

296

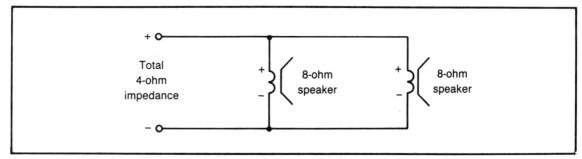

Fig. 12-18. When two 8-ohm speakers are connected in parallel, the total impedance is 4 ohms.

speaker cable may be using up part of the ampli-fier power instead of being applied to the speakers.

Choose number 18 or 16 gauge two-conductor speaker wire for connecting speakers over 25 feet from the amplifier. A thirty-foot piece of number 18 gauge wire would have a total resistance of less than .04 ohms, but a fifty-foot cable of number 16 gauge wire would have about the same resistance. Number 18 lamp or zip cord works nicely for con-necting speakers 30 or 50 feet from the amplifier. The larger the connecting cable, the less power ab-sorbed by the speaker wires.

## CAR RADIO SPEAKERS

The selection of a good car radio speaker is even more important than the radio. In the early car radios the speaker was often mounted right in-side the chassis, or there was a single front deck speaker mounted under the dash. Then a back seat speaker was added for better overall quality along with a speaker switch. The stereo tape player had two speakers in the front dash, two more in the

front doors, and two large rear deck mounted speakers (Fig. 12-20). Today, in some sports cars, an expensive component system may have a mod-ule of speakers at the rear deck.

Car radio speakers come in dash- and flush-mounted rear deck, surface, and component-mounted types. The front dash speakers may vary from 3½" diameter to 6" × 9" units. Most front door speakers are 4" to 6½" flush-mount types. The rear deck speakers may be 6" × 9", two- or three-way pairs which may include special size speakers. The special size speakers may be 4" × 10", 5" × 7", or 8" types mounted either in the front dash or rear deck. Most surface-mounted speakers are mounted on the rear deck. Special trunk-mounted speakers may be from 10 to 15 inches in size.

Instead of the low-wattage speakers found in the old car radio, modern units may have speakers ranging from 15 to 150 watts of power. The fre-quency response may be from 45 to 40,000 Hz on some speakers, but the average response is from 60 to 20,000 Hz. Of course, the 2, 3, and 4-way

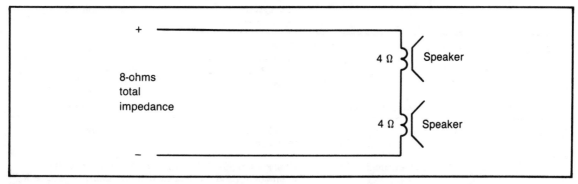

Fig. 12-19. Connect two 4-ohm speakers in series to get a total impedance of 8 ohms. In amplifiers with two different stereo outputs, the speaker switch may place each channel speaker in series.

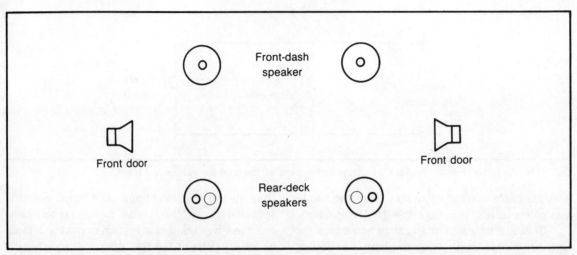

Fig. 2-20. In many autos with stereo 8 tape and cassette decks, two front dash, two front door, and two rear deck speakers are provided for optimum sound.

speaker systems have the greatest frequency response and output wattage. In a 3-way system, the small tweeters are mounted inside the cone area of the large 6 × 9 woofer. The auto component speaker system may contain a 1-inch tweeter, a 2- to 5-inch cone mid-range, and an 8- to 12-inch bass

### Table 12-2. Three-Way Speaker Troubleshooting Chart.

| Speaker | Symptom | Check |
|---------|---------|-------|
| Woofer | No sound | Check the resistance across speaker cable—there should be a clicking noise. If infinity, suspect open voice coil, broken cable wire, poor solder connection on sub terminals, or open network coils. |
| | Mushy-distorted | Sub another speaker to check amp. Cone dropped on woofer speaker. |
| | Intermittent | Check speaker cable. Remove speaker and test with hands while music is playing. |
| | Noisy | Suspect a damaged voice coil. Check cone area for hole damage. Inspect rim of speaker for a loose cone. Check cabinet for noisy panel. |
| Mid-range | No sound | Rotate level control or reset thermal relay if one available. Measure continuity of each driver ( – 4 to 12 ohms). There should be a clicking noise. Check for broken wires to speaker if woofer is normal. Check network components for an open. |
| | Intermittent and distorted | Sub or replace speaker. Check for loose connections. |
| Tweeter | No sound | Check continuity of voice coil. Inspect speaker wiring and terminals. |
| | Sound intermittent | Check for broken level control or thermal cutout. Suspect intermittent voice coil. Inspect network components. Check wiring to speaker terminals. |

reflex woofer. Car speakers may have impedances of 4, 6, or 8 ohms.

**Speaker Damage.** In addition to an open or damaged voice coil, the car speaker may become warped over time from excess moisture. Because cars sit outside most of the time, the speaker cone has a tendency to drop and rub against the magnet pole piece. Sometimes water will seep in and eventually warp the speaker cone. Excessive road dust may accumulate on top of the cone in front and rear deck speakers. In time, this may produce mushy music.

The voice coil may be damaged by excessive or high power applied to the speakers over a long period of time. Most auto players are operated at high volume to combat road noises. Often the excessive power may cause the voice coil to become intermittent, and the music will cut in and out at high volume levels. To locate the intermittent speaker, firmly press up and down on the cone area and note if the music starts and stops. Sub another known speaker to determine if the cable is good. Test the voice coil low-ohm resistance with a VOM or DMM to check for open conditions.

A defective speaker with a suspected open voice coil may be the result of an open or grounded speaker wire. Check where the wire bends for opens in the front door speakers. Each speaker wire may be signal-traced with the ohmmeter. Sometimes the speaker wires may be grounded to the metal frame. Hauling or placing large objects may damage or pull speaker wires loose in the trunk area if they are not protected. Check for grounds under the metal door step and around sharp metal corners. Remove both speaker wires for a good ground test.

Table 12-2 lists a number of additional problems along with their possible causes and troubleshooting suggestions.

# Appendix

# Manufacturers of Consumer Electronics Equipment

THE FOLLOWING IS A LIST OF THE MANY MANufacturers in the various consumer electronics and entertainment fields, listed alphabetically.

## Amplifiers

Acoustat Corp., 3101 SW. First Terrace, Ft. Lauderdale, FL 33315

Akai American Ltd., 800 W. Artesia Blvd., Compton, CA 90220

All Channel Products, 4240 Bell Plaza, Bayside, NY 11361

Amber Electronics, 218 Ridge St., Charlottesville, VA 22901

Analog & Digital Systems, One Progress Way, Wilmington, MA 01887

Andante, P.O. Box 5046, Berkeley, CA 94705

Bozak, Inc., 68 Holmes Rd., Newington, CT 06111

Cower Corp., 19210 33rd Ave., Lynnwood, WA 98036

Concord Systems, Inc., 6025 Golanda Ave., Tarzana, CA 91356

dB Systems, Main St., Ridge Center, NH 03461

Denon America, Inc., P.O. Box 1139, W. Caldwell, NJ 07006

Fisher Corporation, 21314 Lassen St., Chatsworth, CA 91311

General Electric, Consumer Electronics, Portsmouth, VA 23705

Harman Kardon, 240 Crossways Park, W. Woodbury, NJ 11797

Hitachi Sales Corp., 401 Artesia Blvd., Compton, CA 90220

J R Loudspeaker, 165 Broadway, Hudson, NY 10706

JVC America, 41 Slater Dr., Elmwood Park, NJ 07407

Kenwood Electronics, Inc., 1315 E. Watson Center Rd., Carson, CA 90745

Kyocera International, 7 Powder Horn Dr., Warren, NJ 07060

Linear Power, Inc., 11545 D Ave., Suburn, CA 95603

Lyman Division, 3102 Kashiwa St., Torrance, CA 90505

Marantz Co., 20525 Nordhoff St., Chatsworth, CA 91311

NAD (USA), Inc. 675 Canton St., Norwood, MA 02062

Nakamichi USA Corp., 19201 S. Vermont Ave., Torrance, CA 90502

Nikko Audio, 5830 S. Triangle Dr., Commerce, CA 90040

Onkyo USA Corp., 200 Williams Dr., Ramsey, NJ 07446

Panasonic Consumer Electronics, One Panasonic Way, Secaucus, NJ 07094

Pioneer Electronics, Inc., 5000 Airport Plaza Dr., Box 1540, Long Beach, CA 90801

Quad Electroacoustics Ltd., 695 Oak Grove Ave., Menlo Park, CA 94025

RCA Consumer Electronics, 600 N. Sherman Dr., Indianapolis, IN 46201

SAE, 1734 Gage Road., Montebello, CA 90640

Sansui Electronics, 1250 Valley Brook Ave., Lyndhurst, NJ 07071

H.H. Scott, Inc., 20 Commerce Way, Woburn, MA 01888

Sony Corp. of America, Sony Dr., Park Ridge, NJ 07074

Soundcraftsmen, Inc., 2200 S. Rickey, Santa Ana, CA 92075

Speco Division, 1172 Route 109, Box 624, Lyndhurst, NJ 11757

Stanton Magnetics, Inc., Terminal Dr., Plainview, NJ 11803

Studen Revox America, 1425 Elm Hill Pike, Nashville, TN 37210

Tandberg of America, Labriola Ct., Armonk, NY 10504

Technics, One Panasonic Way, Secaucus, NJ 07094

Threshold Corp., 1832 Tribute Rd. Suite E, Sacramento, CA 95815

Vector Research, 20600 Nordhoff St., Chatsworth, CA 91311

Winegard Co., 3000 Kirkwood St., Burlington, IA 52601

Yamaha Electronics Corp., 6660 Orangethorpe Ave., Buena Park, CA 90620

Zeff Advanced Products, 2135 Stone Ave., Modesto, CA 95351

## Auto Cassettes

ARA Manufacturing Co., 606 Fountain Pkwy., Grand Prairie, TX 75050

Afco Electronics, Inc., 471 Roland Way, Oakland, CA 94621

Aiwa America, Inc., 35 Oxford Dr., Moonachie, NJ 07074

Alaron, Inc., P.O. Box 550, Troy, MI 48099

Alpine Electronics of America, 3102 Kashiwa St., Torrance, CA 90505

American Acoustics, Inc., 12841 Western Ave., Garden Grove, CA 92641

American Audio Corp., 636 Forbes Blvd., So. San Francisco, CA 94080

Audiovox Corp., 150 Marcus Blvd., Hauppauge, NY 11727

Blaupunkt, 2800 S. 25th Ave., Broadview, IL 60153

Clarion Corp. of America, 5500 Rosecrans Ave., Lawndale, CA 90260

Concord Systems, Inc., 6025 Yolanda Ave., Tarzana, CA 91356

Craig Corp., 921 W. Artesia Blvd., Compton, CA 90220

Daewoo Electronics, 100 Daewoo Pl., Carlstadt, NJ 07041

Denon American, Box 1139, W. Caldwell, NJ 07006

Electronic Industries, 16940 Vincennes, S. Holland, IL 60473

Epicure Products, Inc., 25 Hale St., Newburyport, MA 01950

Fortune Star Products, 12 W. 23rd St., New York, NY 10010

Fujitsu Corp. of America, 19281 Pacific Gateway Dr., Torrance, CA 90502

Arthur Fulmer Electronics Division, 122 Gagoso, Memphis, TN 38103

Grundig/GR Electronics, Glenpointe Center E., Teaneck, NJ 07666

Hanabashiya Ltd., 39 W. 28th St., New York, NY 10001

J-corp Corp., 1031 Northern Blvd., Baldwin Harbor, NY 11510

JICL LA Corp., 17120 Edwards Rd., Ceritos, CA 90706

JVC America, 41 Slater Dr., Elmwood Park, NJ 07407

Jensen Inc., 4136 N. United Pkwy., Scheller Park, IL 60176

Jordache, 1201 Broadway, New York, NY 10001

K & K Merchandising Group, 10-27 45th Ave., Long Island City, NY 11101

Kendale Technology Corp., 4185 NW. 77th Ave., Miami, FL 33176

Kenwood Electronics, 1315 E. Watson Center Rd., Carson, CA 90745

Kraco Enterprises, Inc., 505 E. Euclid Ave., Compton, CA 90224

MCI, 23 NW. 8th Ave., Hallandale, FL 33009

Marantz Co., 20525 Nordhoff St., Chatsworth, CA 91311

Midland International Corp., 1690 N. Topping, Kansas City, MO 64120

Mitsubishi, 3030 E. Victoria, Rancho Dominguez, CA 90221

Nakamichi USA Corp., 19701 S. Vermont Ave., Torrance, CA 90502

Panasonic Auto Division, One Panasonic Way, Secaucus, NJ 07094

Phillips Auto Radio Division, 230 Duffy Ave., Hicksville, NY 11802

Pioneer Electronics USA, 5000 Airport Plaza Dr., Box 1540, Long Beach, CA 90801

Sansui Corp., 1250 Valley Brook Ave., Lyndhurst, NJ 07071

Sanyo Electronic Inc., 1200 W. Artesia Blvd., Compton, CA 90220

Sony Corp. of America, Sony Park, Park Ridge, NJ 07074

Sparkomatic Corp., Rts. 6 & 209, Milford, PA 18337

TZL International Corp., 1523 NW. 79th Ave., Miami, FL 33126

Tancredi Division, Kukje Pacific, 2318 E. Del Amo Blvd., Compton, CA 90220

Ultimate Sound, 19330 E. San Jose Ave., City of Industry, CA 91748

Vector Research, 20608 Nordhoff St., Chatsworth, CA 91311

Yamaha Electronics Corp., 6660 Orangethorpe Ave., Buena Park, CA 90620

## Compact Disc Players

Akai America Ltd., 800 W. Artesia Blvd., Compton, CA 90220

Denon America, Inc., Box 1139, W. Caldwell, NJ 07006

Fisher Corp., 21314 Lassen St., Chatsworth, CA 91311

General Electric, Portsmouth, VA 23705

Hitachi Sales Corporation of America, 401 W. Artesia Blvd., Compton, CA 90220

JVC America Co., 41 Slater Dr., Elmwood Park, NJ 07407

Kenwood Electronics, 1315 E. Watson Center Rd., Carson, CA 91745

Kyocera International, 7 Powder Horn Dr., Warren, NJ 07060

Luxman Division, 3102 Kashiwa St., Torrance, CA 90505

Magnavox, NAP, Box 6950, 1-40 & Straw Plains Pike, Knoxville, TN 37914

Marantz Co., 20525 Nordhoff St., Chatsworth, CA 91311

Mitsubishi, 3030 E. Victoria, Rancho Dominguez, CA 90221

NAD, Inc., 675 Canton St., Norwood, MA 02062

NEC Home Electronics, 1401 W. Ave., Elk Grove Village, IL 60007

Nakamichi USA Corp., 19701 S. Vermont Ave., Torrance, CA 90502

Onkyo USA Corp., 200 Williams Dr., Ramsey, NJ 07446

Panasonic Corp., One Panasonic Way, Secaucus, NJ 07094

Pioneer Electronics, 5000 Airport Plaza Dr., Box 1540, Long Beach, CA 90801

Quasar Co., 9401 W. Grand Ave., Franklin Park, IL 60131

RCA Consumer Electronics, 600 N. Sherman Dr., Indianapolis, IN 46201

SAE, 1734 Gage Rd., Montebello, CA 90640

Sansui Electronics, 1250 Valley Brook Ave., Lyndhurst, NJ 07071

Sanyo Electric, Inc., 1200 W. Artesia Blvd., Compton, CA 90220

H.H. Scott, Inc., 20 Commerce Way, Woburn, MA 01888

Sharp Electronics, 10 Sharp Plaza, Paramus, NJ 07652

Sony Corporation of America, Sony Dr., Park Ridge, NJ 07074

Studer Revox America, 1425 Elm Hill Pike, Nashville, TN 37210

Technics, One Panasonic Way, Secaucus, NJ 07094

Toshiba America, 82 Totawa Rd., Wayne, NJ 07470

Yamaha Electronics Corp., 6660 Orangethorpe Ave., Buena Park, CA 90620

## Compact Systems

Alaron, Inc., Box 550 Troy, MI 48099

Bang & Olufsen of America, 1150 Feehanville Dr., Mt. Prospect, IL 60056

Brentwood Electronics, 256 W. Ivy Ave., Inglewood, CA 90302

Denon America Inc., Box 1139, W. Caldwell, NJ 07006

Emerson Radio Corp., North Bergen, NJ 07047

Fortune Star Products, 1200 23rd St., New York, NY 10010

Hanimex, Inc., 3125 Commercial Ave., Northbrook, IL 60062

Hitachi Sales Corp., 401 W. Artesia Blvd., Compton, CA 90220

Juliette Electronics, 4615 NW. 77th Ave., Miami, FL 33166

Lloyds Electronics, 180 Raritan Center Pkwy., Edison, NJ 08818

Magnavox Consumer Electronic, Box 6950, 1-40 & Straw Plains Pike, Knoxville, TN 37914

Marantz Co., 20525 Nordhoff St., Chatsworth, CA 91311

Mitsubishi Electric Sales, 3030 E. Victoria, Rancho Dominguez, CA 90221

Panasonic, One Panasonic Way, Secaucus, NJ 07094

Philco Consumer Elec., Box 6950, Knoxville, TN 37914

Pioneer Electronics, 5000 Airport Plaza Dr., Box 1540, Long Beach, CA 90801

Quasar Co., 9401 W. Grand Ave., Franklin Park, IL 60131

Sanyo Corporation of America, 1050 Arthur Ave., Elk Grove Village, IL 60007

Sanyo Electronics, 1200 W. Artesia Blvd., Compton, CA 90220

Teletone Co., Inc. 444 S. 9th. Ave., Mt. Vernon, NY 10550

Toshiba America, 82 Totawa Rd., Wayne, NJ 07470

UCM Corp., 3843 Carson St., Torrance, CA 90503

Yorx Electronics Corp., 405 Minnisink Rd., Totowa, NJ 07512

## Portable Tape Recorders

Aiwa America Inc., 35 Oxford Dr., Moonachie, NJ 07074

Akai America Ltd., 800 W. Artesia Blvd., Compton, CA 90220

Alaron, Inc., Box 550, Troy, MI 48099

Anow Trading Co., Inc., 1115 Broadway, New York, NY 10010

Daewoo Electronics, 100 Daewoo Pl., Carlstadt, NJ 07041

Dejay Corp., 5 Mear Rd., Holbrook, MA 02343

Emerson Radio Corp., One Emerson Ln., N. Bergen, NJ 07047

Fortune Star Products, 12 W. 23rd. St., New York, NY 10010

General Electric Electronics, Electronics Park Bldg. 5, Syracuse, NY 13221

General Electric, Portsmouth, VA 23705

Goldstar Electronics, 1050 Wall St., W. Lyndhurst, NJ 07071

Grundig/GR Electronics, Glenpointe Center East, Teaneck, NJ 07666

Hanabashiga Ltd., 39 W. 28th. St., New York, NY 10001

Hanimex USA, Inc., 3125 Commercial Ave., Northbrook, IL 60062

Hitachi Sales Corp., 401 W. Artesia Blvd., Compton, CA 90220

JVC Corporation of America, 41 Slater Dr., Elmwood Park, NJ 07407

Jordache, 1201 Broadway, New York, NY 10001

Juliette Electronics, 4565 NW 77th Ave., Miami, FL 33166

K & K Merchandising Corp., 10-27 45th Ave., Long Island City, NY 11101

Kenwood Electronics, 1315 E. Watson Center Rd., Carson, CA 90745

Koss Corp., 4129 N. Port Washington Ave., Milwaukee, WI 53212

Lasonic Electronics, 1827 W. Valley Blvd., Alhambra, CA 91803

Lloyds Electronics, 180 Rariton Center Pkwy., Edison, NJ 08818

MCI, 23 NW 8th Ave., Hallandale, FL 33009

Magnavox Electronics, Box 6950 1-40 & Straw Plains Pike, Knoxville, TN 37914

Marantz Co., 20525 Nordhoff St., Chatsworth, CA 91311

Olympus Corp., Crossways Park, Woodbury, NY 11797

Panasonic Electronics, One Panasonic Way, Secaucus, NJ 07094

Pierre Cardan Electronics, 1115 Broadway, New York, NY 10010

Pioneer Electronics, 5000 Airport Plaza Dr, Box 1540, Long Beach, CA 90801

Quasar Co., 9401 W. Grand Ave., Franklin Park, IL 60131

Sanyo Corporation of America, 1050 Arthur Ave., Elk Grove Village, IL 60007

Samsuy Electronics, 301 Mayhill St., Saddlebrook, NJ 07662

Samsung Corp., 1250 Valley Brook Ave., Lyndhurst, NJ 07071

Sanyo Electronics, 1200 W. Artesia Blvd., Compton, CA 90220

Sharp Electronics, 10 Sharp Plaza, Paramus, NJ 07652

Sony Corporation of American, Sony Drive, Park Ridge, NJ 07024

Soundesign, 34 Exchange Pl., Jersey City, NJ 07302

Symphonic Electronics, 1825 Acacia Blvd., Compton, CA 90220

TZL International Corp., 1523 NW 79th Ave., Miami, FL 33126

Tatung Company of America, 2850 El Presido St., Long Beach, CA 90810

Toshiba Corp., 82 Totowa Rd., Wayne, NJ 07470

UCM Corp., 3848 Carson St., Torrance, CA 90503

Wald Sound, 11131 Dora St., Sun Valley, CA 91352

Windsor Industries Inc., 131 Executive Blvd., Farmingdale, NY 11735

Yamaha Electronics Corp., 6660 Orangethorpe Ave., Buena Park, CA 90620

Yorx Electronics Corp., 405 Minnisink Rd., Totowa, NJ 07512

## Receivers

Akai America Ltd., 800 W. Artesia Blvd., Compton, CA 90220

Analog & Digital Systems, One Progress Way, Wilmington, MA 01887

Bang & Olufsen of America, 1150 Feehanville Dr., Mt. Prospect, IL 60056

Carver Corp., 19210 33rd Ave., Lynnwood, WA 98036

Denon America Inc., Box 1139, W. Caldwell, NJ 07006

Fisher Corp., 21314 Lassen St., Chatsworth, CA 91311

General Electric Corp., Portsmouth, VA 23705

Harmon Kardon, 240 Crossway Park W., Woodbury, NY 11797

Hitachi Sales Corp., 401 W. Artesia Blvd., Compton, CA 90220

JVC Company of America, 41 Slater Dr., Elmwood Park, NJ 07407

Kenwood Electronics, 1315 E. Watson Center Rd., Carson, CA 90745

Kyocera International, 7 Powder Horn Dr., Warren, NJ 07060

Luxman Division, 3102 Kashiwa St., Torrance, CA 90505

Marantz Co., 20525 Nordhoff St., Chatsworth, CA 91311

Mitsubishi Electric Sales, 3030 E. Victoria, Rancho Dominguez, CA 90221

NAD (USA) Inc., 675 Canton St., Norwood, MA 02062

Nikko Audio, 5830 S. Triangle Dr., Commerce, CA 90040

Onkyo USA Corp., 200 Williams Dr., Ramsey, NJ 07448

Panasonic Consumer Electric, One Panasonic Way, Secaucus, NJ 07094

Pioneer Electronics, 5000 Airport Plaza Dr., Box 1540, Long Beach, CA 90801

SAE, 1734 Gage Rd., Montibello, CA 90640

Sansui Corp., 1250 Valley Brook Ave., Lyndhurst, NJ 07071

Sanyo Electric Inc., 1200 W. Artesia Blvd., Compton, CA 90220

H.H. Scott Co., 20 Commerce Way, Woburn, MA 01888

Sharp Electronics, 10 Sharp Plaza, Paramus, NJ 07652

Sony Corporation of America, Sony Dr., Park Ridge, NJ 07074

Soundesign, 34 Exchange Pl., Jersey City, NJ 07302

Studer Revox America, 1425 Elm Hill Pike, Nashville, TN 37210

Technics, One Panasonic Way, Secaucus, NJ 07094

Vector Research, 20600 Nordhoff St., Chatsworth, CA 91311

Yamaha Electronics, 6660 Orangethorpe Ave., Buena Park, CA 90620

## Speakers

AAL the Mitek Group, One Mitek Plaza, Winslow, IL 61089

Acoustat Corp. Teledyne, 330 Turnpike, Canton, MA 02031

Adcom, 11 Elkins Rd., East Brunswick, NJ 08816

Advent, 4138 N. United Pkwy, Schiller Park, IL 60176

Aiwa America Inc., 35 Oxford Dr., Moonachie, NJ 07074

Akai America Ltd., 800 W. Artesia Blvd., Compton, CA 90220

Altec-Lansing International, 1515 S. Manchester Ave., Anaheim, CA 92803

Analog & Digital Systems, One Progress Way, Wilmington, MA 01887

Audio-Technia US Inc., 1221 Commerce Dr., Stow, OH 44224

BES, 345 Fischer St., Costa Mesa, CA 92626

BSR USA Ltd., RR 303, Blaurelt, NJ 10913

Bang & Olufsen of America, 1150 Feehanville Dr., Mt. Prospect, IL 60056

Bose Corp., 100 The Mountain Rd., Framington, MA 01701

Boston Acoustics, Inc., 247 Lynnfield St., Peabody, MA 01960

Bozak, Inc., 68 Holmes Rt., Newington, CT 06111

Carter Corp., 1916 11th St., Rockford, IL 61101

Celestion Industries, Box 521, Hollister, MA 01746

Cerwin-Vega, 12250 Montague St., Arleta, CA 91331

Dahlquist, Inc., 601 Old Willets Rd., Hauppauge, NY 11788

Fisher Corp., 21314 Lassen St., Chatsworth, CA 91311

Fortune Star Corp., 12 W. 230 St., New York, NY 10010

Gemini Speaker Systems, 1221 38th St., Brooklyn, NY 11218

General Electric, Portsmouth, VA 23705

Grafex Mitek Corp., One Mitek Plaza, Winslow, IL 61089

GR Electronics Corp., Glenpointe Center, East Teaneck, NJ 07666

Hitachi Sales Corp., 401 W. Artesia Blvd., Compton, CA 90220

Infinity Systems, Inc., 9409 Owensmouth, Chatsworth, CA 91311

Interaudio by Bose, The Mountain Road, Framington, MA 01701

International Component, 105 Maxess Rd., Melville, NY 11747

JBL Inc., 8500 Balboa Blvd., Box 2200, Northridge, CA 91329

J R Loudspeaker, 165 Broadway, Hastings on the Hudson, NY 10706

JVC America Co., 41 Slater Dr., Elmwood Park, NJ 07407

Jasco Products Co., Box 466, Oklahoma City, OK 73145

Jensen Inc., 4136 N. United Pkwy., Schiller Park, IL 60176

KEF, 695 Oak Grove Ave., Menlo Park, CA 94025

Kenwood Electronics, 1315 E. Watson Center Rd., Carson, CA 90745

Koss Corp., 4129 N. Port Washington Ave., Milwaukee, WI 53212

Kyocera International Inc., 7 Powder Horn Dr., Warren, NJ 07060

M & G Electronics, 32 Ranich Rd., Hauppauge, NY 11788

MTX, 629 W. Cermak, Chicago, IL 60616

Marantz Co., 20525 Nordhoff St., Chatsworth, CA 91311

Mitsubishi Electronic Sales, 3030 E. Victoria, Rancho Dominguez, CA 90211

Motorola, Inc., 4800 Alameda Blvd. NE, Albuquerque, NM 87113

NAD, Inc., 675 Canton St., Norwood, MA 02062

OWI, Inc., 1160 Mahalo Pl., Compton, CA 90220

Oaktron Inc., 1000 30th St., Monroe, WI 53566

Onkyo USA Corp., 200 Williams Dr., Ramsey, NJ 07446

Panasonic Consumer Electronics, One Panasonic Way, Secaucus, NJ 07094

Peerless Audio Mfg., 40 Gytek Dr., Leominster, MA 01453

Pioneer Electronics, 5000 Airport Plaza, Box 1540, Long Beach, CA 90801

Polk Audio, 1915 Annapolis Rd., Baltimore, MD 21230

Polydax Speaker Corp., Two Park Ave., New York, NY 10016

Pyle Industries, 501 Center St., Huntington, IN 46750

Quad Electroacoustics, 695 Oak Grove Ave., Menlo Park, CA 94025

Quasar Co., 9401 W. Grand Ave., Franklin Park, IL 60131

RCA Consumer Electronics, 600 N. Sherman Dr., Indianapolis, IN 46201

RTR Speaker Co., 21212 Vanowen St., Canoga Park, CA 91303

Sansui Electronics Corp., 1250 Valley Brook Ave., Lyndhurst, NJ 07071

H.H. Scott Co., 20 Commerce Way, Woburn, MA 01888

Shahinian Acoustics Ltd., 24 Commercial Blvd., Medford, NY 11763

Sharp Electronics, 10 Sharp Plaza, Paramus, NJ 07652

Sony Corp., Sony Dr., Park Ridge, NJ 07074

Soundesign, 34 Exchange Pl., Jersey City, NJ 07302

Speco Division, 1172 Rte. 109, Box 624, Lyndhurst, NJ 11757

Studer Revox America, 1425 Elm Hill Pike, Nashville, TN 37210

Technics, One Panasonic Way, Secaucus, NJ 07094

Vector Research, 20600 Nordhoff St., Chatsworth, CA 91311

Visonik of America, 701 Heinz Ave., Berkeley, CA 95710

Wald Sound, 11131 Dora St., Sun Valley, CA 91352

Wharfedale Loudspeakers, 700 Billings St. Aurora, CO 80011

Yamaha Electronics Corp., 6660 Orangethorpe Ave., Buena Park, CA 90620

## Tape Decks

Adcom, 11 Elkins Rd., East Brunswick, NJ 08816

Aiwa America, Inc., 35 Oxford Dr., Moonachie, NJ 07074

Akai America Ltd., 800 W. Artesia Blvd., Compton, CA 90220

Alaron, Inc., Box 550, Troy, MI 48099

Analog Digital Systems, One Progress Way, Wilmington, MA 01887

Bang & Olufsen of America, 1150 Feehanville Dr., Mt. Prospect, IL 60056

Fortune Star Products, 1200 23rd St., New York, NY 10010

General Electric, Portsmouth, VA 23705

Harman Kardon, 240 Crossways Park, W. Woodbury, NY 11797

Hitachi Sales Corp., 401 W. Artesia Blvd., Compton, CA 90220

JVC Company of America, 41 Slater Dr., Elmwood Park, NJ 07407

Kenwood Electronics, 1315 E. Watson Center Rd., Carson, CA 90745

Kyocera International, 7 Powder Horn Dr., Warren, NJ 07060

Luxman Division, 3102 Kashiwa St., Torrance, CA 90505

Marantz Co., 20525 Nordhoff St., Chatsworth, CA 91311

Mitsubishi Electronics Sales, 3030 E. Victoria, Rancho Dominguez, CA 90221

NAD, Inc., 675 Canton St., Norwood, MA 02062

Nakamichi USA Corp., 19701 S. Vermont Ave., Torrance, CA 90502

Nikko Audio, 5830 S. Triangle Dr., Commerce, CA 90040

Onkyo USA Corp., 200 Williams Dr., Ramsey, NJ 07446

Panasonic Electronics Group, One Panasonic Way, Secaucus, NJ 07094

Pioneer Electronics, 5000 Airport Plaza Dr., Long Beach, CA 90801

RCA Consumer Electronics, 600 N. Sherman Dr., Indianapolis, IN 46201

SAE, 1734 Gage Rd., Montebello, CA 90640

Samsung Electronics Inc., 301 Mayhill St., Saddlebrook, NJ 07662

Sansui Electronics Corp., 1250 Valley Brook Ave., Lyndhurst, NJ 07071

Sanyo Electronics, 1200 W. Artesia Blvd., Compton, CA 90220

H.H. Scott Inc., 20 Commerce Way, Woburn, MA 01888

Sharp Electronics, 10 Sharp Plaza, Paramus, NJ 07652

Sony Corp., Sony Dr., Park Ridge, NJ 07074

Studer Revox America, 1425 Elm Hill Pike, Nashville, TN 37210

Teac Corporation of America, 7733 Telegraph Rd., Montebello, CA 90640

TZL International, 1523 NW 79th Ave., Miami, FL 33126

Tandberg of America, Labriola Ct., Armonk, NY 10504

Technics, One Panasonic Way, Secaucus, NJ 07094

Toshiba America Inc., 82 Totawa Rd., Wayne, NJ 07470

Vector Research, 20600 Nordhoff St., Chatsworth, CA 91311

Yamaha Electronics, 6660 Orangethorpe Ave., Buena Park, CA 90620

## Telephone Answering Machines

AT & T Consumer Products, 5 Wood Hollow Rd., Parsippany, NJ 07054

Cobra/Dynarcan Corp., 6500 W. Courtland St., Chicago, IL 60634

Code-A-Phone Co., Box 5656, Portland, OR 97228

Cosmo Communications, 16501 NW 16th Ct., Miami, FL 33169

Fortel Corp., 19200 S. Laurd Park Rd., Compton, CA 90220

Fortune Star Corp., 12 W. 23rd St., New York, NY 10010

GTE Consumer Products, One Stamford Forum, Stamford, CT 06904

General Electric Co., Electronics Park, Syracuse, NY 13221

Hanabashiya Ltd., 39 W. 28th St., New York, NY 10001

K & K Merchandising Group, 10-27 45th Ave., Long Island City, NY 11101

Kindale Technology, 4185 NW 77th Ave., Miami, FL 33176

Kifkat International Telephone, 40-18 150th St., Flushing, NY 11354

Kraco Enterprises, Inc., 505 E. Euclid Ave., Compton, CA 90224

LETEL Electronics, 17923 Western Ave., Gardena, CA 90248

MCI, 23 NW 8th Ave, Hallandale, FL 33009

Panasonic Electronics Group, One Panasonic Way, Secaucus, NJ 07094

Phone-Mate, Inc., 325 Maple Ave., Torrance, CA 90503

Quasar Microsystems, Record-O-Phone, Brentwood, NY 11717

Sanyo Business Systems, 51 Joseph St., Moonachie, NJ 07074

ITT Systems Corp., 9 E. 36th St., New York, NY 10016

Telephone Company of America, 55 Colony St., Meriden, CT 06450

Toshiba America Inc., 82 Totawa Rd., Wayne, NJ 07470

Unisonic Products, 1115 Broadway, New York, NY 10010

Webcor Electronics, 107 Charles Lindberg Blvd., Garden City, NY 11530

## Tuners

Adcon, 11 Elkins Rd., East Brunswick, NJ 08816

Amber Electronics, 218 Ridge St., Charlottesville, VA 22901

Analog Digital Systems, One Progress Way, Wilmington, MA 01887

Carver Corp., 19210 33rd Ave., Lynnwood, WA 98036

Denon America, Inc., Box 1139, W. Caldwell, NJ 07016

Fisher Corp., 21314 Lassen St., Chatsworth, CA 91311

General Electric Consumer Products, Portsmouth, VA 23705

Harmon Kardon, 240 Crossways Park, W. Woodbury, NY 11797

Hitachi Sales of America, 401 W. Artesia Blvd., Compton, CA 90220

JVC Company of America, 41 Slater Dr., Elmwood Park, NJ 07407

Kyocera International, 7 Powder Horn Dr., Warren, NJ 07060

Marantz Co., 20525 Nordhoff St., Chatsworth, CA 91311

Mitsubishi Electric Sales, 3030 E. Victoria, Rancho Dominguez, CA 90221

NAD USA Inc., 675 Canton St., Norwood, MA 02602

Nakamichi USA Corp., 19701 S. Vermont Ave., Torrance, CA 90502

Nikko Audio, 5830 S. Triangle Dr., Commerce, CA 90040

Onkyo USA Corp., 200 Williams Dr., Ramsey, NJ 07448

Panasonic Consumer Electronics, One Panasonic Way, Secaucus, NJ 07094

Pioneer Electronics Inc., 5000 Airport Plaza Dr., Long Beach, CA 90801

Quad Electroacoustics, 695 Oak Grove Ave., Menlo Park, CA 94205

RCA Consumer Electronics, 600 N. Sherman Dr., Indianapolis, IN 46201

SAE, 1734 Gage Road., Montebello, CA 90640

Samsung Electronics America, 301 Mayhill St., Saddlebrook, NJ 07662

Sansui Electronics, 1250 Valley Brook Ave., Lyndhurst, NJ 07071

H.H. Scott, Inc., 20 Commerce Way, Woburn, MA 01888

Sony Corporation of America, Sony Dr., Park Ridge, NJ 07074

Soundcraftsmen, Inc., 2200 S. Rithey, Santa Ana, CA 92705

Studer Revox America, 1425 Elm Hill Pike, Nashville, TN 37210

TZL International Corp., 1523 NW 79th Ave., Miami, FL 33126

Tandberg of America, Labrida Ct., Armonk, NY 10504

Technics, One Panasonic Way, Secaucus, NJ 07094

Vector Research, 20600 Nordhoff St., Chatsworth, CA 91311

Yamaha Electronics Corp., 6660 Orangethorpe Ave., Buena Park, CA 90620

## Turntables

Acoustic Research, 330 Turnpike St., Canton, MA 02021

Aiwa America Inc., 35 Oxford Dr., Moonachie, NJ 07074

Akai America Ltd., 800 W. Artesia Blvd., Compton, CA 90220

Alaron, Inc., Box 550, Troy, MI 48099

Analog Digital Systems, One Progress Way, Wilmington, MA 01887

Andante, Box 5046, Berkeley, CA 94705

BSR USA Ltd., RR303, Blauvelt, NY 10913

Bang & Olufsen, Inc., 1150 Feehanville Dr., Mt. Prospect, IL 60056

Dejay Corp., 5 Mear Rd., Holbrook, MA 02343

Denon America, Inc., Box 1139 W. Caldwell, NJ 07006

Dynavector Systems, 2217 S. Grand Ave., Santa Ana, CA 92705

Epicure Products Inc., 25 Hale St., Newburyport, MA 01950

Fisher Corp., 21314 Lassen St., Chatsworth, CA 91311

Fortune Star Products, 12 W. 23rd St., New York, NY 10010

General Electric Corp., Portsmouth, VA 23705

Harmon Kardon, 240 Crossways Park, W. Woodbury, NY 11797

Hitachi Sales Corp., 401 W. Artesia Blvd., Compton, CA 90220

J R Loudspeaker, 165 Broadway, Hastings on Hudson, NJ 10706

JVC Company, 41 Slater Dr., Elmwood Park, NJ 07407

Kenwood Electronics, 1315 E. Watson Center Rd., Carson, CA 90745

Kyocera International, 7 Powder Horn Dr., Warren, NJ 07060

Luxman Divisions, 3102 Kashiwa St., Torrance, CA 90505

Marantz Co., 20525 Nordhoff St., Chatsworth, CA 91311

Mitsubishi Electric Sales, 3030 E. Victoria, Rancho Dominguez, CA 90221

NAD USA Inc., 675 Canton St., Norwood, MA 02602

Nakamichi USA Corp., 19701 S. Vermont Ave., Torrance, CA 90502

Nikko Audio, 5830 S. Triangle Dr., Commerce, CA 90040

Onkyo USA Corp., 200 Williams Dr., Ramsey, NJ 07446

Panasonic Consumer Electronics, One Panasonic Way, Secaucus, NJ 07044

Pioneer Electronics, 5000 Airport Plaza Dr., Box 1540, Long Beach, CA 90801

RCA Consumer Products, 600 N. Sherman Dr., Indianapolis, IN 46201

Sansui Electronics Corp., 1250 Valley Brook Ave., Lyndhurst, NJ 07071

Sanyo Electric Inc., 1200 W. Artesia Blvd., Compton, CA 90220

H.H. Scott Inc., 20 Commerce Way, Woburn, MA 01888

Sharp Electronics, 10 Sharp Plaza, Paramus, NJ 07652

Sony Corporation of America, Sony Dr., Park Ridge, NJ 07074

Soundesign, 34 Exchange Place, Jersey City, NJ 07302

Studer Revox America, 1425 Elm Hill Pike, Nashville, TN 37210

Technics, One Panasonic Way, Secaucus, NJ 07091

Vector Research, 20600 Nordhoff St., Chatsworth, CA 91311

Yamaha Electronics, 6660 Orangethorpe Ave., Buena Park, CA 90620

## Video Cassette Recorders (VCRs)

Akai America Ltd., 800 W. Artesia Blvd., Compton, CA 90220

Canon USA Inc., One Canon Plaza, Lake Success, NY 11042

Denon America, Inc., Box 1139, W. Caldwell, NJ 07006

Fisher Corp., 21314 Lassen St., Chatsworth, CA 91311

General Electric Consumer Electronics, Portsmouth, VA 23705

Goldstar Electronics Inc., 1050 Wall St., W. Lyndhurst, NJ 07071

Hitachi Sales Corp., 401 W. Artesia Blvd., Compton, CA 90220

JVC Company of America, 41 Slater Dr., Elmwood Park, NJ 07407

Jensen Inc., 4136 N. United Pkwy., Schiller Park, IL 60176

Kenwood Electronics, 1315 E. Watson Center Rd., Carson, CA 90745

Lloyds Electronics, 180 Rariton Center Pkwy., Edison, NJ 08818

Magnavox Consumer Electronics, Box 6950 1-40 & Shaw Plains Pike, Nashville, TN 37914

Mitsubishi Corp., 3030 E. Victoria, Rancho Dominguez, CA 90221

NEC Home Electronics, 1401 W. Estes Ave., Elk Grove Village, IL 60007

Panasonic Consumer Electronics, One Panasonic Way, Secaucus, NJ 07094

Philco Consumer Electronics, Box 6950, Knoxville, TN 37914

Quasar Co., 9401 W. Grand Ave., Franklin Park, IL 60131

RCA Consumer Electronics, 600 N. Sherman Dr., Indianapolis, IN 46201

RCA Microcomputer Products, New Holland Ave., Lancaster, PA 17604

Sanyo Corp., 1050 Arthur Ave., Elk Grove Village, IL 60007

Samsung Electrics Inc., 301 Mayhill St., Saddlebrook, NJ 07662

Sansui Electronics Corp., 1250 Valley Brook Ave., Lyndhurst, NJ 07071

Sanyo Electric, Inc., 1200 W. Artesia Blvd., Compton, CA 90220

Sharp Electronics, 10 Sharp Plaza, Paramus, NJ 07652

Sony Corporation of America, Sony Dr., Park Ridge, NJ 07074

Sylvania Consumer Electronics, Box 6950, 1-40 & Straw Plains Pk, Knoxville, TN 37914

Symphonic Electric Corp., 1825 Acacia, Compton, CA 90220

Tatung Company of America, 2850 El Presidio St., Long Beach, CA 90810

Technics Electronics Corp., 353 Rt. 46 W., Fairfield, NJ 07470

Toshiba America Inc., 82 Totawa Rd., Wayne, NJ 07470

Toyomenka Inc., 357 County Ave., Secaucus, NJ 07094

Vector Research, 20600 Nordhoff St., Chatsworth, CA 91311

Zenith Electronic Corp., 1000 Milwaukee Ave., Glenview, IL 60025

# Glossary

**acoustic feedback**—A vibration of the turntable and speaker picked up and reamplified by the cartridge, producing a rumble, howling noise, or distortion in the speaker.

**acoustic suspension**—AS or air suspension speakers are enclosed in a sealed enclosure or box to produce natural, low-distortion bass output. More driving power is needed with these less efficient speaker systems.

**adjacent channel selectivity**—The tuner's ability in dB to filter out the station on the band adjacent to the one already tuned in.

**AFC (automatic frequency control)**—The AFC circuits reduce drift by locking the tuner on a certain station. The defeat switch allows weaker stations to be tuned in.

**AFM (audio frequency modulation)**—The process by which both Beta and VHS systems encode the audio track for recording.

**AGC (automatic gain control)**—Adjusts the radio tuner's sensitivity according to the strength of the station tuned in.

**air suspension**—Another name for an acoustic suspension speaker.

**alternate channel selectivity**—The tuner's ability in dB to filter out the alternate station alongside the one already tuned in.

**AM (amplitude modulation)**—The standard broadcast band (550 to 1650 kHz) employs amplitude modulation; the AM process in which the program information is imposed upon a carrier signal of constant frequency to vary its amplitude level in proportion to the level of the program.

**ambience simulation**—Refers to the sound environment of a given space. By means of electronically controlling the reverberation, echo time, and phase relationship with extra speakers a small room may sound like a concert hall.

**amp**—Abbreviation for amplifier.

**AM suppression or rejection**—The ability of an AM tuner to reject FM signals. Multipath reception off of reflected surfaces beyond the tuner's ability to reject these unwanted signals may be harsh and raspy. AM rejection occurs with the AGC which compresses the signal to reduce the change in amplitude.

**ANRS**—A noise-reduction system operating on principles similar to the Dolby system found in JVC products.

**antenna**—Any device used to pick up radio frequency and convert it to electrical energy for use by the radio or TV receiver. The inverted "L" antenna was used in the early radio days with the present dipole antenna mounted on top of the plastic radio cabinet.

**antiskating**—A force applied to the pivoted tone arm to counter-act the tendency of the arm to be pulled towards the center of the record or disc.

**APC (automatic power control)**—The circuit which keeps the laser-diode optical output at a constant level in the compact disc player.

**audio/video control center**—The central control system that controls all audio and VCR operations.

**auto eject**—The tape player feature which automatically ejects the cassette at the end of the playing time.

**auto focus (AF)**—The focus servo which functions to move the objective lens up or down to correct the focus of the compact disc player.

**auto record level**—Automatic control of the recording level.

**auto reverse**—The ability of the cassette player to automatically reverse directions to play the other side of the tape.

**auto size selector**—Puts the tone arm down on the record according to the size of the loaded records. Several different sizes of records may be loaded and played at the same time.

**auto tape selector**—Automatic bias and equalization when the cassette is inserted into the tape deck.

**auto turntable**—A turntable that automatically plays each loaded record and shuts off without help from the operator. The semi-automatic turntable may only lift the arm at the end of play and return the tone arm to the rest post.

**azimuth**—The angle at which the tape head meets the moving tape. A loss of high-frequency response is often caused by improper azimuth adjustment. The azimuth screw is located alongside of the tape head in the cassette player.

**azimuth control**—A control to adjust the angle of the tape head to correct misalignment in the auto stereo tape player.

**baffle**—The board on which the speakers are mounted.

**balance**—The control in the stereo amp equalizes the output audio in each channel.

**bass reflex**—A bass reflex system which vents the backward sound waves through a tuned vent or port, thus improving bass response.

**Beta**—A tape head system developed by Sony for VCR recorders.

**biamplification**—Using two amplifiers and a crossover network to drive separate speakers with one power level, one for the low and the other for the high-frequency range.

**bias**—A high frequency current applied to the tape head winding to prevent low distortion and noise while recording on the tape.

**block diagram**—A diagram showing the different stages of a radio, amplifier, VCR, or compact disc player.

**booster amplifier**—A separate amplifier connected between the main unit and the speakers in a car stereo system.

**bridging**—Combining both stereo channels of the amp to produce a mono signal with almost twice the normal power rating in a car stereo system.

**cabinet**—The box which contains the speakers. The size, materials, and construction all determine how the loudspeaker will sound.

**capstan**—The shaft that rotates against the tape at a constant rate of speed, moving the tape past the tape heads. In the cassette tape player, a rubber pinch roller holds the tape against the capstan. A dirty capstan or pinch roller may cause slow speeds or spilling or pulling of the tape.

**capture ratio**—The measure in dB of how much

stronger the FM station must be to enable the tuner to lock onto the stronger and suppress the weaker station.

**cartridge**—A component which holds the stylus or needle and follows the record groove of the turntable. The up and down and sideways motion of the stylus to the cartridge produces an output voltage for the phono amplifier.

**cartridge mounting**—The cartridge may be held into position with clips or mounting screws. With the new p-mount arms, you simply plug in the cartridge.

**cassette radio**—The combination of an AM-FM tuner, amplifier, and cassette player in one unit.

**cassette tuner**—A tuner and cassette deck in one chassis.

**CH**—The abbreviation for channel. The stereo component may have two channels (left and right). A quadraphonic amp may have four channels as found in the quad-auto cassette deck.

**channel separation**—The degree of isolation between left and right channels, often expressed in decibels. The higher the decibel values, the better the separation.

**chassis**—The frame work which holds the working parts in the amplifier, tuner, radio, cassette, CD player, or VCR recorder. The chassis may be metal, plastic, or a PC board.

**chip devices**—Many kinds of chip devices found in various CD players such as the thick-film chip resistor, multilayer ceramic chip capacitor, mini-mould chip transistor, mini-mould chip diode, and mini-mould chip IC.

**clamper assembly**—The clamper assembly fits over the compact disc after loaded. The clamper assembly must be removed to get at the laser pick-up mechanism in the CD player.

**clear button**—The button which erases the last digit entered or the complete program if pressed immediately after the band button on some CD players.

**clipping**—Removing or cutting off the signal of a waveform containing distortion, which can be seen upon the oscilloscope. Excessive power applied to the amp may produce a clipping level resulting in distortion.

**closed loop drive**—A tape transport system which drives both incoming and outgoing tapes and controlled by contact with the capstan at each end of the head assembly.

**coaxial speaker**—A speaker with two drivers mounted on the same frame. Usually coaxial speakers are found in the car radio system. The tweeter is mounted in front of the woofer speaker.

**color burst sensor**—This sensor in a VCR which senses when color burst signals are present.

**compact disc (CD)**—The compact disc player plays a small record or disc of digitally encoded music. The compact disc provides noiseless high-fidelity music on one side of a rainbow-like surface.

**compliance**—The ease with which a stylus can be deflected by the groove wall. A high-compliance stylus will yield readily to the forces exerted upon it by the record groove.

**CPU**—A computer-type processor used in the master and mechanism circuits of the CD player.

**crossover**—A filter which divides the signal to the speaker into two or more frequency ranges. The highs go to the tweeter and the low frequencies to the woofer.

**crosstalk**—Improper adjustment of the tape head may cause crosstalk between two different tracks. Crosstalk is leakage of one channel into the other.

**cueing lever**—A method of raising or lowering the tone arm using a lever. The tone arm may be moved into another position when the arm is lifted by the cueing control.

**DBX**—The noise-reduction system in which the program is compressed before being recorded and expanded in playback.

**dc**—Direct current such as that found in automobile battery systems; and also, after ac has been filtered and rectified in low-voltage power supplies.

**decibel (dB)**—A measure of gain, the ratio of the output power or voltage with respect to the input, expressed in log units.

**de-emphasis**—A form of equalization in FM

tuners to improve the overall S/N ratio while maintaining the uniform frequency response. The de-emphasis circuit is automatically engaged in the compact disc player when the discs with pre-emphasis are being played. The de-emphasis stage follows the D to A converter.

**dew**—A waining light which may come on in the VCR, indicating too much moisture in the recorder. Some machines will shut down if this occurs.

**digital**—Within tuners, a very precise method of locking in a station without station drift, with the station frequency being displayed on the front panel. Digital recording is found in compact discs.

**dipole**—The element of an antenna which collects signals for the receiver. The folded dipole is a common element in FM and TV antennas. The dipole may refer to a type of speaker which radiates in equal amounts to the front and rear with planor and electrostatic panel speakers.

**direct access volume**—A control feature that lets you simply touch a point on the volume scale to set it.

**direct drive**—A direct drive motor shaft to the turntable without any coupling or belts. The platter or turntable rests directly upon the motor shaft.

**disc holder**—The disc holder or turntable which sits directly on top of the motor shaft in a compact disc player.

**dispersion**—The spread of a speaker's high frequencies measured in degrees, or the angle in which the speaker radiates its sound.

**distortion**—In a simple sine-wave signal, distortions appear as multiples (harmonics) of the input frequency. A type of distortion is the clipping of the audio signal in the audio amplifier. Distortion may be seen when signal tracing with the oscilloscope.

**dither**—A very low level noise added to a digitized signal to reduce high distortion caused by quantizing low-level audio signals. Quantization may be found in the master control IC of compact disc players.

**DNR (dynamic noise reduction)**—A noise-reduction system that reduces the high frequencies when the signal is at a low level.

**Dolby noise reduction**—A type of noise reduction which works by increasing the high frequency treble sounds during recording and decreasing them during playback, thus restoring the signal to the original level and eliminating tape hiss. There are three different Dolby noise-reduction systems (A, B, and C).

**driver**—In a speaker system, each separate speaker is sometimes termed a driver.

**drive system**—The motors, belts, or gears that rotate the turntable. There are no belts or pulleys in a direct-drive system.

**dropout**—Drop-out is caused when the tape does not contact the tape head for an instant. Dropout may occur in the compact disc because of dust, dirt, or deep scratches on the plastic disc. Dropout may also occur in the VCR recorder.

**D to A converter**—In the compact disc player, the device that converts the digital signal to analog or audio.

**dual capstan**—Dual capstan and dual flywheels are found in auto-reverse cassette players and can play the tape in both directions. In some tape decks, a second capstan may be added, creating a closed loop method with more stable tape motion and better performance.

**dynamic**—A dynamic speaker has a voice coil which carries the signal current with a fixed magnetic field (pm magnet), and moves the coil and cone. The same principle applies to the human ear or headphone.

**dynamic range**—The ratio between the maximum signal level and minimum level expressed in decibels (dB). The full dynamic range of the human ear may be recorded on the compact disc.

**E-F balance**—After changing the optical-laser pick-up assembly, the balance of the E-F diodes must be adjusted for tracking error detection in the CD player.

**efficiency**—The percentage of electrical input power to a given speaker that is connected to audio energy. High efficiency may mean less amplifier power is required to reproduce the music for listening.

**EFM signal (8 to 14 bit modulation)**—A very complex encoding scheme used to transform the digital data to a form which can be placed upon the disk. This information is modulated by EFM. The EFM signal is fed into the signal processing LS1.

**electronic speed control**—An electronic method of controlling the speed of the motor.

**electrostatic**—An electrostatic speaker, headphone, or meterphone which uses a thin diaphragm having high voltage applied to it. The electrostatic field is varied by the signal voltage, which moves the diaphragm to create sound.

**equalization (EQ)**—Alteration of the frequency response so that the frequency balance of the output equals the frequency balance of the input. The tape player contains the equalization circuits, which may be switched to accommodate metal, chrome, or high-bias tapes. Equalization is also used to correct response deficiencies within speakers.

**equalizer**—A device to change the volume of certain frequencies in relation to the rest of the frequency range. Sliding controls may be found in auto radio and cassette player equalizers.

**erase head**—A magnetic component with applied voltage or current to remove the previous recording or noises on the tape. The erase head is mounted ahead of the regular play/record head.

**extended play (EP)**—Refers to the six hours of playing time obtainable with a T-120 VHS cassette played in a VCR machine.

**eye pattern**—The rf signal waveform at the rf amplifier in a CD player. The waveform is adjusted so the diamond shapes in the eye pattern are clear and distinct.

**fader**—A control in auto radio or cassette players to control the volume balance between front and rear speakers.

**FF, fast-forward**—A button which speeds up the tape in the forward direction. The button switches a higher voltage or another motor winding into the motor circuit of the cassette, VCR, or compact disc player.

**filter**—A circuit that selectively attenuates certain frequencies but not others, such as those in its passband frequency. The large electrolytic capacitor in the low-voltage power supply is sometimes called a filter capacitor.

**floating ground**—A common ground or chassis above the auto body.

**fluorescent display**—A display showing the status of the receiver functions.

**flutter**—A change in the speed of a turntable or tape transport, also known as "wow."

**FM alternate selectivity**—The tuner must tune in the desired station while rejecting interference from a nearby or distant station of the same frequency.

**FM (frequency modulation)**—A process in which the program information is imposed upon a carrier signal by varying its instantaneous frequency directly to the program level. The FM broadcast band is from 88 to 108 MHz.

**FM noise blanker**—The circuit which silences interstation noise when changing stations.

**FM sensitivity**—The ability of the tuner to receive weak and distant stations. A useful measure of a tuner's sensitivity is how strong the signal needs to be for good reception.

**focus error**—The output from the four optosensing elements are supplied to the error signal amp amplifier and a zero output is produced. The error amp corrects the signal voltage and is sent to the servo IC to correct the focus in the CD player.

**focus offset adjustment**—The offset adjustment which is made at the rf amp with a test disc. The eye pattern is monitored with the scope. A good eye pattern means that the diamond shape in the center of the waveform is clear in the CD player.

**FOK (focus OK circuit)**—The circuit which generates a signal used to determine when the laser spot is on the reflecting surface of the disc. The FOK signal is high when the laser is in focus on the CD player.

**folded horn speaker**—The system which forces the sound of the driver to take a different path to the listener. It is one of the most efficient types of speakers available.

**four track**—The four separate parallel magnetic tracks which can be recorded on the regular tape width found in quad-tape players.

**frequency response**—The range of frequencies a given piece of equipment can pass to the listener. The frequency response of a given amplifier may be 20 to 20 kHz. It is often defined with decibel variation over a flat specified frequency range. A speaker (20 to 20,000 Hz) measurement shows how much of the audio range can be reproduced.

**full-range speaker**—A speaker system with only one driver which reproduces the normal frequency range without help from another speaker.

**FZC circuit (focus zero cross)**—The circuit which detects when the FE signal reaches 0 V. It is used together with the FOK circuit to determine the focus adjustment timing in the CD player.

**gain**—The amplification of an electronic signal. Gain may be given in decibels.

**gain control**—A control to adjust the amount or boost the amount of signal.

**gap**—The critical distance between the pole pieces of a tape head. The gap area of a cassette tape head is quite small compared to a regular or stereo 8 tape head.

**glitch**—A form of audio or video noise or distortion which suddenly appears and disappears during VCR operation.

**graphic equalizer**—An equalizer with a series of sliders which provides a visual graphics display.

**ground**—A point of zero voltage or the common voltage return for the components within a circuit, sometimes referred to as earth ground. The common ground may be a metal chassis in the amplifier or receiver; the common ground of the automobile is the metal chassis or framework. American made cars have negative ground polarity.

**harmonic distortion**—The addition of harmonics not present in the original recording. How well a cassette deck copies the tape signal is indicated by the amount of harmonic distortion. A good tape player should have less than 1% distortion.

**harmonics**—A series of multiples of the fundamental frequency. Harmonics help determine the tonal quality of a sound.

**head**—A magnetic component with a gap area which picks up signals from the revolving tape.

**head unit**—A central control of a car stereo system containing the radio, cassette deck, and amplifier.

**helical scan system**—The diagonal stripe system by which very high video frequencies are placed on the tape in both Beta or VHF format.

**hertz (Hz)**—Cycles per second (cps), the unit of frequency.

**hiss**—The annoying high frequency background noise found in tapes and record players.

**hum**—A type of noise which originates from the 60 cycle power line, due mainly to poor filtering in the low-voltage power supply. Hum pickup may occur in the ungrounded phono cartridge or input circuits. Hum and vibrating noise may be heard in a transformer or motor with loose particles or laminations.

**idler wheel**—The wheel in the phonograph which rotates the turntable. The size of an idler wheel helps determine the speed of the capstan/flywheel in the cassette player.

**IDM (intermodulation distortion)**— Distortion at frequencies which are sums and differences of multiples of the input frequencies.

**impedance**—The degree of resistance (in ohms) that an electrical current will encounter in a given circuit or component. A speaker impedance may be 2, 4, 8, or 16 ohms. The typical car speaker is 4 or 8 ohms impedance.

**index search**—When using a disc with index coding, press track (skip forward) or track (skip reverse) until the desired number appears in the display. If the track or index does not exist on the disc, the player will search to the end of the disc and stop the CD player.

**infinite baffle**—A completely sealed box enclosing the speakers.

**integrated amp**—A single component combining the circuitry and functions of the pre-amp and power output amplifiers.

**integrated circuit (IC)**—A single component with many parts and now found throughout the electronic entertainment field. A single one power output component within the amplifier may include the whole audio circuit.

**interlock**—A safety interlock circuit found in some CD players for loading the disc. The interlock circuit lowers the supply voltage to the laser optical assembly while the loading tray is out and raises the voltage to make the laser disc operate after the disc is loaded in the CD player.

**intermodulation distortion (IMD)**—The presence of unwanted frequencies which are the sum and differences of the test signals. Blurring or smearing of sound is the result of IMD. These levels should be below 0.1%.

**IPS (inches per second)**—The measurement of tape speed.

**jack**—The female part of a plug and receptacle.

**key-off eject**—To prevent damage to the tape and capstan of the auto cassette player, the cassette is ejected when the ignition key is turned off.

**kHz**—1000 Hz or 1000 cycles per second.

**laser assembly**—The assembly which contains the laser diodes, focus, and tracking coils. The optical pickup assembly is also known as the laser assembly.

**laser current**—The laser current measurement may indicate if the laser diodes are defective in a CD player. The exact current measurement is found on a label near the laser pickup assembly. The laser current may be measured with voltage test or with a laser power meter.

**laser diodes**—The diodes which pick up the coded information from the disc along with the optical pickup assembly in a CD player.

**LED (light-emitting diode)**—The low-power diodes used for optical readouts and displays in electronic equipment. They are available in many different colors.

**level**—The strength of a signal; also the alignment of the tape head with the tape. The turntable should be mounted level for normal playing.

**line**—Line input or output jacks are found in the amplifier, cassette, or compact disc player. The line signal is usually a high-level signal.

**loading motor**—The motor in the CD player that moves the loading tray out and pulls the loaded disc and tray back into play position. Also known as the tray motor.

**loading tray**—The tray which holds the small compact disc during loading in the CD player.

**local/DX or distant SW**—A switch that reduces the local strong station and increases the sensitivity of the tuner for distant (DX) stations.

**long play (LP)**—A speed on the VCR which provides four hours of recording on a 120 minute VHS cassette.

**loudness**—The volume of sound. Loudness compensation is controlled by the loudness control of an amplifier.

**loudness circuit**—A switch to change the frequency response contour of the sound by increasing bass and treble at low volume. You may find loudness switches on many deluxe amplifiers.

**loudness compensation**—A switch that boosts a low sound level to compensate for the natural loss of sound at the human ear when the sound level is reduced.

**LSI (large-scale integrated)**—Includes the processors, ICs, and CPUs found in the compact disc player.

**magnetic**—The magnetic cartridge has a magnetic moving vane between the coil assembly. The voltage output is very low and must have a pre-amplifier stage ahead of it unlike the crystal cartridge. The magnetic cartridge coil may be checked with the low-ohm scale of the VOM or DMM.

**memory**—The program memory of a CD player. Some program memories can play up to 15 selected tracks. The tracks can be entered in any sequence or the same track can be repeated several times.

**memory counter**—A system which allows the tape to be rewound to any point on the tape.

**memory preset**—An instant recall feature in computerized tuners. These tuners can also automatically scan for a quick sampling of all the stations on the dial.

**metal tape**—The high-frequency response and maximum output level are greatly improved with metal tape. The pure metal particles on the tape make the cassettes more expensive than the normal oxide cassettes.

**MHz (megahertz)**—One million Hertz or one million cycles per second.

**microprocessor**—A multifunction chip found today in most electronic products. They are used in tape decks, search transports, turntables, tuners, memory operations, and CD players, to name a few.

**MIR (mirror detector circuit)**—The circuits used for detection of the mirror portion of the disc between tracks and outside the lead-out track, and also in the detection of disc flaws.

**modulation**—The way in which one signal modifies or controls another signal for the purpose of carrying information.

**monitor**—To compare signals. The monitor head in the tape player is a playback head positioned just past the record head so that the new recorded tape can be listened to or monitored. A stereo amplifier stage may be monitored to compare the signal with the defective channel. An ordinary TV hooked up to the VCR can be used to view or monitor the tape.

**monophonic**—One channel of audio, such as a single radio speaker. Stereo sound has two channels of music.

**MOSFET**—Metal oxide semiconductor field-effect transistor. They are often used in the front end of the FM receiver.

**MPX filter**—A circuit to filter out the 19 kHz frequencies in the output signal from a stereo FM tuner or receiver.

**multipath distortion**—The distortion which occurs when the receiving antenna picks up the same signal with many paths of deflections. This multipath interference may cause loss of stereo channel separation in the receiver.

**multiplex (MPX)**—A multiplex demodulator in the FM tuner or receiver which converts a single carrier signal into two stereo channels of audio.

**music search**—A feature which finds the beginning of each song automatically and also skips long blank sections of the tape.

**mute switch**—A switch which eliminates interstation noise when tuning the FM band. The switch circuit reduces the weaker station signals and may be found in the audio-output line circuits of the compact disc player.

**noise**—Any unwanted signal unrelated to the desired signal. Noise may be generated during the record and playback functions in the cassette player. Dust on the record may produce a scratching noise. A defective transistor or IC may produce a frying noise in the amplifier system.

**noise suppressor**—A filter to reduce background noise.

**NR**—Abbreviation for noise reduction.

**optical lens**—The lens located in the laser pickup, sometimes called optical-lens assembly of the CD player. The optical lens should be cleaned by wiping off the lens area with cotton swab, cleaning paper, or photolens cleaning products.

**output power**—The output power of an amplifier, rated in watts. To double the volume requires a ten-fold increase in power.

**oxide**—The magnetic coating compound of the recording tape or cassette. After many hours of operation the oxide dust flakes off and may coat the tape head, resulting in weak and distorted music. The excess oxide should be cleaned off the tape head, pinch roller, and capstan for good music reproduction.

**passive radiator**—A second woofer cone that is added but without a voice coil. The efficient second speaker cone is driven from the inside pressure movement of the other speakers and produces enhanced heavy bass tones.

**pause control**—A feature to stop the tape movement without switching the machine. The pause control is found in cassette, VCR, and compact disc players.

**peak**—The level of power or signal. A peak indicator light shows that the signal levels are exceeding the recorder's ability to handle the peaks without distortion.

**phase**—Sound waves that are in sync with one another. The positive terminals of speakers are wired together so the cones will go in and out together or in phase.

**phono plug**—A small plug which transports the cartridge signal to the amplifier. Referred to as the RCA plug.

**pick-up motor**—The pick-up, SLED, or feed motor is used to move the pick-up assembly, in the radial direction or towards the outer edge of the disc.

**piezoelectric cartridge**—The normal crystal cartridge found in record players. The generating element is a piece of ceramic or a crystal which generates voltage when bent or twisted. The output voltage in a crystal cartridge is quite high compared to the magnetic cartridge.

**piezoelectric speaker**—A ceramic element which expands or bends under applied signal voltage in a speaker. The piezoelectric principle is used in some tweeters.

**pitch control**—A control that slightly changes the speed of the turntable motor.

**playback head**—The head which often includes both playback and record in one assembly. In some tape players, the single play head is known as the monitor tape head.

**PLL (phase-locked loop)**—An accurate system with an FM multiplex decoder based on feedback control of the oscillator. A PLL-VCO circuit may be also found in the digital control processor of the compact disc player.

**port**—An opening in a speaker enclosure or cabinet. The port permits the back bass radiation to be combined with the front radiation for total response.

**power**—The output power of any amp is given in watts. A low voltage power supply provides voltage for other circuits.

**preamplifier**—The amp within the cassette player which takes the weak signal from the tape head and amplifies it for the af stages. A preamp also takes the weak signal from the cartridge in the phono and amplifies it for the first audio-amplifier stage.

**pre-amp output**—Low-level output signal from the pre-amplifier to be connected to the main power amp.

**quantization**—The number of possible values available to represent various levels of amplitude of a digital audio system. The resolution of quantization is 16 bits in compact disc players. Quantization takes place within the RAM and control-system processor.

**quartz lock**—The quartz-crystal speed detector which locks in the precise turntable speed for the motor.

**radial tone arm**—A linear-tracking tone arm which moves along a track parallel to the record radius in a phonograph.

**rated power bandwidth**—The frequency range over which the amplifier supplies a certain minimum power factor, usually from 20 to 20,000 Hz.

**recording level meter**—The meter which indicates how much signal is being recorded on the tape. The recording meter may be a vane type, an LED, or a fluorescent panel. It is useful for preventing overloads during normal recording.

**reject level**—A lever which rejects or deletes a given track in a cassette or a record on the record changer.

**remote control**—A means of operating the receiver, compact disc player or VCR from a distance. Today, most remote control transmitters are the infrared types.

**repeat button**—The button which replays the same track of music on the compact disc player.

**rf (radio frequency)**—The radio signal picked up by an antenna. An rf stage in the FM receiver amplifies the rf signal.

**ribbon speaker**—A high-frequency driver or tweeter speaker which uses a light ribbon material suspended in a magnetic field to generate audio sound when current is passed through it.

**rumble**—Low frequency vibrations picked up by the cartridge caused by the turntable motor and which are transmitted into the audio system.

**sample hold**—The circuits which are found in each stereo channel after the digital-to-analog (D to A) processor within the compact disc player.

**sampling frequency**—The rate or the number of times a signal is sampled in digital audio. The sampling rate of a compact disc player is 44.1 kHz.

**saturation**—The inability to receive further information. The recording tape is saturated when it cannot hold anymore magnetic signals. Saturation may also occur in a magnetic tape head.

**scan**—The ability of a tuner to search the band and sample each station for a few seconds.

**seek or search**—The ability of a tuner to search the band until another station is found. Search circuits may also be found in cassette and compact disc players.

**selectivity (SEL)**—The ability of a tuner to reject unwanted stations. Some tuners offer variable selectivity.

**self-erase**—A degrading or partial erasure of information upon the magnetic tape.

**self-powered speakers**—A speaker with a built-in amplifier.

**semi-automatic**—In turntables, semi-automatic operation requires that the tone arm be placed manually on the record to start, but at the end the turntable will shut off and set down the tone arm.

**sensitivity**—A measure of how much signal is needed to provide a combined noise and distortion level in the audio output from 30 to 50 dB below the output signal level. The sensitivity of a speaker is the measured output of the speaker (in dB) compared to the input.

**separation**—The separation of two stereo channels. Placement of the stereo speakers may provide good or poor stereo separation.

**servo**—Refers to the servo or tracking circuits which keep the laser pickup in the grooves at all times.

**servo control**—Refers to the servo control IC which controls the focus and tracking coils, in addition to maintaining accurate tracking.

**signal**—A form of music or voice carried in electrical or electronic form.

**signal processing**—In the compact disc player, converting the laser beam signals to audio with pre-amp and signal processors.

**signal-to-noise ratio (S/N)**—The ratio of the loudest signal to that of hiss or noise. The higher the signal-to-noise ratio the better the sound.

**simulated stereo**—A feature which creates an actual stereo image from mono programs of old records or VCR sound.

**skating**—If the stylus is worn or the pressure is wrong, the stylus may skate across the record. Linear tracking tone arms do not require anti-skating adjustments, in contrast to pivoted tone arms.

**skewing**—A form of visual distortion or bend at the upper part of the picture of the VCR player.

**skip**—Certain compact discs have index points which allow different movements or parts of pieces of music such as symphonies to be selected. To set the index number, press the skip or track index number button.

**solenoid**—A switch consisting of an electric coil with an iron-core plunger which is pulled inside the coil by the magnetic field. The solenoid switch is often used in cassette, tape, and compact-disc recorders instead of mechanical switches.

**speaker enclosure**—The cabinet in which the speakers are mounted. The speaker enclosure may provide AS or bass reflex systems.

**spindle motor**—The disc or turntable motor that is controlled by a constant linear velocity system (CLV). The spindle motor revolutions may vary from 500 to 200 RPM.

**standard play (SP)**—The speed at which a two-hour (T-120) VHS cassette plays a VCR machine.

**standing waves**—A wave created by bouncing or reflecting back the original wave. Standing waves may either cancel themselves or cause distortion.

**subwoofer**—A speaker designed to handle very low frequencies below 150 Hz.

**super tweeter**—A tweeter which handles extremely high frequencies in a 4-way system.

**stylus**—A jewel or diamond tip that rides in the groove of the record. Sometimes referred to as the needle.

**test cassette**—Recorded signals upon a test cassette used for alignment and adjustment procedures on the cassette player.

**test disc**—A compact disc used to make alignments and adjustments on the compact disc player.

**tone control**—A circuit designed to increase or decrease the amplification in a specific frequency range. You may find one or a separate bass and treble tone control.

**total harmonic distortion (THD)**—A percentage of harmonic distortion found in components. To measure how accurate the amp is, a signal is fed in and the harmonics are measured at the output. The lower the percentage the less the distortion.

**tracking**—The tracking force is how much downward pressure is needed for the tone arm to track along the record groove. The vertical tracking angle is between the disc and the diamond stylus. Lower tracking weight means less wear on the record groove.

**tracking servo**—The IC processor which keeps the laser beam in focus and tracking correctly.

**track kick circuit**—The circuit used when the laser beam is skipped to a relatively close pit track during accessing and cue/record mode operations. Skipping is achieved by applying kick and brake pulses to the tracking core with the tracking servo loop open.

**track offset adjustment**—An adjustment made with a test disc and the oscilloscope of the tracking jump waveform on the rf board of a CD player.

**transducer**—A device which converts energy into another form. The speaker changes electrical energy to sound energy. A cartridge converts mechanical movement to electrical energy.

**tray**—The loading tray in which the CD disc to be played is placed.

**tweeter**—A high-frequency driver.

**VCR**—Video cassette recorder.

**vented speaker system**—Any speaker cabinet with a hole or port to let the back waves of the woofer speaker escape. A bass reflex is a type of vented speaker system.

**VHS (video home system)**—The system used today in most VCRs.

**voice coil**—The coil of wire wound over the end of the cone of the speaker in which the amplifier output is connected. The electrical signal is converted to mechanical energy to create audible sound waves.

**watts (W)**—The measurement of electrical power.

**W/CH**—Watts per channel.

**woofer**—The largest speaker in a speaker system and the one that reproduces the low frequencies. The low-frequency driver.

**wow**—Variation in the speed of the tape. Wow is a slow speed fluctuation; fast speed variation is called flutter.

# Index

# Other Bestsellers of Related Interest

**MAINTAINING AND REPAIRING VCRs**
2nd Edition—Robert L. Goodman

". . . of immense use . . . all the necessary background for learning the art of troubleshooting popular brands" said *Electronics for You* about the first edition of this indispensable VCR handbook. Revised and enlarged, this illustrated guide provides complete, professional guidance on troubleshooting and repairing VCRs from all the major manufacturers, including VHS and Betamax systems and color video camcorders. Includes tips on use of test equipment and servicing techniques plus case history problems and solution. 352 pages, 427 illustrations. Book No. 3103, $17.95 paperback, $27.95 hardcover

**BASIC ELECTRONICS THEORY**—3rd Edition
—Delton T. Horn

"All the information needed for a basic understanding of almost any electronic device or circuit . . ." was how *Radio-Electronics* magazine described the previous edition of this now-classic sourcebook. This completely updated and expanded edition provides a resource tool that belongs in a prominent place on every electronics bookshelf. Packed with illustrations, schematics, projects, and experiments, it's a book you won't want to miss! 544 pages, 650 illustrations. Book No. 3195, $21.95 paperback, $28.95 hardcover

**THE CET EXAM BOOK**—2nd Edition—Ron Crow & Dick Glass

An excellent source for update or review, this book includes information on practical mathematics, capacitance and inductance, oscillators and demodulators, meters, dependency logic notation, understanding microprocessors, electronics troubleshooting and more! Thoroughly practical, it is an essential handbook for preparing for the Associate CET test! 266 pages, 211 illustrations. Book No. 2950, $13.95 paperback, $21.95 hardcover

**DESIGNING, BUILDING AND TESTING YOUR OWN SPEAKER SYSTEM—with Projects**
—3rd Edition—David B. Weems

Build low-cost, great-sounding speaker systems that rival the most expensive units with this third edition. You get details on special custom features that commercial models don't have. This expanded edition reflects all the recent advances in audio technology and calls for low cost, reliable, and readily available Radio Shack components. Follow the step-by-step instructions and expert advice. Plus, get professional tips on level and tone control settings, speaker protection, subwoofers, and more. 224 pages, 152 illustrations. Book No. 3374, $16.95 paperback, $24.95 hardcover

**TROUBLESHOOTING AND REPAIRING SOLID-STATE TVs**—Homer L. Davidson

Packed with case study examples, photos of solid-state circuits, and circuit diagrams. You'll learn how to troubleshoot and repair all the most recent solid-state TV circuitry used by the major manufacturers of all brands and models of TVs. This workbench reference is filled with tips and practical information that will get you right to the problem! 448 pages, 516 illustrations. Book No. 2707, $17.95 paperback, $26.95 hardcover

**HDTV: High-Definition Television**—Stan Prentiss

Taking a thorough and comprehensive overview of this highly competitive new technology, engineer and communications expert Stan Prentiss focuses on the most recent developments in HDTV taking place internationally. These include the current standards being developed in Europe, Japan, Canada, and the United States. Among the topics highlighted: engineering approaches, proposed delivery systems, characteristics of HDTV receivers and reception capabilities, FCC guidelines, goals, and decisions, and system test criteria. 240 pages, 90 illustrations. Book No. 3272, $16.95 paperback, $24.95 hardcover

## TROUBLESHOOTING AND REPAIRING VCRs
—Gordon McComb

It's estimated that 50% of all American households today have at least one VCR. *Newsweek* magazine reports that most service operations charge a minimum of $40 just to look at a machine, and in some areas there's a minimum repair charge of $95 *plus the cost of any parts*. Now this time and money-saving sourcebook gives you complete schematics and step-by-step details on general up-keep and repair of home VCRs—from the simple cleaning and lubricating of parts, to troubleshooting power and circuitry problems. 336 pages, 300 illustrations. Book No. 2960, $17.95 paperback, $27.95 hardcover

## COMPACT DISK PLAYER MAINTENANCE AND REPAIR—Gordon McComb and John Cook

Packed with quick and reliable answers to the problems of maintaining and repairing CD players, this illustrated, do-it-yourself guide takes the apprehension out of first-time repairs. Master repairman Gordon McComb takes away the mystery that surrounds these seemingly complicated devices and gives you the confidence you need to repair minor malfunctions (the cause of more than 50% of CD player problems). 256 pages, 193 illustrations. Book No. 2790, $14.95 paperback only

**Prices Subject to Change Without Notice.**

## Look for These and Other TAB Books at Your Local Bookstore

## To Order Call Toll Free 1-800-822-8158
(in PA, AK, and Canada call 717-794-2191)

or write to TAB BOOKS, Blue Ridge Summit, PA 17294-0840.